PEABODY'S
CONTROL OF PIPELINE CORROSION

SECOND EDITION

A.W. PEABODY

Edited by
RONALD L. BIANCHETTI

NACE International
The Corrosion Society
1440 South Creek Drive
Houston, Texas 77084

NACE International
The Corrosion Society

© 1967, 2001 by NACE International

Second Edition 2001. All rights reserved.

Library of Congress Catalog Number 99-80032

ISBN 978-1-57590-092-6

Cover illustration by Mark Lewis, courtesy of the East Bay Municipal Utility District.

NACE Press:
Director of Publications: Jeff Littleton
Manager of NACE Press: Neil Vaughan

NACE International
1440 South Creek Drive
Houston, Texas 77084
http://www.nace.org

Table of Contents

Preface

This book was originally published in 1967 by Sam Peabody and is the most quoted and used document in the corrosion industry for pipeline corrosion control and testing. When the original book was published, specific criteria for cathodic protection for underground pipelines were still under evaluation and consideration. Not until 1969 was the first documented standard approved by NACE International on criteria RP0169. The depth and vision that Peabody incorporated in the first version of the book has stood the test of time.

This revised version of the 1967 book is not an attempt to make radical changes to the original document. Much of the original text and concepts remain intact. We attempted, however, to incorporate original traditional elements of the book with updates and expanded discussions on equipment, testing techniques and criteria, coatings, survey methods, and data analysis.

An integral part of this revision is a CD-ROM that contains formulas of key design calculations, case examples of corrosion control designs which provide a set-by-step overview of how to design various components of cathodic protection systems, and an electronic copy of the revised book edition.

As described in the Preface of the original 1967 edition, every attempt has been made to check the accuracy of all statements and other data. However, it is unreasonable to assume that everything in this book is accurate and exact. Any suggestions will be considered when future editions of this book are prepared.

About the Author

1915–1998

This updated version of NACE International's book titled *Control of Pipeline Corrosion* is dedicated to the memory of its original author, A.W. (Sam) Peabody. Since its publication in 1967, the book has been translated into at least seven different languages and is considered by most as the definitive work on pipeline corrosion.

Sam received his bachelor's degree from the University of Maine and pursued graduate studies at the Brooklyn Polytechnic Institute in New York. He worked for Ebasco Services Inc. (no longer in existence) for over 40 years until his retirement in 1980 as Director of Corrosion Engineering. He was an active member of NACE since 1947. His accomplishments, awards, and recognitions are too many to list here. His biggest legacy, especially to those of us who had the privilege of working for and with him, is that he was the perfect example of "a gentleman and a scholar." He was an excellent teacher who always emphasized professional integrity, a quality he instilled in so many.

Contributors

John A. Beavers

John A. Beavers is Vice President of Research at CC Technologies, a corrosion engineering and research company. He received B.S. and Ph.D. degrees in metallurgical engineering from the University of Illinois at Urbana-Champaign in 1973 and 1977, respectively. Dr. Beavers has directed and contributed to numerous research programs on corrosion performance of structural materials. These programs included failure analyses, critical literature reviews, and laboratory and field evaluations of metallic and non-metallic material. Dr. Beavers has utilized state-of-the-art electrochemical, surface analytical, and mechanical techniques for the evaluation of materials performance. A major emphasis of his research has been the mechanistic and practical aspects of corrosion and stress corrosion cracking (SCC) on underground pipelines. Dr. Beavers worked at Battelle Memorial Institute from 1977 to 1987, where he was a Senior Research Leader in the Corrosion Section. He joined CC Technologies in 1987.

Dr. Beavers has authored over 80 papers in the field of corrosion and has received two U.S. Patents. An active member of NACE, he was Chairman of the Research in Progress Symposium in 1994 and of the Publications Committee in 1991 and 1992.

Editor's Note: Sincere appreciation to John Beavers for investing a lot of time on a detailed and productive review of the final draft on the eve before printing.

Ronald L. Bianchetti

Ronald L. Bianchetti is currently a Senior Engineer at East Bay Municipal Utility District (EBMUD) in Oakland, California. He received a B.S. in engineering in 1975 from the University of California, Davis and an MBA in 1981 from St. Mary's College of California. He is a Registered Professional Engineer and has over 25 years of experience. Prior to holding his current position, Mr. Bianchetti worked in the private sector as a consultant in the corrosion industry from 1975 to 1992. His work includes planning, designing, testing, and the construction management of cathodic protection systems for underground pipelines, tanks, refineries, power plants, and marine structures. He has served in NACE International as Past

Chairman of the Publications Committee, ad-hoc member to the Board of Directors, Past Western Region Chairman and Past Section Chair of the San Francisco Section.

Mr. Bianchetti has published over 30 papers in the field of corrosion and has given hundreds of presentations on corrosion and corrosion control.

Kevin C. Garrity, P.E.

Kevin C. Garrity, P.E., is currently Vice President of Engineering at CC Technologies, a corrosion engineering and research company. He received a B.S. in electrical engineering in 1974 from the Polytechnic Institute of Brooklyn. He is a NACE Certified Cathodic Protection Specialist and a Registered Professional Engineer in seven states. Mr. Garrity has 26 years of experience in the design, installation, monitoring, and assessment of cathodic protection systems for buried pipelines, underground storage tanks, concrete structures, and marine structures. Mr. Garrity worked at Ebasco Services from 1974 to 1982, where he was a Senior Corrosion Engineer, and at Harco Corporation from 1982 to 1989, where he was Vice President of Engineering. He joined CC Technologies in 1989.

In 1996, Mr. Garrity received the Colonel George W. Cox Award for outstanding contributions to the field of underground corrosion control. He has published more than 20 papers in the field of corrosion control. Mr. Garrity delivered the plenary lecture at Corrosion'98.

Mark Lewis

Mark Lewis is Assistant Corrosion Engineer at the East Bay Municipal Utility District (EBMUD) in Oakland, California. He is a graduate of Kent State University and attended Bethany College in West Virginia. He has worked in the cathodic protection and corrosion engineering field since 1980, both within the United States and internationally. He is a Past Chairman of the San Francisco Bay Area Section of NACE International.

He is the author of several technical and historical articles on cathodic protection and has made numerous presentations on the subject. Mr. Lewis has a patent pending for a distribution system rectifier design.

Brenda J. Little

Brenda J. Little, Senior Scientist for Marine Molecular Processes at the Naval Research Laboratory, has a Ph.D. in chemistry from Tulane University and a B.S. in biology and chemistry from Baylor University. She is a member of the American Chemical Society and the National Association of Corrosion Engineers (NACE International). She is a NACE International Fellow and the recipient of a 1999 NACE International Technical Achievement Award.

Dr. Little serves on the editorial board for Biofouling and is the author of one book, 20 book chapters, and over 80 peer-reviewed journal articles.

Steve McKim

Since 1989, Steve McKim has been Vice President of American Construction & Supply, Inc. Based in Mill Valley, California, his company specializes in cathodic protection construction services. Mr. McKim previously worked with Harco Corporation and Chevron USA. He has been in the corrosion industry since he graduated from the University of Illinois with a B.S. in mechanical engineering in 1983. He is a Past Chairman of the NACE San Francisco Bay Area Section.

Richard N. Sloan

The late Richard Sloan, was an authority in the field of pipeline coatings. He worked for over 45 years with a company that was first known as HC Price. (The company changed its name several times: HC Price, Ameron Price, Bredero Price, and Energy Coatings.) He attended Drexel University and graduated with a bachelor's degree in Industrial Administration.

During his professional career, Richard Sloan taught various short courses in pipeline coatings, and was a speaker at numerous seminars on the subject. The late Mr. Sloan was an active and long-standing member of NACE, AWWA, and Western Pipeliners.

Michael J. Szeliga

Michael J. Szeliga, P.E., is the Chief Engineer for Russell Corrosion Consultants, Inc. He has more than 23 years of experience in corrosion control engineering. Much of his work has involved the analysis and control of stray current from DC-powered transit systems and from impressed current cathodic protection systems. A Licensed Professional Engineer in several states and certified by NACE International as a Corrosion Specialist and a Cathodic Protection Specialist, Mr. Szeliga has been and is the principal corrosion consultant for the design, construction, and maintenance of many light and heavy rail transit systems. He is presently chairman of the NACE (05)024X Committee on Interference Problems Associated with Rail Transit. Mr. Szeliga is also chairman of the ASTM subcommittee on stray current.

He has edited a book for NACE International titled *Stray Current Corrosion* and has published several articles on the subject.

Patricia Wagner

Patricia Wagner retired from the Naval Research Laboratory in 1998 after 14 years of extensive experience in microbiologically influenced corrosion. She is the coauthor of one book and the author of numerous articles on corrosion.

Publisher Note

Regarding the frequently used equations on the CD-ROM, NACE Press would like to extend its gratitude to Jeff Didas, who provided the original ideas and formulas, and to Jack Tinnea, who provided a technical review of the equations.

Chapter 1

Introduction to Corrosion

John A. Beavers

WHAT IS CORROSION?

One general definition of corrosion is the degradation of a material through environmental interaction. This definition encompasses all materials, both naturally occurring and man-made and includes plastics, ceramics, and metals. This book focuses on the corrosion of metals, with emphasis on corrosion of carbon and low-alloy steels used in underground pipelines. This definition of corrosion begs the question; why do metals corrode? The answer lies in the field of thermodynamics, which tells whether a process such as corrosion will occur. A second logical question is what is the rate of corrosion or how long will a pipeline last? Corrosion kinetics can help provide an answer to this question. Both topics are discussed in greater detail in Chapter 16. Chapter 1 contains an introduction to the subject of underground corrosion. A glossary of terms is included in Appendix A of this book to help with the sometimes confusing terminology.

A significant amount of energy is put into a metal when it is extracted from its ores, placing it in a high-energy state. These ores are typically oxides of the metal such as hematite (Fe_2O_3) for steel or bauxite ($Al_2O_3 \cdot H_2O$) for aluminum. One principle of thermodynamics is that a material always seeks the lowest energy state. In other words, most metals are thermodynamically unstable and will tend to seek a lower energy state, which is an oxide or some other compound. The process by which metals convert to the lower-energy oxides is called corrosion.

Corrosion of most common engineering materials at near-ambient temperatures occurs in aqueous (water-containing) environments and is electrochemical in nature. The aqueous environment is also referred to as the electrolyte and, in the case of underground corrosion, is moist soil. The corrosion process involves the removal of electrons (oxidation) of the metal [Equation (1)] and the consumption of those electrons by some other reduction reaction, such as oxygen or water reduction [Equations (2) and (3), respectively]:

$$Fe \rightarrow Fe^{++} + 2e^- \tag{1}$$

$$O_2 + 2H_2O + 4e^- \rightarrow 4OH^- \tag{2}$$

$$2H_2O + 2e^- \rightarrow H_2 + 2OH^- \tag{3}$$

The oxidation reaction is commonly called the anodic reaction and the reduction reaction is called the cathodic reaction. Both electrochemical reactions are necessary for corrosion to occur. The oxidation reaction causes the actual metal loss but the reduction reaction must be present to consume the electrons liberated by the oxidation reaction, maintaining charge neutrality. Otherwise, a large negative charge would rapidly develop between the metal and the electrolyte and the corrosion process would cease.

The oxidation and reduction reactions are sometimes referred to as half-cell reactions and can occur locally (at the same site on the metal) or can be physically separated. When the electrochemical reactions are physically separated, the process is referred to as a differential corrosion cell. A schematic of a differential corrosion cell is given in Figure 1.1. The site where the metal is being oxidized is referred to as the anode or anodic site. At this site, direct electric current (defined as a positive flow of charge) flows from the metal surface into the electrolyte as the metal ions leave the surface. This current flows in the electrolyte to the site where oxygen, water, or some other species is being reduced. This site is referred to as the cathode or cathodic site. There are four necessary components of a differential corrosion cell.

1. There must be an anode
2. There must be a cathode

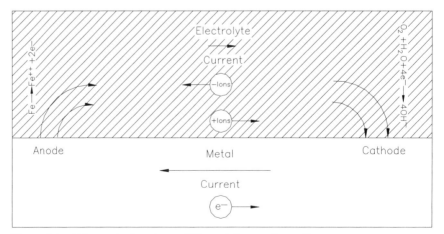

Figure 1.1   Schematic showing a differential corrosion cell.

3. There must be a metallic path electrically connecting the anode and cathode. (Normally, this will be the pipeline itself.)

4. The anode and cathode must be immersed in an electrically conductive electrolyte (normally, moist soil).

Underground corrosion of pipelines and other structures is often the result of differential corrosion cells of which a variety of different types exist. These include differential aeration cells, where different parts of a pipe are exposed to different oxygen concentrations in the soil, and cells created by differences in the nature of the pipe surface or the soil chemistry. Galvanic corrosion is a form of differential cell corrosion in which two different metals are electrically coupled and exposed in a corrosive environment. Further discussion of these differential corrosion cells is given below and in Chapter 16.

HOW DO WE DETECT CORROSION?

The electrochemical nature of the corrosion process provides opportunities to detect and mitigate corrosion of underground structures. We can monitor the voltages and the currents associated with the corrosion process.

When a piece of metal is placed in an electrolyte, such as soil, a voltage will develop across the metal–electrolyte interface because of the electrochemical nature of the corrosion process. We cannot measure this voltage directly but, using a voltmeter, we can measure a voltage between two different metals that are placed in the soil. We also can measure the voltage difference between a metal and a reference electrode, commonly called a half-cell electrode. This voltage is referred to as a corrosion potential, an open circuit potential, or a native potential for that metal in the environment in which the measurement is being obtained. For soil environments, the most common reference electrode used is the copper–copper sulfate reference electrode (CSE).

Potential measurements can be used to estimate the relative resistance of different metals to corrosion in a given environment. Noble metals, such as gold and platinum, have more positive potentials and are more resistant to corrosion than are the more common engineering metals such as steel and aluminum. A galvanic series is a list of metals and alloys arranged according to their relative corrosion potentials in a given environment. Table 1.1 shows a galvanic series for metals and other materials in neutral soils and water, indicating that carbon has the most positive potential of the materials listed and magnesium has the most negative potential. The potentials measured for the different metals in a galvanic series vary somewhat, depending on the nature of the environment, but the relative position of the metals is similar for natural environments such as soil and seawater.

Another use for corrosion potential measurements is to establish whether galvanic corrosion is likely to occur. When two metals are electrically coupled in an environment, the more negative (active) member of the couple will become the anode in the

Table 1.1 Practical Galvanic Series for Materials in Neutral Soils and Water

Material	Potential Volts (CSE)[a]
Carbon, Graphite, Coke	+0.3
Platinum	0 to −0.1
Mill Scale on Steel	−0.2
High Silicon Cast Iron	−0.2
Copper, Brass, Bronze	−0.2
Mild Steel in Concrete	−0.2
Lead	−0.5
Cast Iron (Not Graphitized)	−0.5
Mild Steel (Rusted)	−0.2 to −0.5
Mild Steel (Clean and Shiny)	−0.5 to −0.8
Commercially Pure Aluminum	−0.8
Aluminum Alloy (5% Zinc)	−1.05
Zinc	−1.1
Magnesium Alloy (6% Al, 3% Zn, 0.15% Mn)	−1.6
Commercially Pure Magnesium	−1.75

[a]Typical potential normally observed in neutral soils and water, measured with respect to copper sulfate reference electrode.

differential corrosion cell, and the more positive (noble) member of the couple will become the cathode in the cell. In general, the severity of the galvanic couple increases as the difference in potential between the two members of the couple increases, although this is not always the case. The galvanic series shown in Table 1.1 indicates that, where copper is electrically coupled to mild steel in soil, the copper will become the cathode and the steel will become the anode, accelerating corrosion of the steel. A further discussion of galvanic corrosion is given in Chapter 16.

Table 1.1 also shows that the potential of mild steel can differ depending on whether the surface is clean or covered with mill scale. The potential of steel also is a function of soil properties, including pH, ion concentration, oxygen, and moisture content. The potential differences that develop on underground pipelines and other structures as a result of these factors can result in severe corrosion. Further discussions of these differential corrosion cells are given in Chapter 16.

Potential measurements are commonly used on underground pipelines to detect the presence of these types of differential corrosion cells. An electrical connection is made to the pipe, and the potential of the pipe is measured with respect to a reference electrode placed over the pipe. This process is shown schematically in Figure 1.2. Normally, the reference electrode is connected to the negative lead of a digital voltmeter to obtain a negative reading. As shown in Table 1.1, most potentials in soils are negative. With this type of measurement, the most negative regions of the structure are the anodes and are undergoing accelerated corrosion due to the differential corrosion cells.

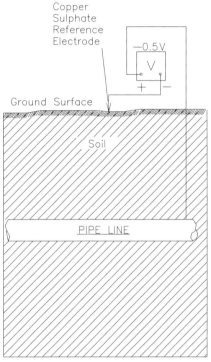

Figure 1.2 Schematic showing a pipe-to-soil potential measurement.

Current measurements also can be used to detect differential corrosion cells if the anodes and cathodes are large. These large cells create long-line currents that can be detected by measurements made over the pipe or other underground structure. Through Ohm's law (V = IR, where V is the voltage, I is the current, and R is the resistance) we know that current flow in the soil will create a voltage gradient. This gradient can be detected by placing identical reference electrodes over the pipe and measuring the voltage difference. The voltage measurements can be used to indicate the direction of the differential cell current. The anodic and cathodic sites on the pipeline can be located by performing a series of cell-to-cell potential measurements taken along the pipeline. Another possible source of current flow in the ground is stray currents. These issues are discussed further in Chapter 5.

HOW DO WE MITIGATE CORROSION?

The principal methods for mitigating corrosion on underground pipelines are coatings and cathodic protection (CP). Although each will be treated in greater detail in the following chapters, these two methods are briefly described here.

Coatings normally are intended to form a continuous film of an electrically insulating material over the metallic surface to be protected. The function of such a coating is to isolate the metal from direct contact with the surrounding electrolyte (preventing the electrolyte from contacting the metal) and to interpose such a high electrical resistance that the electrochemical reactions cannot readily occur. In reality, all coatings, regardless of overall quality, contain holes, referred to as holidays, that are formed during application, or during transport or installation of mill-coated pipe. Holidays in coatings also develop in service as a result of degradation of the coating, soil stresses, or movement of the pipe in the ground. Degradation of the coating in service also can lead to disbonding from the pipe surface, further exposing metal to the underground environment. A high corrosion rate at a holiday or within a disbonded region can result in a leak or rupture, even where the coating effectively protects a high percentage of the pipe surface. Thus, coatings are rarely used on underground pipelines in the absence of CP. The primary function of a coating on a cathodically protected pipe is to reduce the surface area of exposed metal on the pipeline, thereby reducing the current necessary to cathodically protect the metal. Further discussion of coatings is given in Chapter 2.

One definition of CP is a technique to reduce the corrosion rate of a metal surface by making it the cathode of an electrochemical cell. This is accomplished by shifting the potential of the metal in the negative direction by the use of an external power source (referred to as impressed current CP) or by utilizing a sacrificial anode. In the case of an impressed current system, a current is impressed on the structure by means of a power supply, referred to as a rectifier, and an anode buried in the ground. In the case of a sacrificial anode system, the galvanic relationship between a sacrificial anode material, such as zinc or magnesium, and the pipe steel is used to supply the required CP current. Further discussions of CP are given in Chapters 3 and 16.

Chapter 2

Pipeline Coatings

Richard N. Sloan

When the first edition of *Control of Pipeline Corrosion* by A.W. Peabody was published in 1967, there were few governmental regulations to contend with. Today the Department of Transportation–Office of Pipeline Safety (DOT/OPS), Occupational Safety and Health Administration (OSHA), and the Department of Environmental Resources (DER) are among the many regulatory agencies influencing or controlling the pipeline industry. Governmental regulations, along with the development, introduction, and acceptance of new pipeline coatings, have made major changes and will continue to affect the selection and use of pipeline coatings in the future.

Economics, while still a factor, is being replaced by safety and environmental concerns to obtain the best available pipe-coating systems. This trend was first apparent in Europe where permanence, instead of cost, led to the use of multi-layer systems that have proven to be most effective and more economical over the life of the pipeline. In today's regulated environment, all new hazardous pipelines (carrying oil, gas, or other potentially dangerous substances) are required by federal regulation to use an effective coating and cathodic protection (CP).

EFFECTIVENESS OF COATINGS AS A MEANS OF CORROSION CONTROL

First attempts to control pipeline corrosion relied on the use of coating materials and the reasoning that if the pipeline metal could be isolated from contact with the surrounding earth, no corrosion could occur. This concept is entirely reasonable and logical. Furthermore, a coating would be completely effective as a means of stopping corrosion if the coating material:

• Is an effective electrical insulator,

- Can be applied with no breaks whatsoever and will remain so during the backfilling process, and
- Constitutes an initially perfect film that will remain so with time.

While this is possible with some of the advanced multi-layer systems, it may not be practical from an initial cost analysis.

Although coatings by themselves may not be the one perfect answer to corrosion control, they are extremely effective when properly used. Most operators plan coatings and cathodic protection (CP) for all their pipelines as a matter of course. A properly selected and applied coating will provide all the protection necessary on most of the pipeline surface to which it is applied. On a typical well-coated pipeline this should be better than 99% and, along with the CP, should give total protection.

It is not the intent of the chapter to make specific recommendations for coating materials to be used. However, the capabilities and limitations of various pipeline coating materials will be discussed as well as desirable characteristics and how to get the most of any material used. Types of coatings now used on pipeline systems will be described briefly.

NACE Standard RP0169-96 Section 5: Coatings, is a comprehensive guide to pipe coatings, and is required reading for a better understanding of their importance. This Standard lists the following desirable characteristics of coatings:

1. **Effective electrical insulator.** Because soil corrosion is an electrochemical process, a pipe coating has to stop the current flow by isolating the pipe from its installed environment/electrolyte. To assure a high electrical resistance, the coating should have a high dielectric strength.
2. **Effective moisture barrier.** Contrary to the theory that water absorption is good because it increases the effectiveness of CP, water transfer through the coating may cause blistering and will contribute to corrosion by prohibiting isolation.
3. **Applicability.** Application of the coating to the pipe must be possible by a method that will not adversely affect the properties of the pipe and with a minimum of defects.
4. **Ability to resist development of holidays with time.** After the coating is buried, two areas that may destroy or degrade coatings are soil stress and soil contaminants. Soil stress, brought about in certain soils that are alternately wet and dry, creates forces that may split or cause thin areas. To minimize this problem, one must evaluate the coating's abrasion resistance, tensile strength, adhesion, and cohesion. The coating's resistance to chemicals, hydrocarbons, and acidic or alkaline conditions should be known for evaluating their performance in contaminated soils.
5. **Good adhesion to pipe surface.** The pipe coating requires sufficient adhesion to prevent water ingress or migration between the coating and the pipe, along with cohesion to resist handling and soil stress. Soil stress is the main cause of pipe coating failure. "Soil stress effects can be seen on flexible PE coatings with elastomeric adhesives as a characteristic wrinkling. However, other types of coatings can fail by blistering fusion-bonded epoxy (FBE) or fatigue cracking coal tar enamel (CTE)

that are exacerbated by soil movement. . . . resistance to shear must be combined with a measurement of the resistance of the backing material (or outer jacket) to deformation and tensile force. The two properties combine to determine the ability of a pipeline coating to resist damage to soil movement." Soil stress resistance is measured by shear resistance, not by peel strength.

6. **Ability to withstand normal handling, storage (UV degradation), and installation.** The ability of a coating to withstand damage is a function of its impact, abrasion, and flexibility properties. Pipe coatings are subject to numerous handlings between application and backfill. Their ability to resist these forces vary considerably, so those factors need to be evaluated to know if any special precautionary measure should be used. Ultraviolet rays can be very destructive to pipe coatings. Storage life may vary from 6 months to 5 years so resistance to ultraviolet is a very important consideration.

7. **Ability to maintain substantially constant electrical resistivity with time.** The effective electrical resistance of a coating per average square foot depends on the following.

   - Resistivity of the coating material
   - Coating thickness
   - Resistance to moisture absorption
   - Resistance to water vapor transfer
   - Frequency and size of holidays
   - Resistivity of the electrolyte
   - Bond or adhesion of coating

   If the effective resistance is unstable, the CP required may double every few years. It is easy to obtain misleading higher resistance measurements if the soil has not settled around the pipeline and if the moisture has permeated to any holidays in the coating. Experience is necessary to evaluate the validity of these resistance measurements and to use them for designing the CP system.

8. **Resistance to disbonding.** Because most pipelines are cathodically protected, the coating must be compatible with CP. The amount of CP required is directly proportional to the quality and integrity of the coating. The negative aspects of CP are that it may drive water through the coating and that the interface bond surrounding a holiday may have a tendency to disbond. No coating is completely resistant to damage by CP. When large amounts of current are required, stray current and interference problems may arise. This emphasizes the importance of proper coating selection, application, and installation.

9. **Ease of repair.** Because the perfect pipe coating does not exist, we can expect to make some field repairs as well as field-coating of the weld area. Check for compatibility and follow the manufacturer's recommendations. A field repair is never as good as the original coating. Tight inspection should be maintained.

10. **Nontoxic interaction with the environment.** Some coating materials have been modified, restricted, or banned because of environmental and health standards. Asbestos felts and primers with certain solvents have required substitution of glass reinforcements and modification of solvents; changes in fusion-bonded epoxy powders

to eliminate carcinogenic agents have also been necessitated by health and environmental concerns. This has been a major influence of change on today's pipe coatings.

In addition to the above characteristics, the following typical factors should be considered when selecting a pipe coating.

- Type of environment
- Accessibility of pipeline
- Operating temperature of pipeline
- Ambient temperatures during application, storage, shipping, construction, and installation
- Geographical and physical location
- Type of coating on existing pipeline
- Handling and storage
- Installation methods
- Costs
- Pipe surface preparation requirements

Good practice in modern pipeline corrosion control work comprises the use of good coatings in combination with CP as the main lines of defense. Supplementary tactics, such as the use of insulated couplings and local environmental control may be used to reinforce these basic control methods.

In selecting a coating system for a given pipeline project, one of the most important characteristics to design for is stability. By this we mean a coating combination that will have a high electrical resistance after the pipeline has been installed and the backfill stabilized and will lose the least electrical resistance over time.

Those characteristics are important in any event but particularly so where CP is used to supplement the coating. When used with an unstable coating, a CP system that is fully adequate during the early life of a pipeline may no longer provide full protection as the coating deteriorates (as indicated by a reduction in the effective electrical resistance of the coating), which will require additional current. This means that continued expenditures will be necessary for additional CP installations. The overall economics of the coating-plus-CP concept are adversely affected by poor coating performance.

In a review of 50 years of literature on pipeline coatings, the following concepts emerged:

- Selection of the best coating and proper application are very important.
- CP must supplement the coating for 100% protection.
- In-the-ground tests are more reliable than laboratory tests.
- Results of adhesion tests do not correlate with those of cathodic disbondment tests.
- Cathodic disbondment tests are the best tests to measure coating performance.
- The current required for CP is the best measure of coating performance.

- Optimum coating thickness is important.
- Soil stress is one of the main problems.
- Resistance to cathodic disbondment and soil stress are very important requirements of a pipe coating. For a pipe coating to be effective, it should meet these criteria: adhesion, adequate thickness, low moisture absorption/transfer, chemical resistance (especially alkalis from CP), and flexibility.
- Selection of the best appropriate system is important, but proper application is the most important consideration.

A major cause of pipeline coating failure is improper application. A quality material poorly applied is of little value, and the quality of a pipe coating is only as good as the quality of application. To assist in the evaluation of an applicator, the following points should be considered.

1. **Experience.** Research and trial and error have gone into the development of every coating, with close cooperation between applicator, coating manufacturer, equipment manufacturer, and customer. The transition from laboratory to production line is usually a costly experience, which should not be ignored.
2. **Reputation.** This is an asset earned by consistent performance. Not only good quality work but also solving problems and correcting mistakes help to develop a reputation.
3. **Reliability.** Many variables affect the application of coatings. A reliable work force, well-maintained equipment, and consistent quality performance are prerequisites for an applicator.
4. **Conformance to the coating manufacturer's specifications.** The manufacturer's established minimum specifications for application of materials should be met.
5. **Modern automated equipment.** Capital expenditure on automated application equipment is an important part of the success of plastic coatings. Elimination of human errors through automation and controls continues to be an important factor in improved pipe coatings.
6. **Quality control.** Conformance to specifications has to be checked regularly. Knowledge of the applicator's quality control procedures on materials, application, and finished product is essential in the selection of an applicator.

SPECIFICATIONS

Pipeline coating should not be attempted without rigid specifications that precisely spell out every step of the coating procedure to be used. Such specifications are necessary to ensure that the materials being used are applied in a manner that will permit development of the best coating of which those materials are capable.

Because many materials may be used, no specific example of coating specifications will be attempted here. Specifications can be prepared in accordance with the manufacturer's recommendations with such modifications as may be dictated by conditions applicable to the particular project and requirements of the pipeline system in which the coated pipe is to be used.

Areas to be covered by specifications should include the following.

- Cleaning the pipe surface
- Priming, if required
- The coating materials to be used and (if more than one material) the order in which they are to be applied
- Total thickness with permissible tolerances
- Specifications applicable to the particular materials to be used, such as application temperature and thickness, tension (for tapes or wrappers), and other items of a similar nature
- Handling requirements for coating materials, such as storage provisions and maintenance of dry and clean conditions
- Inspection requirements
- Procedure for repair of coating defects
- Basis for rejection of unacceptable coating
- Requirements for handling and transporting the coated pipe
- Details of coating field joints when factory coated pipe is used
- Backfilling requirements

INSPECTION PROCEDURES

Once the coating system and applicator are selected, an important part of a quality installation is good inspection. Inspection should begin with the stockpile of bare pipe through coating operations, load out, coated pipe stockpile, field inspection, joint coating procedure, and backfill of coated pipe. Knowledge of the coating system, plant facilities, quality control methods, shipping requirements, handling, joint coating, field conditions, field holiday detection, and repair are requirements for proper installation. Experience and common sense in interpretation of specifications and analysis of test results will contribute to obtaining the best possible coating results.

As a final backup to application supervision exercised by the coating inspector, usual pipelining practice includes a final test with a holiday detector (or "jeep"). This device impresses an electrical voltage across the coating. An electrode is passed over the entire coating surface and, as it passes over a coating defect, there is an electrical discharge between electrode and pipe. This discharge, or spark, actuates a signaling device, which warns the operator that a holiday has been detected. The operator marks the defect for the repair crew and continues.

Refer to the proper NACE specification when examining for holidays: RP02-74 (latest revision) for the thicker coatings, or RP04-95 (latest revision) for the thinner coating systems.

Plant Holiday Inspection

Pipe coated at a coating plant normally is passed through a holiday detector before shipment. Both mill-coated pipe and that coated over the ditch should be subjected to a final holiday test before being placed in the ditch.

The fewer the defects in a coating which is to be repaired, the better the quality of the completed coating. Nevertheless, if all holidays are picked up by a detector in proper operating conditions, and if they are repaired to conform to an effective procedure, then the quality of the coating as it enters the ditch will at least approach an optimum.

Field Holiday Inspection

Several types of holiday detectors are suitable for field use at the pipeline construction site. The most common ones are usually battery operated and equipped with some type of pipe-encircling electrode. The electrode is arranged so that the ring may be pushed or rolled along the pipe by the operator, allowing the electrode to sweep all portions of the coating surface.

The holiday detector should be operated in strict accordance with the manufacturer's instructions. The coating inspector should be sure the operator has been trained properly and is using the equipment correctly. Some practical operating procedures that apply to any type of holiday locator include the following.

1. Use only adequately charged batteries in battery-operated models.
2. Use detectors that are set to operate at a voltage suitable for the coating being applied. Thick coatings require a high voltage to spark through at defects. On the other hand, too high a voltage may break down thin film coatings such as tapes or other thin plastic coatings.
3. Verify periodically that the detector is operating properly. This may be done by purposely making a coating defect (such as a pinhole made with a knife) and passing the detector over the hole. Failure to detect the hole properly indicates the need for prompt corrective adjustment. During production work, verification should be made at least twice a day and at such other times as the inspector may suspect poor performance.
4. Keep the contact electrodes clean. A buildup of coating material on electrodes may interfere with efficient detection or even prevent it entirely. This possibility is greater with some materials than others. Where found to be a factor, keeping the electrodes clean of the insulating coating material must be insisted on.
5. Maintain a good ground. To be complete, the detector circuit must contact the earth, with a trailing ground wire for example. This trailing wire should be checked for damage daily (or whenever faulty detector operation is suspected) and replaced or repaired if faulty. When working on long sections of line, there usually will be sufficient

conductance between line and earth to permit adequate detector operation. On the other hand, a short length of well-coated pipe on dry skids may have to be grounded to the pipe to establish an adequate circuit.

TYPES OF PIPELINE COATINGS

The types of pipeline coatings and their characteristics are summarized in Table 2.1.

Table 2.1   Types of Pipeline Coatings

Pipe coating	Desirable characteristics	Limitations
Coal tar enamels	80+ years of use Minimum holiday susceptibility Low current requirements Good resistance to cathodic disbondment Good adhesion to steel	Limited manufacturers Limited applicators Health and air quality concerns Change in allowable reinforcements
Mill-applied tape systems	30+ years of use Minimum holiday susceptibility Ease of application Good adhesion to steel Low energy required for application	Handling restrictions—shipping and installation UV and thermal blistering— storage potential Shielding CP from soil Stress disbondment
Crosshead-extruded polyolefin with asphalt/butyl adhesive	40+ years of use Minimum holiday susceptibility Low current requirements Ease of application Nonpolluting Low energy required for application	Minimum adhesion to steel Limited storage (except with carbon black) Tendency for tear to propagate along pipe length
Dual-side-extruded polyolefin with butyl adhesive	25 years of use Minimum holiday susceptibility Low current requirements Excellent resistance to cathodic disbondment Good adhesion to steel Ease of application Nonpolluting Low energy required for application	Difficult to remove coating Limited applicators
Fusion-bonded	35+ years of use Low current requirements Excellent resistance to cathodic disbondment Excellent adhesion to steel Excellent resistance to hydrocarbons	Exacting application parameters High application temperature Subject to steel pipe surface imperfections Lower impact and abrasion resistance High moisture absorption
Multi-layer epoxy/ extruded polyolefin systems	Lowest current requirements Highest resistance to cathodic disbondment Excellent adhesion to steel Excellent resistance to hydrocarbons High impact and abrasion resistance	Limited applicators Exacting application parameters Higher initial cost Possible shielding of CP current

Enamels

Bituminous enamels today are formulated from coal tar with a low carbon content, plasticized by the digestion of coal and heavy aromatic coal tar distillates followed by the addition of an inert mineral filler. Petroleum asphalts with select air-blown asphalts are still used internationally as a pipe coating but their use today in North America is almost nonexistent.

The early coal tar enamel (CTE) coatings usually had an outerwrap of rag felt to provide a backfill shield. However, the rag felt did not prevent the tendency of the CTE to creep and cold-flow under soil stresses at the higher operating temperature range of the pipeline. The use of asbestos felt minimized this problem but the manufacture of asbestos wraps has been discontinued; resin-bonded glass fiber mats are being used at present. CTE systems have been used over 80 years, and a recently introduced two-component epoxy primer when used with special hot service enamel has increased the exposure temperature of a CTE coating system to 230 °F. Today an inner and outer glass fiber mat are incorporated into the CTE coating system simultaneously with the application of the hot CTE. The inner glass mat is pulled into the center of the coating. The outer glass mat is usually presaturated with coal tar to assist wetting and is pulled into the outer surface of the CTE. Extra-heavy-duty outer reinforcement wraps have been developed with woven glass filaments and resin-bonded glass mats to further guard against the effects of soil stresses.

The use of CTE is not expected to increase in the future because of the increased acceptance of fusion-bonded epoxy (FBE), extruded polyolefin, and the FBE–polyolefin combination coatings; decreasing numbers of suppliers; and restrictive regulations.

Extruded Asphalt Mastic

Introduced over 75 years ago, this thick (1/2 to 5/8 in [1.2 to 1.6 cm]), dense mixture of select graded sand, crushed limestone, and glass fiber bound with an air-blown asphalt proved to be a prominent pipe coating. Its weight, cost, and limited availability, however, led to its manufacture being discontinued.

Mill-Applied Tape Coating Systems

Fabric-reinforced petrolatum-coated tapes were first used over 65 years ago. Polyethylene tapes for pipeline coatings were introduced 46 years ago, and mill-applied tape systems were introduced 20 years ago. The mill-applied tape systems consist of a primer, a corrosion-preventative inner layer of tape, and one or two outer layers for mechanical protection. Concern regarding shielding of CP on a disbonded coating has led to development of fused multi-layer tape systems and also of a backing that will not shield CP. Environmental restrictions on solvent-based primers is being resolved by

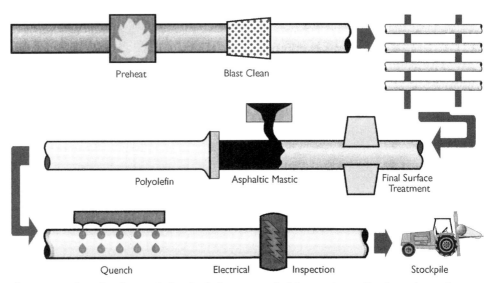

Figure 2.1   Crosshead extruded polyolefin over asphaltic mastic application schematic.

introducing environmentally acceptable primers. In spite of these limitations, the ready availability, ease of application, and cost mean the use of mill-applied tape systems will continue.

Extruded Polyolefin Systems

The first extruded polyolefin system was introduced in 1956 as a crosshead-extruded polyethylene over an asphalt mastic adhesive. Originally introduced for small-diameter pipe (up to 4 1/2 in [11.4 cm]), the material is now available for pipe up to 24 in (61 cm) in diameter; the most popular size is 16 in (40.6 cm). Recent improvements in the adhesive yield better adhesion, and selection of polyethylenes has increased stress crack resistance. Available with polypropylene for use at higher temperatures (up to 190°F [88°C]), these systems have been used in Europe since the mid-1960s, along with the side extrusion method for larger diameters through 60 in (152.4 cm). A copolymer adhesive is applied to eliminate cold flow and minimize shrink-back of the coating. This is followed by the application of an epoxy primer. In late 1972, the side-extrusion method was introduced in the United States. This is a dual-side extrusion, where the butyl rubber adhesive is extruded onto the pipe, followed by the polyethylene extrusion. Side extrusion can coat pipes as great as 145 in (368 cm) in diameter, the only restriction being cleaning and pipe-handling capacity. The extrusion process is a dependable production method with exacting controls. The extruder heats, melts, mixes, and extrudes the materials onto the steel pipe at the desired temperature and pressure. One may select the best polyolefin to meet the end-use requirements, and the process consistently produces holiday-free

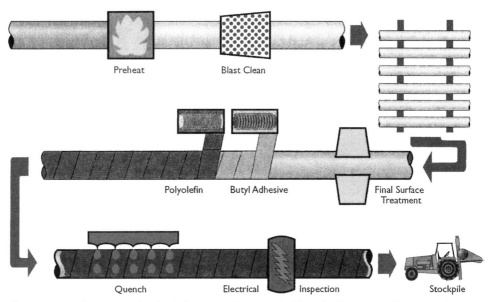

Figure 2.2   Side extruded polyolefin over side extruded butyl adhesive application schematic.

coatings. Extrusion systems are nontoxic and do not degrade air quality. Use of these systems will continue to grow because of handleability, moisture resistance, and overall consistent reproducibility.

Fusion-Bonded Epoxy

Fusion-bonded epoxy (FBE) coatings were first commercially available in late 1961. For many years they were available only on 3/4 to 8 5/8 in (1.9 to 21.9 cm) pipe but now are available in North America for pipe up to 48 in (122 cm) in diameter. For many years FBE was applied at 8–10 mil (203.2–254.0 μm) to be more competitive with other coatings. At present, it is applied at 12 mil minimum up to 25 mil (304.8–635 μm). Over the past 35 years, the resins have evolved through those requiring a primer and some requiring post application heat. None of the present epoxy pipe coatings require a primer, and most plant applications do not require post application heat. Most of the FBE pipe-coating powders have remained the same for the last 18 years. Newer dual-FBE systems were introduced in the early 1990s, to improve resistance to moisture absorption and abrasion.

FBE coatings require great care to apply them properly. In addition to the NACE No. 2 near-white metal finish, a phosphate wash and demineralized water rinse have proven essential to remove potential chloride contamination and improve performance properties. Among the advantages of FBE is that it does not cover up any steel defects present, thus permitting inspection of the pipe after the FBE has been applied. Resistance

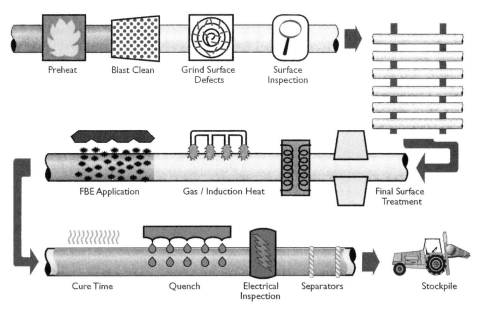

Figure 2.3   Fusion-bonded epoxy powder application schematic.

to soil stress and cathodic disbondment has made FBE the most specified pipe coating in the United States. The trend is to thicker applications with 16 mil (406.4 μm) being the norm. FBE will continue its prominence in the near future but will gradually share this position with improved extruded polyolefin coating systems and the multi-layer (FBE–extruded polyolefin) coating systems.

Liquid Coating Systems

Epoxy coal tars and urethanes are currently the most used liquid pipe-coating systems. They are applied in custom coating or modified plant systems, usually on larger-diameter pipes or ductile iron pipes that may not be compatible with existing pipe-coating plants. Specific manufacturers' specifications must be strictly followed with emphasis on surface cleaning, preparation, and times for cure and overcoat.

These systems are constantly evolving. The largest growth has been in the use of urethane systems.

Multi-Layer Epoxy/Extruded Polyolefin Systems

First introduced in Europe in the mid-1960s as a hard adhesive under polyethylene, followed by the addition of an epoxy primer (FBE or liquid), multi-layer epoxy/polyolefin

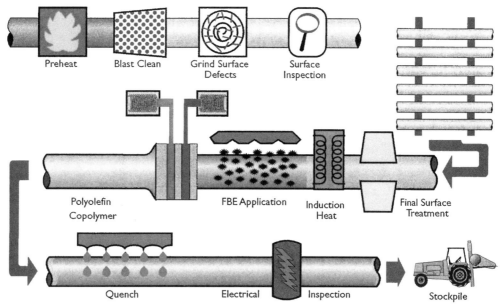

Figure 2.4   3–Layer copolymer coating application schematic.

systems are the most-used pipe-coating systems in Europe. These systems are now available throughout the world.

CONCLUSION

In summarizing this chapter on coatings, pipeline corrosion engineers should stress two areas of knowledge:

- Full information on all details of characteristics, performance, and limitations of the coatings considered for various pipeline projects.
- As complete a summary as practical of the conditions existing along the route of proposed pipeline projects together with information on the manner in which the pipeline will be operated.

When well informed in these matters, corrosion engineers will be able to advise management effectively in the selection of suitable protective coating systems. They also will be able to prepare application specifications and plan inspection programs that will, if effectively implemented, ensure getting the best possible coating job.

BIBLIOGRAPHY

J.D. Kellner, "Shear Strength Testing of Pipeline Coatings and Soil Stress," Corrosion '96, paper no. 199 (Houston, TX: NACE, 1996).

NACE Standard RP0169-92, Section 5, "Coatings" (Houston, TX: NACE, 1967).

A.W. Peabody, Control of Pipeline Corrosion (Houston, TX: NACE, 1967).

W. Roder, Personal correspondence to R.N. Sloan, Oct 3, 1997.

R.N. Sloan, "50 Years of Pipe Coatings—We've Come a Long Way," Corrosion '93, paper no. 17 (Houston, TX: NACE, 1993).

R.N. Sloan and A.W. Peabody, Steel Structures Painting Council, Steel Structures Painting Manual, Vol. 1 (Pittsburgh, PA), 1982.

Chapter 3

Cathodic Protection— How It Works

John A. Beavers

Over the years, cathodic protection (CP) has continued to be treated as a somewhat mysterious term by those not fully conversant with this most useful means of corrosion control. Apparently, many feel that CP is a complicated procedure. In actuality, the basic idea of CP is very simple. Any complications arise during the application of this basic idea. Trained pipeline corrosion engineers, however, are equipped with the knowledge needed to apply the basic concept of CP to pipeline systems and to attain a very high level of effective corrosion control.

In this chapter, a simple theory of CP is described. Factors involved in application as well as limitations that must be kept in mind also are outlined. A more detailed description of the theory of CP is provided in Chapter 16.

BASIC THEORY OF CATHODIC PROTECTION

As defined in Chapter 1, CP is a technique to reduce the corrosion rate of a metal surface by making it the cathode of an electrochemical cell. This definition is explained in greater detail here.

Various conditions that cause pipeline corrosion are described in Chapter 1, and in greater detail in Chapter 16. In each case, anodic areas and cathodic areas are present on the pipe surface. At the anodic areas, current flows from the pipeline steel into the surrounding electrolyte (soil or water) and the pipeline corrodes. At the cathodic areas, current flows from the electrolyte onto the pipe surface and the rate of corrosion is reduced.

In light of the above, it becomes obvious that the rate of corrosion could be reduced if every bit of exposed metal on the surface of a pipeline could be made to collect current.

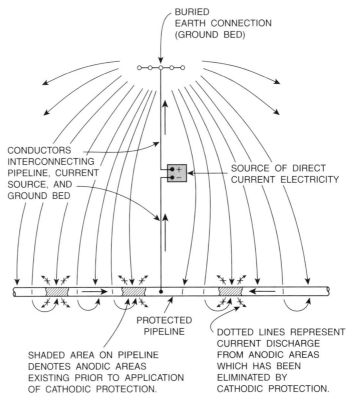

BURIED
EARTH CONNECTION
(GROUND BED)

CONDUCTORS
INTERCONNECTING
PIPELINE, CURRENT
SOURCE, AND
GROUND BED

SOURCE OF DIRECT
CURRENT ELECTRICITY

PROTECTED
PIPELINE

SHADED AREA ON PIPELINE
DENOTES ANODIC AREAS
EXISTING PRIOR TO APPLICATION
OF CATHODIC PROTECTION.

DOTTED LINES REPRESENT
CURRENT DISCHARGE
FROM ANODIC AREAS
WHICH HAS BEEN
ELIMINATED BY
CATHODIC PROTECTION.

Figure 3.1   Basic CP installation.

This is exactly what CP does. Direct current is forced onto all surfaces of the pipeline. This direct current shifts the potential of the pipeline in the active (negative) direction, resulting in a reduction in the corrosion rate of the metal. When the amount of current flowing is adjusted properly, it will overpower the corrosion current discharging from the anodic areas on the pipeline, and there will be a net current flow onto the pipe surface at these points. The entire surface then will be a cathode and the corrosion rate will be reduced. This concept is illustrated in Figure 3.1. A major activity of a CP engineer is to determine the actual level of CP required to reduce the corrosion rate to an acceptable level. Monitoring, in conjunction with the application of CP criteria, are used for this determination. Details of these activities are given in Chapters 4 and 5 of this book.

If, as shown by Figure 3.1, current is forced to flow onto the pipe at areas that were previously discharging current, the driving voltage of the CP system must be greater than the driving voltage of the corrosion cells that are being overcome. The original cathodic areas on the pipe collect current from the anodic areas. Under CP, these same cathodic areas (which were corroding at a negligible rate in the first place) collect more current from the CP system.

For the CP system to work, current must be discharged from an earth connection (ground bed). The sole purpose of this ground bed is to discharge current. In the process of discharging current, the anodes in the ground bed are consumed by corrosion. It is desirable to use materials for the ground bed that are consumed at a much lower rate (pounds/per ampere/per year) than are the usual pipeline metals. This will ensure a reasonably long life for the anodes. Further discussion of ground-bed design is covered in Chapter 7.

PRACTICAL APPLICATION OF CATHODIC PROTECTION

With the simple theory of CP in mind, a preliminary discussion of the techniques of putting CP into actual use is given below. Details of each of these techniques are covered in later chapters.

Cathodic Protection with Galvanic Anodes

The corrosion cell resulting from contact of dissimilar metals is discussed in Chapters 1. In such a cell, one metal is active (negative) with respect to the other and corrodes. In CP with galvanic anodes, this effect is taken advantage of by purposely establishing a dissimilar metal cell strong enough to counteract corrosion cells normally existing on pipelines. This is accomplished by connecting a very active metal to the pipeline. This metal will corrode and, in so doing, will discharge current to the pipeline as shown in Figure 3.2. In the case of CP with galvanic anodes, CP does not eliminate corrosion; rather, it displaces corrosion from the structure being protected to the galvanic anodes.

Under normal circumstances, the current available from galvanic anodes is limited. For this reason, CP by galvanic anodes normally is used where the current required for protection is small. Similarly, the driving voltage existing between pipe steel and galvanic anode metals is limited. Therefore, the contact resistance between the anodes and the earth must be low for the anodes to discharge a useful amount of current. This means that, for normal installations, galvanic anodes are used in low-resistivity soils. A normal installation, as considered here, is one in which the current from a galvanic anode installation is expected to protect a substantial length of pipeline. There are also instances where galvanic anodes are placed at specific points on a pipeline (often termed hot spots) and may be expected to protect only a few feet of pipe, especially where the line is bare. This is an application of the close anode concept, as discussed later in the chapter. Details of the design of galvanic anode installations are discussed further in Chapter 9.

Cathodic Protection with Impressed Current

To be free of the limited driving voltage associated with galvanic anodes, current from some outside power source may be impressed on the pipeline by using a ground bed and

WORKING GALVANIC ANODE OF ZINC OR MAGNESIUM BURIED IN EARTH AND CONNECTED TO PIPELINE WITH WIRE WILL DISCHARGE CURRENT AND PROTECT PIPELINE AS SHOWN.

DRIVING VOLTAGE CAN BE DEMONSTRATED BY CONNECTING ANODE AND UNPROTECTED PIPELINE TO VOLTMETER AS SHOWN. TYPICALLY, PIPELINE COULD BE APPROXIMATELY 1.0 VOLT POSITIVE TO MAGNESIUM ANODE AND 0.5 VOLT POSITIVE TO ZINC ANODE.

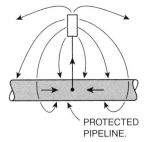
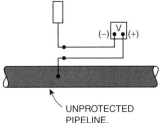

PROTECTED PIPELINE.

UNPROTECTED PIPELINE.

Figure 3.2 Cathodic protection with galvanic anodes.

a power source. Figure 3.1 illustrates this situation. The most common power source is the rectifier. This device converts alternating current (AC) electric power to low-voltage direct current (DC) power. Rectifiers usually are provided with the means for varying the DC output voltage, in small increments, over a reasonably wide range. Although the maximum output voltage may be less than 10 V or close to 100 V, most pipeline rectifiers operate in the range between 10 and 50 V and can be obtained with maximum current outputs ranging from less than 10 A to several hundred amperes. This serves to illustrate the flexibility in choice of power source capacity available to the corrosion engineer when planning an impressed current CP system.

Any other reliable source of DC electric power can be used for impressed current CP systems. Some of these are discussed in Chapter 10. Details of the design of rectifier installations are treated in Chapter 8.

Criteria for Cathodic Protection

Although the basic theory of CP is simple (impressing DC on a structure to reduce the corrosion rate), the obvious question that arises is: How do we know when we have attained adequate protection on a buried structure? The answer to this question is that various criteria have been developed over the years that permit a determination of whether adequate protection is being achieved. Those criteria in more common usage involve measuring the potential between the pipeline and earth. The measurement permits a rapid and reliable determination of the degree of protection attained. Basically, potential criteria are used to evaluate the changes in structure potential with respect to the environment that are caused by CP current flowing to the structure from the surrounding soil or water. The potential measurement criteria, as well as other criteria, are discussed in detail in Chapter 4.

The potential of a pipeline at a given location is commonly referred to as the pipe-to-soil potential. The pipe-to-soil potential can be measured by measuring the voltage between the pipeline and a reference electrode placed in the soil directly over the pipeline. The most common reference electrode used for this purpose is a copper-copper sulfate reference electrode, which is commonly given the acronym CSE. The potential is referred to as an *on* potential if the measurement is made with the CP system energized. The *off* or *instant off* potential estimates the polarized potential when the measurement is made within one second after simultaneously interrupting the current output from all CP current sources and any other current sources affecting that portion of the pipeline. See Chapters 4 and 5 for further details on potential measurements.

Selection of Type, Size, and Spacing of a Cathodic Protection System

Some of the questions to be resolved when planning a pipeline CP system include the following:

1. Shall galvanic anodes be used or would an impressed current system be a better choice?
2. How much total current will be required to attain adequate CP?
3. What should be the spacing between installations, and what will be the current output required from each installation?
4. What provisions should be made to permit testing the completed installation?
5. Are there special conditions at certain locations that will require modifications in the general plan for CP?

These questions cannot be answered using only material covered up to this point. The needed information that will influence the decision includes such items as:

- The corrosivity of the environment;
- The soil structure and resistivity;
- Whether the pipeline is bare or coated;
- If coated, the quality and electrical strength of the coating and the presence of environmental conditions that may cause the coating to deteriorate;
- The metal or alloy used in the pipeline;
- The size of the pipeline and its ability to conduct CP current;
- The presence of metallic structures from other resources (usually termed foreign structures) crossing or close to the pipeline to be protected;
- The presence of stray current from man-made or natural sources.

As this list makes apparent, an appreciable quantity of information and data must be accumulated with respect to the pipeline for which CP is planned. Once reliable information is obtained in sufficient detail, answers to the questions posed earlier in this section can be developed and a sound engineering design can be prepared. Chapters 5 through 12 are concerned with getting the needed data and using it in the CP design.

Effect of the Coating on Cathodic Protection

In the discussion of coatings in Chapter 2, it was stated that better than 99% of the surface of a well-coated pipe would be completely free of corrosion. Also, it was stated that CP would be relatively easy to apply because only minute areas of exposed steel would require protection. Let us look at these statements again and get an idea of their significance in terms of the amount of current that must be supplied for CP.

Figure 3.1 illustrates the pattern of current flow that is expected for protection of a section of bare pipeline. The picture is quite different with a high-resistance barrier coating between the pipeline and the environment, as illustrated by Figure 3.3.

In Figure 3.3, current from the CP ground bed is shown flowing to all areas where pipe metal is exposed. In so doing, the original corrosive current discharge from defects in anodic areas is reduced. In addition to the current shown flowing to defects, current also flows through the coating material itself. No coating material is a perfect insulator (even when absolutely free of any defects whatsoever) and will conduct some current. The amount will depend on the electrical resistivity of the material (expressed in ohm-cm) and its thickness. When a high-resistivity coating is used, the current passing directly

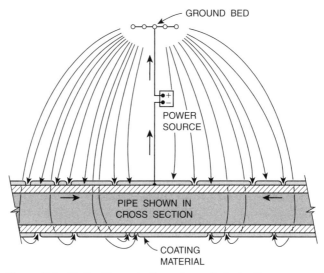

Figure 3.3   Cathodic protection of a coated pipeline.

Table 3.1   Range of Current Required for Protection of 10 Miles
of 36-in Diameter Pipe (under conditions stated in text)

Effective coating resistance in ohms for one average square foot	Current required in amperes
Bare Pipe[a]	500
10,000	14.91
25,000	5.964
50,000	2.982
100,000	1.491
500,000	0.2982
1,000,000	0.1491
5,000,000	0.0298
Perfect coating	0.000058

[a]Bare pipe assumed to require a minimum of 1 mA/ft^2.

through the coating will be negligible compared with that flowing to coating defects unless the number and size of the defects are unusually small.

Table 3.1 gives some idea of the CP current range that may be encountered. The current required to protect a 10-mile section of 36-in diameter pipeline is compared for a wide range of coating resistances, from bare pipe to a holiday-free coating 3/32 in thick with a resistivity of 1×10^{13} ohm-cm. The pipeline section is assumed to be in soil having an average resistivity of 1×10^3 ohm-cm. The current required is that needed to cause a 0.3 V drop across the effective resistance between the pipeline and remote earth (polarization effects are neglected).

The effective coating resistances given in Table 3.1 all could be obtained with the same coating for which the perfect coating current figure is given but with varying numbers of coating defects. For the examples used in the table, effective resistances of 1×10^4 to 2.5×10^4 ohms for one square foot of coating reflect either poor handling and installation of the coated pipe or degradation of the coating after installation. For pipelines in 1×10^3 ohm-cm soil, average resistances of 1×10^5 to 5×10^6 ohms for one square foot of coating indicate good to superior construction work and little or no degradation of the coating with time.

The table shows that a bare pipeline can accept thousands of times more current than the same line with a superior coating. An ordinary two-cell flashlight bulb drawing ~0.5 A can take nearly 17 times as much current as that required to cathodically protect 10 miles of 36-in diameter pipe with a superior coating (5×10^6 ohms for one square foot). In contrast, the current required to protect a line with a poorly applied coating (2.5×10^4 ohms for one square foot) could be at least 200 times more than the current required if the same coating were applied and handled in a superior manner. The examples given are meant to stress a most important point. Because of the wide variation possible, the pipeline corrosion engineer must know the present condition of the coating on the pipeline before determining how much current will be needed from a proposed CP system. The engineer also must be able to estimate the rate of degradation of the coating so that the CP system can be designed to protect the pipeline as the coating degrades.

Very long lengths of pipeline can be protected with a single CP system. For example, it is frequently possible to protect over 50 miles of cross-country pipeline from one location, if the pipeline has a large-diameter and is well coated. Oddly enough, it is easier to protect long lengths of large-diameter pipe than of small-diameter pipe from a single CP installation. In a CP installation such as that shown in Figure 3.1, current flow at any location on the pipe is inversely proportionally to the total resistance of the system at that location, based on Ohm's law. Once the current enters the mass of the earth from a ground bed, it is in a very low resistance conductor and theoretically will travel great distances if there is a suitable return conductor. In pipeline work, the pipe itself is the return conductor. For a given wall thickness, large-diameter pipe has a lower resistance than small-diameter pipe because the former has a larger cross-sectional area and the resistance of a conductor is inversely proportional to the cross-sectional area. Therefore, a larger-diameter pipe will permit extension of effective CP for substantially greater distances. It also follows, then, that better coatings cause less rapid buildup of current in the pipe and extend the distance of effective protection from a single CP installation.

Over-Protection of Coated Lines

Under some conditions, excessive amounts of CP current to a coated pipeline may damage the coating. This process is called *cathodic disbondment*. The current flow promotes water and ion migration through the coating and an increase in the electrolyte pH at the pipe surface. If the polarized potential is sufficiently negative, hydrogen can also evolve in the form of gas bubbles on the pipe surface. All of these processes are detrimental to coatings and promote degradation and disbondment.

The polarized potential at which significant damage to a coating occurs is a function of many factors, including the inherent resistance of the coating to degradation, the quality of the coating application, the soil conditions, and the pipeline temperature. As a rule of thumb, off-potentials that are more negative than −1.1 V (CSE) should be avoided to minimize coating degradation. In this connection, it should be noted that damaging conditions can be created readily by an improperly adjusted impressed current CP system, and can sometimes result when using high-potential galvanic anodes such as magnesium, but seldom if ever will develop when using low-potential galvanic anodes such as zinc.

Remote vs Close Ground Beds

Flow of current from an external source to a pipeline (as is true when the pipeline is cathodically protected) will be accompanied by a potential difference between the earth and the pipeline, the earth being positive (+) and the pipeline negative (−). The potential difference is used in certain criteria for determining the degree of CP, as will be covered in Chapter 4. Developing the desired potential difference can be accomplished in either of two ways:

- By making the pipeline negative with respect to remote earth, or
- By making the earth positive with respect to the pipe in local areas.

The first method uses remote ground beds, from which substantial lengths of pipeline can be protected. The second method uses close ground beds or anodes, which afford protection only in their immediate vicinity.

Remote Ground Beds

The sketch in Figure 3.1 may be used yet again to illustrate the remote ground bed type of installation. Current discharge, from an anode or group of anodes forming the ground bed, will cause voltage drops in the earth between points along lines radiating from the ground bed. Close to the ground bed, the voltage drop per unit of distance is relatively high. As one moves away from the ground bed, this voltage drop per unit of distance becomes less and less until a point is reached beyond which no further significant voltage drop can be observed. This point may be considered as remote earth and establishes the radius of what is termed the area of influence surrounding the ground bed.

Exactly as described above, current flowing to the protected pipeline also will cause a voltage drop in the soil adjacent to the line, and there will be an area of influence surrounding the pipeline. The ground bed shown in Figure 3.1 may be said to be remote from the pipeline if it is far enough away such that there is no significant overlap between the area of influence surrounding the ground bed and the area of influence surrounding the pipeline. Under such conditions, current flows from the ground bed into the general mass of the earth, which may be considered a resistance-less, or infinite, conductor. Current will then flow from this infinite conductor to the pipeline to be protected and cause a voltage drop across the resistance between the pipeline and this infinite conductor. The simple equivalent circuit shown in Figure 3.4 illustrates this concept. Under these conditions, the pipeline will be made negative with respect to remote earth and, if made sufficiently negative, effective CP will result.

With current flowing in an infinite conductor as illustrated, the resistance of the pipeline itself may limit the length of pipeline that can be protected from one ground bed. As described above, pipelines having lower incremental longitudinal resistances (large diameter lines) can have longer sections protected from one ground bed, other conditions being equal. A limitation at the most remote point from the ground bed is the minimum potential required for adequate CP. A limitation near the ground bed is the need to maintain the pipe-to-soil polarized potential at values that are less negative than about 1.1 V (CSE) to avoid coating damage and hydrogen effects in susceptible steels.

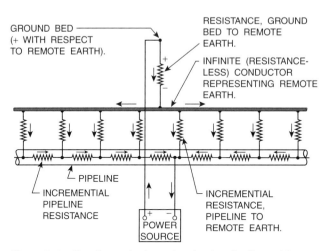

Figure 3.4   Simple equivalent circuit of a pipeline with a remote ground bed.

Close Ground Beds

The use of close anodes, or a series of anodes, is quite different from the remote type of installation just described. Their successful use depends on the area of influence surrounding each ground bed anode as has been discussed in general terms. For a better understanding of how close anodes are used, the conductive path between a ground bed anode and remote earth is examined in greater detail.

The current per unit of cross-sectional area of earth (current density) flowing away from a ground bed anode is highest close to the anode and decreases with distance. Where the current density is highest, the greatest point-to-point potential drops can be observed in the earth. The net result of this effect is that most of the potential drop to remote earth of a single anode normally is encountered within the first few feet. This is illustrated by Figure 3.5, which shows the percentage of the total resistance or potential drop (with respect to remote earth) as a function of distance from an anode that is discharging current.

The curves in Figure 3.5 are based on a 3-in diameter × 60-in long anode discharging 2 A of current in 1×10^3 ohm-cm resistivity soil. Other anode sizes will result in somewhat different shaped curves, but the one illustrated is typical. Non-uniform soil conditions also will change the shape of the curve. The curve is based on the following formula from Rudenberg (1945):

$$V_x = \frac{0.038 I \rho}{\pi y} \log_{10} \frac{(y + \sqrt{y^2 + x^2})}{x} \tag{1}$$

where:

V_x = Potential at x (see Figure 3.5) in volts caused by ground anode current
I = Ground anode current in amperes

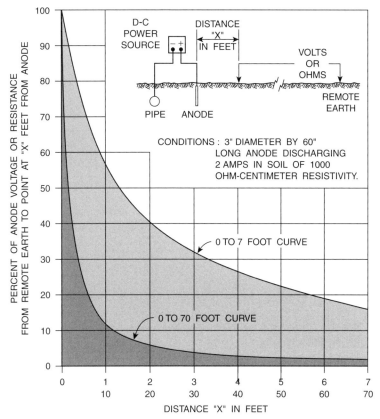

Figure 3.5 Gradients at a ground bed anode.

ρ = Earth resistivity in ohm-centimeters
y = Length of anode in earth in feet
x = Distance from anode in feet

If x is greater than $10y$, then

$$V_x = \frac{0.0052 I \rho}{x} \tag{2}$$

Note that the same curve may be used to indicate the percentage of total voltage drop as well as resistance. This is because both properties are directly related through Ohm's law, which says that the voltage drop across a resistance is equal to the value of the resistance multiplied by the current flowing through it (volts = amps × ohms; $V = \text{IR}$). Therefore, if current flows from a ground anode to a point that is far enough away to include 50% of the total resistance of the anode to remote earth, then the voltage drop between the anode and that point will be 50% of the total voltage drop between the anode and remote earth. Further, it is important to note that the earth within the area

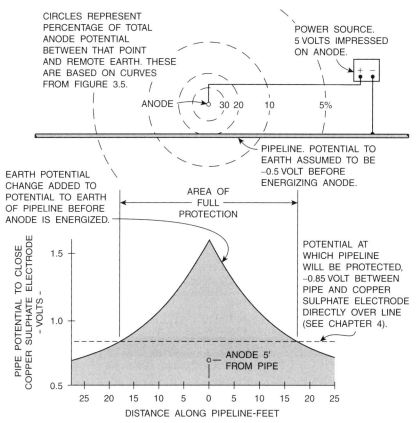

Figure 3.6 Protective potentials impressed on a pipeline by a close ground bed anode.

of influence surrounding a current-discharging anode will be positive with respect to remote earth and the most-positive earth will be closest to the anode. Let's see how this positive potential gradient can be used to advantage.

In the upper portion of Figure 3.6, it can be seem that a pipeline will pass through the area of influence surrounding a ground bed anode located close to the pipe. This means it will pass through earth that is at a positive potential with respect to remote earth. As shown in the potential plot in the lower half of Figure 3.6, there will be a limited area along the pipeline opposite the anode in which the net potential difference between the pipe and adjacent soil will, because of this effect, be sufficient to attain CP. This is in accord with the criterion for protection of steel (pipe-to-soil potential of at least −0.85 V [CSE]). For the analysis shown in Figure 3.6, it is assumed that the IR voltage drop error in the pipe-to-soil potential measurement is negligible. Where this assumption does not hold, the area of full protection will be smaller. A further discussion of criteria and their application is given in Chapter 4.

Figure 3.6 indicates that approximately 35 ft of the pipeline would be protected under the conditions given when 5 V are impressed on the anode. A galvanic anode will operate similarly, but because its voltage output is less (see Chapter 9), the length of pipeline protected likewise would be less. Typically, with anodes spaced 1 foot from the pipe, protection could be expected for 4 to 5 ft if using zinc anodes and 8 to 10 ft if using magnesium anodes.

When only a few anodes are close to a large pipeline (particularly if uncoated), not enough current will be discharged from them to change the potential of the pipeline to remote earth to any appreciable degree. If, however, many such close anodes are used, enough current may be flowing to all portions of the line to make the line more negative with respect to remote earth. This would approach the results discussed previously for remote ground beds.

The region of a pipe protected by a single anode is analogous to a flashlight beam that is shined on a wall. As the flashlight is moved closer to the wall, the area illuminated decreases but the light intensity increases (the light gets brighter). In this analogy, the brightness of the light is equivalent to the current flow to the pipe. The objective of optimizing a CP design is to select the type and location of the anode ground beds to deliver the optimum level of protection that covers the largest area of the structure.

Electrical Shielding and Cathodic Protection

An electrical shield can be defined as any barrier that will prevent or divert from a pipeline, for which protection is intended, the flow of CP current from soil or water. This electrical shielding can be of two types. One may result from a nonmetallic insulating barrier that prevents current flow. The other involves diversion of current to other metallic structures surrounding and in electrical contact with a pipeline to be protected. Each type will be discussed.

Shielding by an Insulating Barrier

Figure 3.7 illustrates a condition in which part of a coated pipeline is surrounded by a loose insulating barrier. The space between this barrier and the pipeline may be filled with earth or water. In the absence of CP, the exposed steel will be subject to corrosion if there are defects in the pipeline coating. If the pipeline is under CP, the protective current may not reach the exposed steel at coating defects under this barrier.

One may argue that CP current could flow to the shielded coating defects through the soil or water between the insulating barrier and the pipeline. In fact, it can, but often not in sufficient amounts for protection. The amount of current reaching bare metal at a coating defect will be a function of the longitudinal resistance of the layer of soil or water between the shield and the pipe through which the current must flow. The closer the spacing between the shield and the pipeline, the higher the per-unit longitudinal resistance of the electrolyte (soil or water) because of a reduced cross-sectional area carrying the

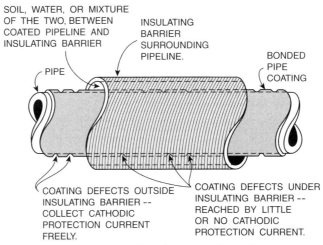

Figure 3.7 Electrical shielding by an insulating barrier.

protective current. This means that the ability of electrical current to penetrate such spaces is not great. As a practical matter, one normally should not expect to force current into the space a distance greater than about 3 to 10 times the thickness of the layer between the shield and the pipeline. This figure is not rigorous but serves as a guide to the approximate relationships involved.

The foregoing discussion applies to a completely insulating barrier. It need not completely encircle the pipe, as is shown in Figure 3.7, but may partially shield an area, the way a large rock might. If the barrier is an insulating material but is sufficiently porous to absorb moisture and become conductive, enough current may pass to partially or completely protect the pipe at coating defects. Such a barrier would not, then, act as a complete shield.

Shielding by Shorted Cased Crossing

Figure 3.8 illustrates a common situation involving a metallic shield that diverts CP current from its intended path. This condition occurs at cased pipeline crossings where the casing is in metallic contact with the pipeline. In the example, water has accumulated between the casing and the pipeline but the metallic contact prevents CP of the pipe within the casing.

With the short circuit in place, CP current collects on the outside of the casing and flows along the casing to the point of contact between the pipe and the casing. At the point of contact, the CP current flows to the carrier pipe through the metallic contact and then along the carrier pipe back to the CP installation. Under these conditions, essentially no CP current will flow through the casing wall to the pipe surface, leaving pipe inside the casing free to corrode even though the rest of the line is fully protected.

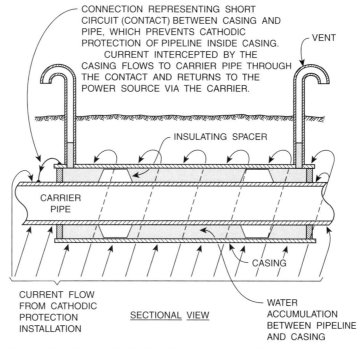

Figure 3.8   Electrical shielding by a shorted pipeline casing.

If the casing pipe is free of a metallic contact with the carrier pipe (i.e., properly insulated), the metallic casing material simply serves as part of the conducting environment. Cathodic protection current then is able to flow straight through the casing walls to those portions of pipeline in contact with any electrolyte inside the casing. It should be recognized that current discharging from the inner surface of the casing wall would corrode the inside of the casing. Furthermore, the level of protection of a cased carrier pipe will be less than that afforded an uncased carrier pipe, even in the absence of a short, because of the voltage drops across the metal-electrolyte interfaces on the ID and OD surface of the casing. For these reasons, it is important to keep the number and size of coating defects to a minimum on the carrier pipe within a casing.

Figure 3.8 shows a pipeline in half-section as well as a casing installed with end seals and insulating spacers. The spacers and seals are intended to keep the casing completely free from metallic contact with the pipeline. This is not always accomplished. Contacts may develop from such conditions as the following:

- Improperly installed end seals
- Insufficient number of, or failed, spacers
- Crooked or out-of-round casing
- Curved carrier pipe
- Welding icicles inside the casing

- Test point wiring (see Chapter 12) contacting the end of a casing or vent pipe
- Metallic objects or scrap inadvertently left in the casing during construction

Whatever the cause, the condition may be represented by a connection bond as shown in Figure 3.8.

If the pipe inside the casing is coated perfectly or if the space between the pipe and casing is dry, there would be no corrosion problem other than atmospheric corrosion of exposed steel. These conditions are not likely to be present. Pipeline coatings are likely to be damaged when coated pipe is being pushed into a casing, and the longer the casing, the greater the probability of damage. Water sometimes enters the casing through defective end seals, or it can condense from air entering through the vents. Figure 3.8 shows water in the space between the pipe and casing, as is found in a surprisingly large percentage of cased crossings. If the oxygen supply to the water accumulated inside a casing is restricted sufficiently, this will tend to slow the rate of corrosion. But failures do occur and when they do, repair is much more involved and expensive than at places where pipe is buried directly in earth along the right-of-way. The critical nature of cased crossings from the standpoint of safety hazards and repair difficulty justifies taking pains to ensure that pipe inside casings is protected properly.

For new construction, cased crossings should be avoided whenever structural analyses indicate they are not needed and codes/regulations permit uncased crossings. Where the use of casings cannot be avoided, care must be exercised in selecting the proper materials and design for casing spacers and end seals.

Recent practices have incorporated pumping mortar/concrete into the annular space between the carrier pipe and the casing. This is a questionable practice because stresses may result in cracking of the concrete, potentially causing coating damage. At road crossings, chlorides from deicing salts may migrate to the areas of coating damage, and cause corrosion damage to the carrier pipe.

On some pipeline systems, bare or poorly coated casing pipe is used on well-coated pipelines. If such casings are shorted to the line, there is a disadvantage in addition to the loss of protection on the pipe inside the casing. This is because a single bare cased crossing in contact with the coated pipe can absorb as much CP current as several miles of pipeline. Therefore, shorted casings impose an unnecessary load on the CP installations.

Chapter 13 includes suggested procedures for clearing short circuits at cased crossings. Also, if the short circuit cannot be cleared because of inaccessibility, suggestions are given for corrosion-proofing the pipe inside the casing by methods other than CP.

Shielding by Reinforcing Wire in Weight Coating

A shielding action, similar to that encountered at a shorted cased crossing, can occur if reinforcing wire in concrete weight coating is accidentally in electrical contact with the pipe. The condition is illustrated in Figure 3.9. Although the reinforcing wire mesh or spiral wound wire does not form a solid shield as with a shorted cased crossing, the closely spaced wires can intercept most of the CP current if the wires are in electrical

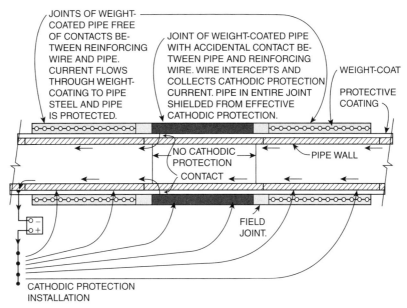

Figure 3.9 Electrical shielding by shorted reinforcing wire in weight coating.

contact with the pipe. Just one point of contact in a length of weight-coated pipe can shield the entire length.

Wire reinforcement applied at a coating mill should not contact pipe steel. Furthermore, particular care must be taken at field joints if reinforcing wire is applied to them after welding and coating. Careful inspection is necessary to ensure that wire is applied in such a manner that contact does not occur. This is very important because such contacts will reduce or completely nullify the beneficial effects of CP in their vicinity.

Furthermore, in underwater installations, the weight-coated pipe will, for all practical purposes, be inaccessible for elimination of the contacts. To ensure that contacts do not exist, it is good practice to make resistance measurements between the pipe steel and wire mesh. Instrumentation and techniques for such measurements are discussed in Chapter 6. This problem can be completely avoided by using nonmetallic reinforcing wires in concrete weight coating.

Shielding in Congested Areas

Piping in congested areas, such as pumping stations and tank farms, may encounter a form of shielding that is the result of the close proximity of the underground metal structures. In Figure 3.10, a condition is represented wherein a network of piping in a restricted area is protected by a remote-type ground bed. The remote ground bed and suitably sized rectifier may change the potential of the entire structure sufficiently to

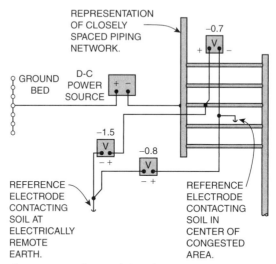

Figure 3.10   Electrical shielding in congested areas.

give an indication of full protection when measured with respect to a remote reference electrode, such as the −1.5 V indicated in Figure 3.10. But, if a measurement is made between remote earth and earth in the midst of the congested area, the potential of the whole earth mass in the area may have been changed as indicated by the −0.8 V reading. When this occurs, there may be relatively low potentials between the pipe and adjacent earth. This is indicated by the −0.7 V reading in Figure 3.10, which is less than full protection using the −0.85 V (CSE) criterion (see Chapter 4). The shielding effect will tend to be greatest near the center of the congested area.

Conditions at each such congested area will determine whether or not the effect described in the preceding paragraph will be serious. The effect may not be important if all piping is well coated and if there are no other underground metallic structures (particularly uncoated ones) in electrical contact with the piping to be protected. In this situation, the protected pipe can polarize readily and the amount of current flowing in the earth within the congested area may not be sufficient to change the potential of the earth mass itself to any substantial degree. In an area such as a pumping station, however, there may be contacts with such things as the station grounding system, reinforced concrete foundations, the electrical system, tanks, and water piping. Total current flow to the area then may be enough to cause potential gradients in the earth, which will create the shielding effect described. If all bare piping (rather than coated piping) were used, the effect could be very severe.

Where congested area shielding is a problem, it may not be practical to rely on a remote type of CP system. Cathodic protection still can be attained by the use of the close anodes discussed earlier in this chapter. Such anodes (either galvanic or impressed current) must then be distributed throughout the congested area in such a way that the areas of influence surrounding the anodes overlap sufficiently to permit development of protective potentials on the entire interconnected structure. See Chapter 7 for further discussion. Chapter 9 also mentions the use of galvanic anodes for electrical grounding to help relieve the congested area shielding effects at pumping stations and similar areas.

EFFECTIVENESS OF CATHODIC PROTECTION

Stopping the Development of Pipeline Leaks

That CP, properly designed and maintained, can control pipeline corrosion effectively on steel systems has been demonstrated in countless instances. Chapter 4 describes criteria for determining whether adequate corrosion control has been achieved. Chapter 5 describes field-monitoring techniques required for the assessment of these criteria.

The proof of the effectiveness of CP is most apparent where protection has been applied to old piping systems that had been developing leaks at a rapidly increasing rate. Suitable protection systems can stop the development of further leaks in dramatic fashion. Woody (Collection of papers on underground pipeline corrosion, Vol. IX) provides an example of such results on a section of natural gas mains in Houston, Texas, which had been under protection for over 20 years. Reduction in the number of leaks was impressive, as shown in Figure 3.11. The curve shows that further leak development was stopped once CP was applied to the pipeline. This study was made on mains in corrosive soil, where leaks were becoming so numerous that abandonment was seriously considered prior to the decision to apply CP. Stetler (1980) reported a similar impressive reduction in the frequency of leaks on a cast iron water main after application of CP.

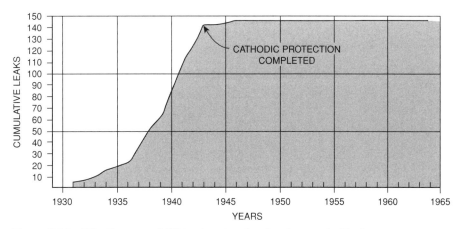

Figure 3.11   Effectiveness of CP in stopping the development of leaks.

Presence of Stray Current

Where stray current corrosion is a factor, CP alone may not be the best method of controlling corrosion. The stray currents can be man-made or natural direct currents from sources other than galvanic corrosion cells on the pipeline itself. The applicability of CP depends to a great extent on the severity and degree of variation of the stray currents picked up and discharged by the pipeline. Low-level steady-state (static) currents or currents that vary within reasonable narrow limits may be controlled with CP systems. Larger stray currents, particularly those showing wide variation and reversals in direction of flow (dynamic stray currents), usually require special analysis and corrective measures, as discussed in Chapter 11.

Aluminum Pipe

Cathodic protection of aluminum pipe is a special problem, in that aluminum is sensitive to alkali (high-pH environments). As previously discussed, the cathodic reactions in a CP circuit generate alkali at the cathode surface. If too much CP is applied, the alkalinity at the surface of an aluminum pipe may become sufficient to break down the passive films on aluminum, resulting in significant rates of attack, even in the presence of CP. This process, sometimes termed cathodic corrosion, does not occur on iron or steel pipelines. The danger is that a buried aluminum pipeline under strong CP actually may corrode faster than it would if it had not been cathodically protected at all.

Precise limitations for CP of aluminum pipe have not been established. Experience indicates that low-level CP can be beneficial. As a guide, the protective potentials on aluminum pipe should be maintained at a less negative value than about -1.00 to -1.10 V (CSE). Because of this limitation, the CP design for an aluminum pipeline generally requires greater care and precision than one for a steel pipeline. Criteria for effective CP of aluminum piping are discussed in greater detail in Chapter 4.

EFFECT OF CATHODIC PROTECTION ON OTHER STRUCTURES

It is quite possible to design a CP system for a pipeline that will protect the line, but, through stray current effects, may promote corrosion of neighboring underground metallic structures. It is important that the corrosion engineer be fully informed about conditions that can result in such adverse effects to these foreign structures. The designs can then minimize this possibility, and the engineer will know where to look for other structures that may be subject to damage.

Corrosion damage to an underground structure caused by a CP system on another structure is commonly called interference. This is actually the result of a form of stray current corrosion. Corrective measures for such problems are treated in Chapter 11. This form of stray current damage is most commonly associated with impressed current CP systems. Galvanic anode systems, because of their low voltage, are not as likely to cause trouble, but they are not completely free of the possibility.

One way to think of interference effects is to consider the earth between a ground bed and a pipeline under CP as one resistance path for the current flow. A foreign pipeline or other metallic structure forms a second resistance path, where the current can jump onto and off of the structure to complete the circuit. According to Ohm's law, the relative amount of current in the two paths is inversely proportional to the relative resistances of those paths.

Another way to consider the problem of interference effects is to consider the voltage gradients associated with the flow of current in the earth. As previously described in this chapter, the resistance and voltage drops are directly related. A further discussion of the problem, with this in mind, follows.

Foreign Pipelines Close to Cathodic Protection Ground Beds

A CP ground bed installed too close to a foreign pipeline can be harmful. Two general conditions will be discussed.

Case 1

In Figure 3.12, a foreign pipeline is shown passing through the zone of positive earth potentials (area of influence) surrounding an impressed current ground bed and then crossing the protected pipeline at a more remote location. The positive earth potentials will force the foreign pipeline to pick up current at points within the area of influence. This current must then complete the electrical circuit and return to the negative terminal of the rectifier power source. Figure 3.12 illustrates this by showing most of the picked-up current flowing along the foreign line toward the point where the two lines cross and then leaving the foreign line in the vicinity of the crossing. This current is then picked up by the protected pipeline and returned to the rectifier. Where the current leaves the foreign line in the vicinity of the crossing, accelerated corrosion of the foreign pipeline occurs.

Usually, a small amount of current will flow along the foreign pipeline in the opposite direction from the ground bed area. This is indicated as endwise current in the figure. This current will leave the foreign pipeline at remote locations, usually in areas of relatively low soil resistivity. The severity of the effect is largely a function of the impressed voltage on the ground bed and the proximity of the foreign pipeline to the ground bed. Where the impressed voltage is high and the foreign pipeline is close to it, current forced onto the foreign pipeline tends to be high and can cause damage. In such instances, the foreign pipeline can fail within a short time if corrective action is not taken. Aluminum and lead structures can suffer corrosion damage at both the pick-up and discharge points because of the mechanism described in the section on aluminum piping.

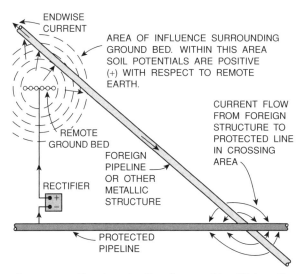

Figure 3.12   Foreign pipeline damaged by CP installation—Case 1.

In cases where the current pickup by the foreign pipeline is not too great, a metallic bond can be installed between the two lines as discussed in Chapter 11. However, severe cases may necessitate abandonment of the ground bed when an adequate bond between the two systems circulates so much of the rectifier current through the foreign pipeline that little is left for CP of the pipeline for which the CP system was installed. This emphasizes the need for care in selecting CP installation sites so that conditions such as these can be avoided.

Case 2

Figure 3.13 illustrates a condition where a foreign pipeline (or other buried metallic structure) closely approaches a CP ground bed but does not cross the protected pipeline. In this case, as in the preceding case, the foreign pipeline is forced to pick up current in the area of positive earth potentials surrounding the ground bed. Current will flow endwise along the foreign pipeline in both directions from the ground bed. This stray current must then leave the foreign pipeline in more remote areas (such as at areas of low soil resistivity) to flow to the protected pipeline and then back to the rectifier to complete the circuit. This means there may be many areas of current discharge and damage to the foreign pipeline rather than a single discharge area as in the preceding case.

Corrective actions may include the use of bond cables from the foreign pipeline to the negative terminal of the rectifier or the installation of CP systems on the foreign pipeline to reverse the flow of endwise current, all of which are discussed further in Chapter 11. As in the preceding case, current pickup by the foreign pipeline may be so intense that

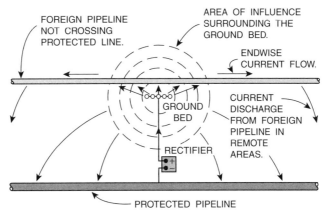

Figure 3.13   Foreign pipeline damage caused by CP installation—Case 2.

correction of the condition may not be practical if the ground bed is too close to the foreign pipeline. The ground bed then may have to be abandoned.

In selecting ground bed sites for impressed current systems, the presence of foreign pipelines, which could be adversely affected, must be carefully explored. In areas of high soil resistivity, where relatively high voltage rectifiers may be used, the area of influence surrounding a ground bed may extend for several hundred feet. Small units in low-resistivity soil will not create as extensive a problem. In any event, tests must be made by the corrosion engineer to assure that neighboring pipelines will not be damaged or, if there is some influence, that the possibility of damage can be corrected economically.

In many major metropolitan areas, corrosion control coordinating committees regularly meet to manage interfering systems. The corrosion engineer has an ethical responsibility to inform and cooperate with representatives of neighboring facilities when designing and installing a potentially interfering source of stray current. Coordinating committees are discussed further at the end of this chapter.

In the preceding sections, impressed current CP systems were used to illustrate stray current corrosion on foreign pipelines because these systems are most likely to promote this form of corrosion. The same conditions can be established with galvanic anodes but the anodes would have to be very close to the foreign pipeline for the line to pick up any appreciable portion of their output. This is because the area of influence surrounding galvanic anodes is relatively small. Nevertheless, the corrosion engineer must make certain not to establish conditions that will lead to stray current corrosion, regardless of the type of CP system used. As with impressed current systems, care must be used in selecting galvanic anode installation sites; however, much closer spacing to foreign pipelines is permissible in most cases. Usually, a spacing of 15 ft would be ample, although the corrosion engineer should check for current pickup on foreign structures this close. Even closer spacing might be tolerated in instances where tests show that the area of influence surrounding the galvanic anodes is sufficiently limited.

Foreign Pipelines Crossing Bare Cathodically Protected Lines

Earlier in the chapter, a potential gradient in the earth surrounding a cathodically protected pipeline was mentioned. This gradient is caused by current flowing onto the pipeline from remote earth and is the reverse of the potential gradient or area of influence surrounding a ground bed that is discharging current. As a result of this gradient, the earth in the immediate vicinity of the pipeline is negative with respect to remote earth. This is illustrated by Figure 3.14.

The size of the area (zone) of influence around a protected pipeline is a function of the amount of current flowing to the line per unit area of pipe surface (current density). The greater the current density, the greater the zone of influence. For well-coated pipelines, the current is so small that potential gradients in the earth around the line are negligible. A cathodically protected bare line, however (or large holidays on coated lines), can collect so much current that substantial voltage drops can be measured in the earth around the line. A foreign pipeline or other buried metallic structure crossing the protected bare line will pass through the potential gradient region and be subject to possible corrosion damage. This is illustrated by Figure 3.15.

Within the potential gradient region, the foreign pipeline tends to become positive with respect to adjacent soil. This is most pronounced at the point of crossing. The voltage difference between pipe and earth can force the foreign pipeline to pick up CP current in electrically remote sections and discharge it to the protected line in the crossing area. The foreign pipeline will be damaged by such discharge to earth, with the point of greatest probable damage being directly at the point of crossing with the protected bare line.

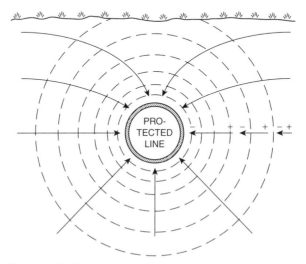

Figure 3.14 Potential gradients in earth around cathodically protected pipeline.

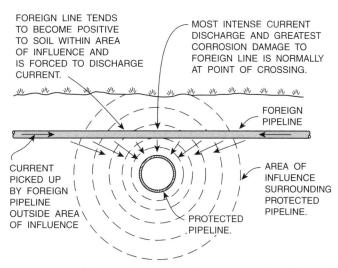

FOREIGN LINE TENDS TO BECOME POSITIVE TO SOIL WITHIN AREA OF INFLUENCE AND IS FORCED TO DISCHARGE CURRENT.

MOST INTENSE CURRENT DISCHARGE AND GREATEST CORROSION DAMAGE TO FOREIGN LINE IS NORMALLY AT POINT OF CROSSING.

FOREIGN PIPELINE

CURRENT PICKED UP BY FOREIGN PIPELINE OUTSIDE AREA OF INFLUENCE

AREA OF INFLUENCE SURROUNDING PROTECTED PIPELINE.

PROTECTED PIPELINE.

Figure 3.15 Effect on foreign pipeline passing through earth potential gradients around cathodically protected bare line.

A foreign pipeline can develop leaks in a short time in extreme instances. If the foreign pipeline happens also to be too close to an impressed current ground bed on the protected line, as previously discussed, the two effects are additive and the rate of corrosion at the point of crossing with the protected line will increase. Damage to the foreign pipeline can occur even if it has a CP system of its own. This takes place if the potential gradients surrounding the cathodically protected bare line are strong enough to offset the protective potential on the foreign pipeline and force it to discharge current (and accelerate corrosion) at the point of crossing.

If the foreign pipeline had a perfect coating, there could be no current discharge and no corrosion despite the existence of potential gradients where it passed through the zone of influence around the cathodically protected bare line. This, however, is unlikely for typical pipeline coatings and field conditions. Even a single coating defect within the gradient can cause a leak. The rate of penetration would tend to increase with increasing coating quality because the current discharge would be concentrated at smaller breaks in the coating.

The existence of a possibly damaging effect on a foreign pipeline at a point of crossing can be ascertained readily. This is accomplished by measuring potentials between the foreign pipe and a close electrode located directly over the foreign line. The measurements are obtained at close intervals because the rate of potential change, point-to-point, can be quite rapid. Thus, these measurements simply comprise a close interval survey of the foreign line in the area near the crossing of the two pipelines. Typically, the plotted result will look like Figure 3.16. This figure illustrates the effect on a cathodically protected foreign pipeline and shows a severe potential dip at the point of crossing.

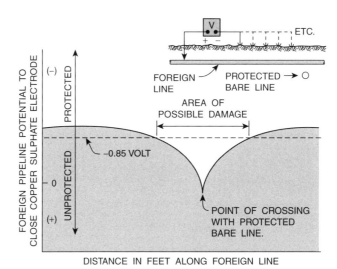

Figure 3.16   Pipe-to-soil potentials on foreign pipeline passing through area of influence around cathodically protected bare line.

Damage to the foreign pipeline would be expected unless its coating is perfect. Such a plot clearly identifies the length of foreign pipeline affected. The length of foreign pipeline subject to depressed potentials can vary from just a few feet in mild cases to hundreds of feet when the potential gradients are severe and the angle between the two crossing lines is small. Other factors being equal, the amount of foreign pipeline subjected to depressed potentials is least for a right-angle crossing.

If there is any question that the potential dip is caused by the CP system on the bare pipeline, the CP current sources can be turned off and the potential measurements along the foreign pipeline repeated. If the dip disappears, or nearly so, this is adequate proof that the CP system on the bare line is the cause of the trouble.

Corrective measures are discussed in Chapter 11. Metallic bonds are suitable in some instances. In other cases, the bare, cathodically protected pipeline may be coated in the vicinity of the crossing to reduce the intensity of potential gradients by locally reducing the amount of current flow to the pipeline per unit area. Galvanic anodes can be used to advantage where conditions are favorable, as described in Chapter 11 in the subsection on use of galvanic anodes.

Sources of Information on Interference

It is desirable, and usually saves considerable time, to seek the help of a corrosion coordinating committee when a pipeline is being installed in an area in which a committee exists. Corrosion coordinating committees are made up of representatives from many of the principal owners of underground metallic structures in an area (usually a metropolitan district where many pipelines cross) that work cooperatively to solve their corrosion problems. Many of these committees have been in existence for decades and have accumulated useful data, maps, and other information that will help avoid the destructive effects associated with interfering CP systems. These committees can assist in locating underground structures in the area, ascertaining the extent and nature of existing CP systems, and making cooperative surveys or cooperative contracts for protection.

REFERENCES

R. Rudenberg, Grounding Principles and Practices, I—Fundamental Considerations on Ground Currents, *Electrical Engineering*, January 1945.

F.E. Stetler, Accelerating Leak Rate in Ductile Cast Iron Water Mains Yields to CP, *Materials Performance*, Vol. 19, No. 10, October 1980.

C.L. Woody, Is 0.85 Volts to Cu/CuSO$_4$ the Only Criteria for Protection? Collection of papers on Underground Pipeline Corrosion, Vol. IX, Library of Congress Catalog Number: 59-54031.

Chapter 4

Criteria for Cathodic Protection

John A. Beavers and Kevin C. Garrity

In Chapter 3, the theory and principles of how cathodic protection (CP) works were presented and discussed. To assure that CP is applied in accordance with these principles, criteria and methods of assessment are required. This chapter describes the industry-accepted criteria, and Chapter 5 describes the survey methods and techniques used to assess whether the criteria are met. The discussion below is a review of the NACE criteria presented in NACE Standard RP-01-69 (1996 Revision) *Control of External Corrosion of Underground or Submerged Metallic Piping Systems*. This document lists criteria and other considerations for CP that will indicate, when used either separately or in combination, whether adequate CP of a metallic piping system has been achieved. The document states that the corrosion control programs are not limited to the primary criteria listed: "Criteria that have been successfully applied on existing piping systems can continue to be used on those systems. Any other criteria used must achieve corrosion control comparable to that attained with the criteria herein," referring to the three primary criteria described below. Other criteria that have been used for underground piping include the 300 mV shift criterion, the E-log I criterion, and the net current flow criterion.

CRITERIA FOR STEEL AND CAST IRON PIPING

Three primary criteria for CP of underground or submerged steel or cast iron piping are listed in Section 6 of NACE Standard RP-01-69 (1996 Revision):

1. −850 mV (CSE)[a] with the CP applied,
2. A polarized potential of −850 mV (CSE)
3. 100 mV of polarization.

[a]Saturated copper-copper sulfate reference electrode.

A fourth criterion, the net protective current criterion, is also listed in Section 6 under a special conditions section, for bare or poorly coated pipelines where long-line corrosion activity is the primary concern. The application and limitations of each are given below.

−850 mV with Cathodic Protection Applied Criterion

The full criterion states that adequate protection is achieved with:

a negative (cathodic) potential of at least 850 mV with the CP applied. This potential is measured with respect to a saturated copper/copper sulfate reference electrode contacting the electrolyte. Voltage drops other than those across the structure-to-electrolyte boundary must be considered for valid interpretation of this voltage measurement. Consideration is understood to mean application of sound engineering practice in determining the significance of voltage drops by methods such as:

- measuring or calculating the voltage drop(s),
- reviewing the historical performance of the CP system,
- evaluating the physical and electrical characteristics of the pipe and its environment
- determining whether or not there is physical evidence of corrosion.

Applications

Of the three primary criteria listed above, the first, −850 mV criterion with CP applied, is probably the most widely used for determining if a buried or submerged steel or cast iron structure has attained an acceptable level of CP. In the case of a buried steel or cast iron structure, an acceptable level of protection is achieved, based on this criterion, if the potential difference between the structure and a CSE contacting the soil directly above and as close as possible to the structure is equal to or more negative than (larger in absolute value) −850 mV. As described above, voltage drops other than those across the structure-to-electrolyte boundary must be considered for valid interpretation of this voltage measurement. These voltage drops are a result of current flow in the electrolyte (soil) and are generally referred to as ohmic or IR voltage drops. IR voltage drops are more prevalent in the vicinity of an anode bed or in areas where stray currents are present and generally increase with increasing soil resistivity.

For bare or very poorly coated structures, IR voltage drops can be reduced by placing the reference electrode as close as possible to the structure. For the majority of coated structures, most of the IR voltage drop is across the coating, and the measurement is less affected by reference electrode placement. The IR voltage drop can also be minimized or eliminated by interrupting all of the direct current sources of the CP system and measuring the instantaneous off-potential. Details on this measurement technique are given in Chapter 5. The off-potential will be free of the IR voltage drop errors if all of the current sources, including sources of stray currents, have been properly interrupted and if long-line currents are negligible. Long-line currents occur on a structure as a result of the presence of macro-cells, as described in Chapter 1 and Chapter 16. The difference between the on- and the off-potential indicates the magnitude of the IR voltage drop error when the measurement is made with the protective current applied.

This criterion was originally adopted based on the observation that the most negative native potential observed for coated underground steel structures was about −800 mV (CSE). The assumption was made that macro-cell corrosion would be mitigated if sufficient CP current were applied to raise (in the negative direction) the potential of the entire structure to a value that is more negative than the native potential of the local anodic sites. A potential of −850 mV was adopted to provide a 50 mV margin of protection. The effectiveness of the criterion has been demonstrated over many years of application.

Limitations

This criterion has a number of limitations. The potential reading should be taken with the reference electrode contacting the electrolyte directly over the structure, to minimize ohmic voltage drop errors in the measurement and to minimize the extent of averaging over large areas of the structure. Alternative criteria may be required where the reference electrode cannot be properly placed, such as at river crossings or road crossings. The criterion also is most commonly used for well-coated structures, where it can be economically met. For poorly coated or bare structures, the high CP currents required to meet this criterion can be prohibitive, such that alternative criteria are typically used.

Potentials can vary significantly from one area of an underground structure to another as a result of variations in soil conditions, coating damage, interference effects, etc. This creates the possibility that potentials less negative than −850 mV (CSE) exist between the measurement points. This problem can be addressed for pipelines by means of close-interval surveys, as described in Chapter 5. If the close-interval survey establishes that this problem exists, one should maintain more-negative potentials at the test stations to ensure that adequate protection is achieved on the entire structure. However, the more negative potentials required will result in increased power consumption.

Potentials more negative than −850 mV (CSE) also are required in the presence of bacteria or with a hot pipeline. In the latter case, the current required for CP can increase by a factor of two for every 10°C (18°F) increase in temperature of the pipe. The potential criterion is adjusted to compensate for the increased anodic current kinetics. Typically, a potential of −950 mV (CSE) is used for hot pipelines. In the case of microbes, the kinetics of the corrosion reaction and the environment at the pipe surface are altered such that a more-negative potential is typically required to mitigate corrosion. Where the presence of microbes is confirmed or suspected, a minimum potential criterion of −950 mV (CSE) is typically used. A more detailed discussion of microbially influenced corrosion (MIC) and CP is given in Chapter 14.

Care should be exercised to avoid overprotection, which can result in coating damage and may promote hydrogen damage of susceptible steels. The potential above which coating damage can occur is a function of many variables, including the soil composition and moisture content, the temperature, the coating type, the quality of the coating application, and the presence of microbes. The general consensus in the industry is to avoid polarized (instant off) potentials more negative than −1.05 to −1.1 V (CSE).

The older steels generally contain higher levels of impurities, such as sulfur and phosphorus, and exhibit greater susceptibility to hydrogen damage than do the newer, cleaner steels. In the older steels, the microstructures associated with hard spots and welds typically are more susceptible to hydrogen damage than is the microstructure of the wrought base metal. Again, the general consensus in the industry is to avoid polarized (instant off) potentials more negative than −1.05 to −1.1 V (CSE) to minimize hydrogen damage in these steels.

Potentials also can vary seasonally as a result of variation in the soil moisture content. Thus, some pipeline companies perform annual surveys at the same time each year, so that trends in the behavior of a pipeline can be properly interpreted. This approach does not, however, preclude the possibility that the criterion is not being met on some parts of the structure during portions of the year.

Limitations also exist in the ability to accurately measure the potential of the structure in the presence of telluric currents or where shielding by disbonded coatings, rocks, thermal insulation, etc., has occurred. Similarly, the accuracy of the potential measurement is compromised by stray currents that cannot be interrupted or by the presence of multiple pipelines in a right-of-way where the pipelines have varied coating conditions.

Dynamic stray currents, from sources such as DC transit systems and mining activities, pose a significant challenge in applying this criterion. Where dynamic stray currents are suspected, it is generally necessary to obtain potential values over the duration of the stray current activity, typically for twenty-four hours or longer. For example, for DC transit systems, it is often possible to obtain fairly stable on-potentials of the structure in the early morning hours when the transit system is not operating. These potentials can provide baseline data for use in evaluating other measurements. Of course, appropriate interpretation of such data is required. DC stray currents not only affect the ability to obtain accurate off-potentials, but also influence the polarized potential of the pipe. Nevertheless, the −850 mV criterion with CP applied is the criterion most commonly used in areas of significant dynamic stray current activity. It is generally accepted that the structure is protected at a test location if the potential of the structure remains more negative than −850 mV (CSE) at all times, even with significant fluctuations associated with the dynamic stray currents. It may be necessary to increase the number of test points and the frequency of surveys in areas of dynamic stray DC currents.

Polarized Potential of −850 mV Criterion

This criterion states that adequate protection is achieved with "a negative polarized potential of at least 850 mV relative to a saturated copper/copper sulfate reference electrode." The polarized potential is defined as the "potential across the structure/electrolyte interface that is the sum of the corrosion potential and the cathodic

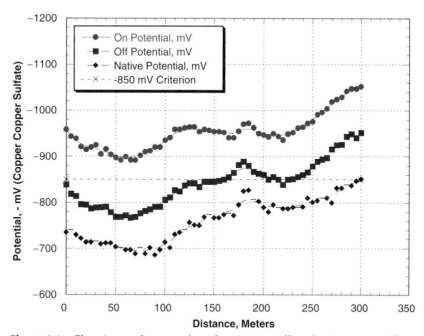

Figure 4.1   Close interval survey data showing on, off, and native potentials.

polarization." The polarized potential is measured directly after the interruption of all current sources and is often referred to as the off- or instant off-potential. The difference in potential between the native potential and the off or polarized potential is the amount of polarization that has occurred as a result of the application of the CP. As previously stated, the difference in potential between the on-potential and the off-potential is the error in the on-potential introduced as a result of voltage drops in the electrolyte (soil) and the metallic return path in the measuring circuit. Typical close interval survey data showing these potentials are given in Figure 4.1.

Applications

This second criterion is more direct than the −850 mV criterion with CP applied by clearly defining the method by which voltage drops errors in the on-potential are considered. In the second criterion, these errors are minimized or eliminated. The voltage drop errors, which are often referred to as ohmic potential drop or IR drop errors, occur as a result of the flow of CP or stray current in the electrolyte (soil) or in the structure. They are measurement errors because the cathodic polarization at the structure-to-electrolyte interface is the only part of the on-potential measurement that contributes to a reduction in the rate of corrosion of the structure. As described above, polarization is defined as the difference in potential between the native potential and the off- or polarized potential; it is referred to as cathodic polarization if the potential shift is in the negative direction.

This criterion is most commonly applied to coated structures where the sources of DC current can be readily interrupted. An example would be an FBE-coated gas transmission pipeline in a rural area with an impressed current CP system.

Limitations

An important limitation of this criterion is the requirement that all sources of DC current be interrupted. For standard survey techniques, the interruption must be performed simultaneously on all current sources. On gas transmission pipelines, interrupting all current sources may require the use of a large number of synchronous interrupters for all rectifiers, sacrificial anodes, and bonds affecting the section of pipeline that is being evaluated. In some cases, the number of rectifiers affecting a test section is not known without experimental verification. On gas distribution systems, sacrificial anodes are more commonly used for CP and the electrical leads for the anodes are usually bonded directly to the pipe with no means available to interrupt the current. For those situations, this criterion cannot be used. Achieving the criterion also may require the application of high CP currents, resulting in overprotection of some portions of the structure and related problems such as cathodic disbondment of coatings and hydrogen embrittlement of susceptible steels. As described above, a potential more negative than −850 mV (CSE) may be required to mitigate corrosion on hot pipelines or in the presence of MIC, further increasing the likelihood of overprotection.

Many of the difficulties of accurately measuring pipe-to-soil potentials that were described under limitations to the −850 mV criterion with CP applied apply to the polarized potential of −850 mV criterion as well. These include access to the structure, seasonal fluctuations in the potential between testing times, spatial fluctuations in potential between test stations, the presence of multiple pipelines with different levels of coating quality in a right-of-way, telluric current effects, and shielding of the structure surface by disbonded coatings, rocks, and thermal insulation.

100 mV of Polarization Criterion

This criterion states that adequate protection is achieved with "a minimum of 100 mV of cathodic polarization between the structure surface and a stable reference electrode contacting the electrolyte. The formation or decay of polarization can be measured to satisfy this criterion." Of the three criteria, this criterion has the most sound fundamental basis. As described in Chapters 3 and 16, the corrosion rate decreases and the rate of the reduction reaction on the metal surface increases as the underground structure is polarized in the negative direction from the native potential. The difference between the corrosion rate (expressed as a current) and the rate of the reduction reaction is equal to the applied CP current. These processes can be shown graphically in a diagram of E versus log I, referred to as an Evans diagram (see Chapter 16). The slope of the anodic (corrosion) reaction is referred to as the anodic Tafel slope and typically has a value of ~100 mV per decade of current. With this Tafel slope, the corrosion rate of a structure decreases by a factor of 10 (an order of magnitude) for every 100 mV cathodic shift in the polarized potential. An order of magnitude decrease in the corrosion rate of an underground structure typically is more than adequate to effectively mitigate corrosion.

The cathodic polarization also promotes beneficial changes in the environment at the pipe surface, such as reducing oxygen, increasing the pH, and moving halides such as chlorides away from the metal surface, which further decreases the corrosion rate. These beneficial changes in the environment at the metal surface are referred to as environmental polarization, in that the environmental changes typically result in a shift in the free corrosion potential of the pipe in the negative direction. Thus, the total potential shift from the native potential (excluding IR voltage drops in the soil) includes components attributable to environmental polarization and cathodic polarization.

As described in the criterion, the magnitude of the polarization shift can be determined by measuring its formation or decay. To determine the magnitude of the shift as a result of the formation of polarization, one must first determine the native potential of the underground structure at test locations before applying CP. The potential is then re-measured after the CP system is energized and the structure has had sufficient time to polarize. Typically, the on-potential is continuously monitored at one test location directly after energization the CP system, and an off-potential reading is made when there is no measurable shift in the on-potential reading for several minutes. The off-potential is then compared with the native potential; if the difference exceeds 100 mV, then the 100 mV criterion has been satisfied at that location. These measurements are shown graphically in Figure 4.2. Off-potential readings are then obtained at the other test locations to determine whether the criterion is met at these locations. The time required for sufficient polarization to develop is highly dependent on the nature of the structure (coating condition, underground environment, types and number of bonds, and so forth) and the design of the CP system. From a practical standpoint, it is wise to reexamine the overall structure and the CP system if a reasonable amount of polarization does not develop within a few hours of energizing the CP system.

An alternative method of assessing the formation of cathodic polarization is to measure the on-potential immediately after energizing the CP system and then re-measure the on-potential after a few hours to days of operation. If the on-potential shifts in the cathodic (negative) direction by >100 mV, then one can conservatively assume that the criterion has been met. Because the applied CP current generally decreases with time, the magnitude of the IR voltage drop also decreases. Thus, the total shift in the on-potential must be a result of the sum of the additional cathodic polarization and the environmental polarization of the pipeline, both of which reduce the corrosion rate of the structure and are included in the 100 mV of polarization in the criterion. If this method is used, the engineer should confirm that the applied CP current decreased with time.

Measuring the positive potential shift associated with polarization decay that occurs after de-energizing the CP system is the most common method to determine the amount

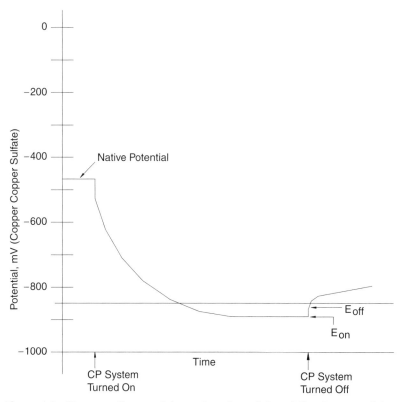

Figure 4.2   Pipe-to-soil potential as a function of time following energizing CP system.

of polarization. Figure 4.3 is a schematic that shows the pipe-to-soil potential follow-ing de-energizing of a CP system. When a CP system is de-energized, the pipe-to-soil potential undergoes an instantaneous positive shift as a result of elimination of the IR voltage drop in the soil. The potential measured at this time is referred to as the off-potential, as previously described, and is used as the starting point for assessing the polarization shift. There may be a spike in the potential reading immediately after inter-ruption of the CP system, a result of inductive effects of the pipeline and the CP system. Because this spike may last a few hundred milliseconds, the off-potential is typically measured 200 to 500 ms after the interruption.

The potential will then exhibit an exponential decay with time in the positive direction as the capacitor across the structure-to-electrolyte boundary discharges. This component of the potential shift is the cathodic polarization of the structure as a result of the applied cathodic current. A gradual linear decay in the potential will then occur over minutes to weeks as a result of a return of the environment at the pipe surface to its native condition. This component of the potential shift is the environmental polarization. To obtain the total polarization shift, the final potential after polarization decay is measured

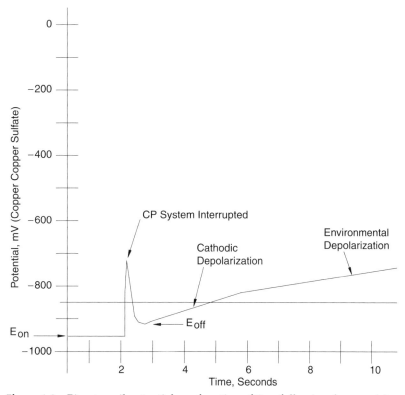

Figure 4.3 Pipe-to-soil potential as a function of time following de-energizing CP system.

and subtracted from the off-potential. If this difference is >100 mV, then the criterion has been satisfied.

Applications

The 100 mV polarization criterion is most commonly used on poorly coated or bare structures where it is difficult or costly to achieve either of the −850 mV criteria. In many cases, 100 mV of polarization can be achieved where the off-potential is less negative than −850 mV (CSE). The application of the 100 mV polarization criterion has the advantage of minimizing coating degradation and hydrogen embrittlement, both of which can occur as a result of overprotection. In piping networks, the 100 mV polarization criterion can be used for the older, poorly coated pipes; whereas, a −850 mV (CSE) polarized potential criterion can be used for the newer piping in the network. Because of its fundamental underpinnings, the 100 mV polarization criterion also can be used on metals other than steel, for which no specific potential required for protection has yet been established.

Limitations

This criterion has several limitations. The time required for full depolarization of a poorly coated or bare structure can be several days to several weeks, making the method very time-consuming and leaving the structure unprotected for an extended period of time. Fortunately, much of the depolarization occurs within a few hours and waiting for the full decay frequently is not necessary, except where the total polarization is very close to 100 mV. Once the criterion has been met, it is not necessary to continue waiting for further depolarization. At the other extreme, if a depolarization of <50 mV is measured within a few hours, it is questionable whether the 100 mV polarization criterion can be achieved. At this point, it may be prudent to assess whether a longer wait for total depolarization is justified.

The 100 mV polarization criterion is frequently used to minimize the costs for up-grading CP systems, and the associated increase in power costs, in areas with degrading coatings. Because of the complicated nature of the measurements, the cost of conducting surveys for the assessment of the 100 mV polarization criterion is considerably higher than for the −850 mV criteria. Thus, an economical analysis may be required to determine whether an actual cost savings is associated with application of the 100 mV polarization criterion.

The 100 mV polarization criterion should not be used in areas subject to stray currents because 100 mV of polarization may not be sufficient to mitigate corrosion in these areas. It is generally not possible to interrupt the source of the stray currents to accurately measure the depolarization. To apply this criterion, all DC current sources affecting the structure, including rectifiers, sacrificial anodes, and bonds must be interrupted. In many instances, this is not possible, especially on the older structures for which the criterion is most likely to be used.

The 100 mV polarization criterion should not be used on structures that contain dissimilar metal couples because 100 mV of polarization may not be adequate to protect the active metal in the couple. This criterion also should not be used in areas where the intergranular form of external stress corrosion cracking (SCC), also referred to as high-pH or classical SCC, is suspected. The potential range for cracking lies between the native potential and −850 mV (CSE) such that application of the 100 mV polarization criterion may place the potential of the structure in the range for cracking.

Net Protective Current Criterion

RP0169-96 (latest revision) states under paragraph 6.2.2.2 (Special Conditions): "On bare or ineffectively coated pipelines where long-line corrosion activity is of primary concern, the measurement of a net protective current at predetermined current discharge points from the electrolyte to the pipe surface, as measured by an earth current technique, may be sufficient" for CP to be achieved.

This statement establishes the fourth criterion for CP of underground piping, referred to as the net protective current criterion. This criterion was originally based on the concept that if the net current at any point on a structure is flowing from the electrolyte to the structure, there cannot be any corrosion current discharging from that point on the structure. The theory of electrochemical kinetics, described in Chapter 16, shows that corrosion can occur at a point on a structure that is collecting net cathodic current from the electrolyte, as long as the polarized potential is more positive than the equilibrium potential. Nevertheless, the criterion can be effective, from a practical standpoint, because the collection of net cathodic current at any point along the structure produces beneficial cathodic polarization and also promotes beneficial changes in the environment at the structure surface, as described above.

Typically, the criterion is applied by first performing, with the CP system de-energized, a close-interval pipe-to-soil potential survey, or a cell-to-cell potential survey to locate the anodic discharge points along the pipeline. Further details on these survey methods are given in Chapter 5. For the surveys to be effective, the CP systems must be de-energized long enough for all polarization to decay. The CP system is then energized and the structure is allowed to polarize. A side drain method is then used at the anodic discharge points to determine whether the structure is receiving cathodic current at these locations. With the side drain method, the potential difference between an electrode placed directly over the structure and one placed on either side of the structure is measured. If the electrode located over the pipe is negative with respect to the other two electrodes, then current is collecting on the pipe at the location and the criterion is satisfied.

Applications

The net protective current criterion is normally used on poorly coated or uncoated pipelines, where the primary concern is long-line corrosion activity. The technique also is normally only used in situations where other criteria cannot be easily or economically met. With these exceptions, this criterion is not a standard criterion for establishing the effectiveness of a CP system.

Limitations

There are a number of limitations to this criterion. First and foremost is the fact that the criterion essentially states that any magnitude of net current flow to the structure (and therefore, any amount of cathodic polarization of the structure) is adequate to mitigate corrosion. In general, that is not the case and therefore, the criterion should be considered for use only as a last resort. Application of the criterion should be avoided in areas of stray current activity or in common pipeline corridors because of the possibility of misinterpretation of the potential readings. The criterion also may not be effective in areas with high-resistivity soils, for deeply buried pipelines, or where the separation distance of the corrosion cells is small. Finally, the side drain measurements at a given location are indicative of the direction of current flow at that location only and are not necessarily representative of behavior elsewhere on the pipeline. Thus, for the application of this criterion, it is generally necessary to perform side drain measurements at close intervals (2 to 20 ft) along the pipeline.

Other Criteria for Steel and Cast Iron

The four criteria listed for steel and cast iron piping are the only acceptable criteria listed in RP-01-69-96 for underground or submerged metallic piping. However, other criteria can be used on a piping system for which they have been used in the past and it can be demonstrated that their use has resulted in effective CP. Other criteria are also useful for underground structures such as reinforced concrete pipe and piling. The two most common other criteria that have been used in the past for underground structures are the 300 mV potential shift criterion and the E-log I curve criterion.

300 mV Potential Shift Criterion

The 300 mV potential shift criterion was contained in the original version of RP 01-69 and stated that adequate protection is achieved with "a negative (cathodic) voltage shift of at least 300 mV as measured between the structure surface and a saturated copper-copper sulfate half cell contacting the electrolyte. Determination of this voltage shift is to be made with the protective current applied." This criterion is similar to the 100 mV polarization criterion, which is assessed on the basis of the formation of polarization on a structure. With both criteria, it is first necessary to determine the native potential of the underground structure at test locations before CP is applied. The potential is then re-measured after the CP system is energized and the structure has had sufficient time to polarize. The difference between the two criteria is that, in the case of the 300 mV potential shift criterion, the on-potential is used for assessment of the criterion; whereas, in the case of the 100 mV polarization criterion, the off-potential is used for assessment. Regarding the 300 mV potential shift criterion, the standard states "The Corrosion Engineer shall consider voltage (IR) drops other than those across the structure-electrolyte boundary for valid interpretation of the voltage measurements." Thus the relationship between the 300 mV potential shift criterion and the 100 mV polarization criterion is analogous to the relationship between the −850 mV (CSE) with CP applied criterion and the polarized potential of −850 mV (CSE) criterion.

The 300 mV potential shift criterion has mainly been used for mitigation of moderate rates of uniform corrosion of bare steel pipelines. It has been applied for protection of entire pipelines and also for hot-spot protection. On these pipelines, native potentials of −200 to −500 mV (CSE) are common and a 300 mV shift has been found to be adequate to mitigate corrosion in some instances. Thus, the development of the criterion was empirically based. The 300 mV potential shift criterion is more applicable to impressed current CP systems than to galvanic anode systems because galvanic anodes may not have sufficient driving voltage to meet the criterion when negative native potentials are encountered.

Probably the most successful application of this criterion has been on steel reinforced concrete structures. These structures typically have native potentials in the range of -200 to -400 mV (CSE) and passive steel surfaces, with the exception of hot spots, such that a potential shift of 300 mV can be readily achieved. Application of this criterion avoids problems associated with overprotection.

Many of the limitations associated with the 100 mV polarization criterion are applicable to the 300 mV potential shift criterion as well. These include the time required for polarization, the possibility of moving the potential into the cracking range for SCC, and difficulties in areas containing stray currents or galvanic couples. In general, the 300 mV potential shift criterion should not be used where high-pH SCC is confirmed or suspected, or where stray currents or galvanic couples are present. The original version of RP 01-69 states, "This criterion of voltage shifts applies to structures not in contact with dissimilar metals."

Probably the single greatest limitation of the 300 mV potential shift criterion is that situations will exist in the field where the criterion will appear to be applicable yet corrosion may not be mitigated. In some situations, the majority of the potential shift will be the result of IR voltage drops in the soil or across the coating, and very little polarization of the structure will occur. For this reason, the criterion was removed from the primary list of criteria in the 1992 and 1996 revisions of RP-01-69.

E-Log I Curve Criterion

The E-log I curve criterion also is found in the original version of RP-01-69, which states that adequate protection is achieved with "a voltage at least as negative (cathodic) as that originally established at the beginning of the Tafel segment of the E-log I curve. This voltage shall be measured between the structure surface and a saturated copper-copper sulfate half cell contacting the electrolyte." The criterion was originally developed based on an incorrect interpretation of a plot of potential versus the log of the current (E-log I curve). The cathodic E-log I curve, which is generated as a structure is polarized from the native potential, was thought to exhibit a break that had some fundamental significance. This break was thought to occur at the beginning of the Tafel region. A review of the theory of CP, given in Chapter 16, indicates that the net cathodic current measured at any applied cathodic potential is equal to the difference between the rate of the reduction reaction and the rate of the oxidation reaction. An E-log I curve shows a smooth transition from zero current, at the native potential, to the linear Tafel region. The Tafel region starts when the rate of the oxidation (corrosion) reaction is negligibly small in comparison with the rate of the reduction reaction. Depending on the Tafel slopes for the oxidation and reduction reactions, the beginning of the Tafel region can vary between 50 and 100 mV cathodically from the native potential.

At present, the E-log I curve criterion is rarely used for evaluating existing CP systems. However, the measurement technique, originally developed for applying the E-log I curve criterion, is now most commonly used to determine the minimum current required for protection. The pipe-to-soil potential, determined by using a remote reference electrode, is plotted as a function of the current output of a CP system. Typically, it is necessary to use an interruption technique and off-potentials for constructing the E-log I plot in order to accurately establish the curve. The potential required to achieve a desired minimum current value is identified on the curve. This value should be at least as negative as the value at the beginning of the Tafel region of the E-log I curve. Once the potential and current values have been established, future surveys consist of checking the current output of the CP system and the potential of the structure with respect to the remote reference electrode, placed in the same location as was used in the original E-log I tests.

Because of the elaborate nature of the technique, its use is generally limited to structures where conventional means of assessment are difficult. Examples include river crossings for pipelines, well casings, and piping networks in concentrated areas such as industrial parks. The technique can give erroneous results in areas of stray currents. The reference electrode must be placed in the same location each time the potential is measured. Furthermore, there is no guarantee that a repeat E-log I curve will yield the same results as the original curve.

CRITERION FOR ALUMINUM PIPING

RP0169-96, lists a single criterion for aluminum piping, identical to the 100 mV polarization criterion used for cast iron and steel. According to paragraph 6.2.3.1, "The following criterion shall apply; a minimum of 100 mV of cathodic polarization between the structure and a stable reference electrode contacting the electrolyte. The formation or decay of this polarization can be used in this criterion."

Two precautionary notes included in Section 6.2.3.2 are unique to aluminum piping: one dealing with excessive voltages (paragraph 6.2.3.2.1) and one dealing with alkaline conditions (paragraph 6.2.3.2.2).

Paragraph 6.2.3.2.1, states that:

Notwithstanding, the minimum criterion in Section 6.2.3.1, if aluminum is cathodically protected at voltages more negative than −1200 mV measured between the pipe surface and a saturated copper/copper sulfate reference electrode contacting the electrolyte and compensation is made for the voltage drops other than those across the pipe-electrolyte boundary, it may suffer corrosion as a result of the buildup of alkali on the metal surface. A polarized potential more negative than −1200 mV should not be used unless previous test results indicate that no appreciable corrosion will occur in the particular environment.

Paragraph 6.2.3.2.2 states that:

Aluminum may suffer from corrosion under high-pH conditions and application of CP tends to increase the pH at the metal surface. Therefore, careful investigation or testing should be made before applying CP to stop pitting attack on aluminum in environments with a natural pH in excess of 8.0.

The basis for these cautionary notes is the incompatibility of aluminum in high-pH environments. The protective passive films on aluminum break down in high-pH electrolytes, leading to significant increases in the corrosion rate, even at relatively negative potentials. In addition to these precautionary notes, several of the limitations for the 100 mV polarization criterion for steel and cast iron also apply to aluminum. These include the time-consuming nature of the measurement technique, difficulties associated with interrupting all current sources, and limitations in applying the criterion to structures with dissimilar metals and in the presence of stray currents. Because no other criterion is applicable to aluminum, good engineering practice must be used to address these limitations. For example, sources of stray current should be identified and eliminated, if possible. Aluminum piping should be isolated from other metals before CP is applied (isolation of aluminum is required for the CP criterion of dissimilar metals under Section 6.2.5 of RP0169; see below).

CRITERION FOR COPPER PIPING

RP0169-96 has a single criterion for copper piping. According to paragraph 6.2.4.1, "The following criterion shall apply; a minimum of 100 mV of cathodic polarization between the structure and a stable reference electrode contacting the electrolyte. The formation or decay of this polarization can be used in this criterion."

This criterion is identical to the 100 mV polarization criterion used for cast iron, steel, and aluminum. There are no precautionary notes with this criterion, but several of the limitations with the 100 mV polarization criterion for steel and cast iron also apply to copper. These include the time-consuming nature of the measurement technique, difficulties associated with interrupting all current sources, and limitations in applying the criterion on structures with dissimilar metals and in the presence of stray currents. Sources of stray current should be identified and eliminated, if possible. Because copper is a noble metal, steel, cast iron, or other metals usually will undergo preferential galvanic attack when coupled to copper. Therefore, it is desirable to eliminate such dissimilar metal couples before applying CP.

Criterion For Dissimilar Metal Piping

RP0169-96 contains a single criterion for dissimilar metal piping. Under paragraph 6.2.5.1, the following criterion is listed: "A negative voltage between all pipe surfaces and a stable reference electrode contacting the electrolyte equal to that required for the protection of the most anodic metal should be maintained."

There is one precautionary note, under Paragraph 6.2.5.2: "Amphoteric materials that could be damaged by high alkalinity created by CP should be electrically isolated and separately protected." Amphoteric metals include aluminum, titanium, and zirconium.

In practice, this criterion applies only where carbon steel or cast iron is coupled to a more noble metal such as copper. In this situation, either of the 850 mV criterion would apply: −850 mV (CSE) with the CP applied or a polarized potential of −850 mV (CSE). Other criteria, such as the 100 mV of polarization criterion would not be applicable.

Chapter 5

Survey Methods and Evaluation Techniques

Ronald L. Bianchetti

Various testing methods and techniques may be used on underground pipelines during the course of field surveys.

DATA ASSEMBLED BEFORE STARTING A FIELD SURVEY

Before any field survey, the corrosion engineer should gather as much information as possible about the pipeline to be studied. This may provide valuable data on corrosion conditions to be expected and should be helpful in planning a survey program that will yield useful data for design purposes.

The following items of information are typical of those which should be accumulated before planning and starting the field survey.

- Pipe material: Steel (including grade of steel), cast iron, wrought iron, or other material of known electrical resistance.
- Is the line bare or coated? If coated, what is the coating material and what coating specifications were used?
- If it is an existing line, is there a leak record? If so, information on the location and date of occurrence of each leak will positively indicate the more serious problem areas.
- Pipe diameter, wall thickness, and weight per foot; data on any changes in these items along the route of the line.
- Size or sizes of casing pipe used, with wall thickness or weight per foot; grade of steel used; data on insulators used between pipe and casing and on casing end

seals; if coated casing was or is to be used, type of coating and application specifications.
- Location and construction details of all corrosion test points that have been installed along the line. If no test points have been installed for corrosion test purposes, determine locations where contact can be made with the pipeline for test purposes (other than by driving contact bars down to the pipe).
- Is the line of all-welded construction, or are mechanical couplers used?
- Location of branch taps.
- Location of insulated flanges or couplers, if any, purposely used to sectionalize the line or to isolate it electrically from other portions of the system or from piping of other ownership.
- Route maps and detail maps giving as much data as is available.
- Location of underground structures of foreign ownership that cross the pipeline to be surveyed; if any of these structures are cathodically protected, determine the location of cathode protection (CP) current sources (particularly rectifiers) that may be close to the line being surveyed.
- Location of possible sources of man-made stray current (such as DC electric transit systems or mining operations) that could affect the line under study.
- Do any sections of the pipeline closely parallel (within 200 ft or so) high voltage electric transmission lines? If so, what is the length of such exposure, how close is the pipeline to the towers, at what voltage does the electric line operate, and what method is used for grounding the towers? (This information is significant because rectifier installations and insulated joints in well-coated pipes closely parallel to high voltage electric lines may be damaged by induced AC voltage surges under electric system fault conditions if preventive measures are not taken.)
- Is the line now operated at elevated temperature or will it be so operated in the foreseeable future. (High temperature could cause deterioration of coatings used.)

SURVEY METHODS AVAILABLE

The actual field survey should be organized to use several or all of the following procedures. The actual selection and the relative importance of data obtained from each method selected will depend on the particular situation. Survey methods for different situations are listed below to guide the corrosion engineer. These tests should supplement information gathered under *Data Assembled Before Starting a Field Survey*.

Survey of Pipeline Routes before Construction

- Measurement of the electrical resistivity of the soil environment around the pipeline
- Determination of conditions suitable for anaerobic bacterial corrosion

- Determination of various chemical constituents in the soil environment (chlorides, sulfate, sulfides, bicarbonates)

Survey of Pipeline Not under Cathodic Protection

- Measurement of the electrical resistivity of the soil environment around the pipeline
- Determination of conditions suitable for anaerobic bacterial corrosion
- Determination of various chemical constituents in the soil environment (chlorides, sulfate, sulfides, bicarbonates)
- Potential surveys: measurements of potentials between pipeline and environment
- Line current survey: measurement of electrical current flowing on the pipeline
- Measurement of the effective electrical resistance of any coating on the pipeline being studied
- Bellhole examinations for evidence of corrosion activity
- Use of recording instruments for the study of unstable (stray current) conditions
- If cathodic protection (CP) is deemed necessary: evaluation of electric current requirements for CP.

Survey of Pipeline under Cathodic Protection

- Potential surveys: measurements of potentials between pipeline and environment
- Line current survey: measurement of electrical current flowing on the pipeline
- Measurement of the effective electrical resistance of any coating on the pipeline being studied
- Bellhole examinations for evidence of corrosion activity
- Use of recording instruments for the study of unstable (stray current) conditions

From the listings above, a corrosion survey might seem to be a rather involved process. It is the responsibility of the corrosion engineer to select the proper survey "tools" that will be best suited for a specific situation and provide adequate design information at the least expense. It is easily possible to "overengineer" corrosion surveys and to put the greatest emphasis on what may turn out to be relatively unimportant data. This is where knowledge and—particularly—experience are important.

MEASUREMENT PROCEDURES AND SURVEY METHODS

In this section, we will discuss some of the more important field test measurement procedures for typical test equipment described in Chapter 6. These measurements procedures will be incorporated into survey methods commonly utilized for assessing pipelines both with and without CP.

Potential Measurements

Measurement of potential between a pipeline and a copper sulfate reference electrode (CSE) is the most frequent test performed in the corrosion industry. All discussions in this book that deal with potential measurements will be referenced to the CSE.

Pipe-to-earth potential measurements are performed by placing the electrode over the pipeline for "close" readings or at remote earth for "remote" readings. The porous plug, with cap removed, should be in firm contact with moist earth. This may require "digging in" at places where the earth's surface is dry. In extremely dry areas, it maybe necessary to moisten the earth around the electrode with fresh water to obtain good contact. Do not permit grass or weeds (particularly when wet) to contact exposed electrode terminals because that may affect the observed potential.

For the purposes of standardized convention in this book the reference electrode will be connected to the negative terminal of a high-impedance voltmeter and the positive terminal to the pipeline (via test point terminal, probe rod, or direct contact with pipeline), as shown in Figure 5.1.

Pipelines Not under Cathodic Protection

Potentials reveal several things about the pipeline being evaluated. These include a general idea of the extent to which corrosion has progressed, the location of hot spots where corrosion is most severe, and the location of areas that are subject to stray current electrolysis.

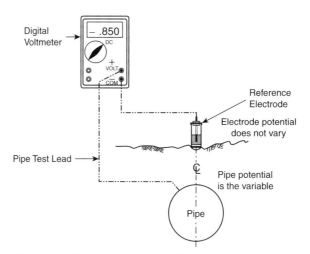

Figure 5.1   Pipe-to-earth potential measurement.

A general idea of corrosion extent can obtained from the average pipeline potential. When potentials are measured with respect to a reference electrode every mile or so along a pipeline or at test stations and the readings are then plotted (excluding those subject to stray current or other external influences), the newer and less corroded pipelines will typically have more negative potential values. Newly laid, coated steel pipelines may have an average potential in the range of −0.5 to −0.7 V, whereas old, bare steel lines may have an average potential more in the range of −0.1 to −0.3 V (CSE).

Location of "hot spots" (corroding areas) can be determined by making what is known as an over-the-line potential survey. This technique is particularly useful on both bare and coated pipelines. In an over-the-line survey, measurements are taken at fairly close intervals (about 3 ft apart) between the pipeline and copper sulfate electrode directly over the line.

Pipelines under Cathodic Protection

Protection criteria based on potential measurements are a logical development of understanding how CP works. As demonstrated in Chapter 3, a flow of current to a cathodically protected pipeline from its environment causes a change in potential, a combination of the voltage drop across the resistance between pipeline and environment and the polarization potential developed at the pipe surface. The resistance between pipeline and environment includes the resistance of the pipeline coating, if any. The net result is that the pipeline will become more negative with respect to its environment. This is illustrated by Figure 5.2.

As discussed in Chapter 4, if cathodic areas on a corroding pipeline are polarized to the open circuit potential of the anodic areas, corrosion will be mitigated. Ideally, based on this concept, potentials should be measured directly across the interface between the pipeline and its environment. This location is represented by the terminals marked "polarization potential" on the equivalent circuits shown in Figure 5.2. However, this is difficult when working with buried pipelines. In common practice, the usual approach is to measure the potential between the pipeline and the earth at the surface directly above the pipeline. As shown by the equivalent circuits, the observed potential thus includes the polarization potential plus a potential created by current flowing through a portion of the resistance (IR drop) between pipeline and earth.

Under some conditions, it is not necessarily desirable to approach the ideal measurement of polarization potential indicated previously. A measurement of potential between pipeline and remote earth then may be in order. This alternative location is indicated in Figure 5.2. Reasons for using a remote earth location are discussed in the section on Remote vs Close Potential Measurements.

Assuming that potential measurement is a reasonable approach to a workable criterion, the next question is how much potential should be present to indicate protection and how is it measured. The actual potential measured varies with the method used to contact the pipeline environment. The contact must be made by means of a reliable and stable reference that will permit reproducible results.

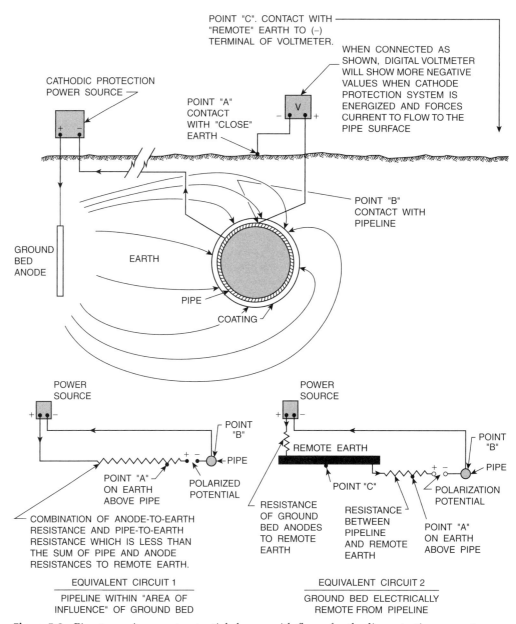

POINT "C". CONTACT WITH
"REMOTE" EARTH TO (–)
TERMINAL OF VOLTMETER.

WHEN CONNECTED AS
SHOWN, DIGITAL VOLTMETER
WILL SHOW MORE NEGATIVE
VALUES WHEN CATHODE
PROTECTION SYSTEM IS
ENERGIZED AND FORCES
CURRENT TO FLOW TO THE
PIPE SURFACE

CATHODIC PROTECTION
POWER SOURCE

POINT "A"
CONTACT
WITH "CLOSE"
EARTH

POINT "B"
CONTACT WITH
PIPELINE

GROUND
BED
ANODE

EARTH

PIPE

COATING

POWER
SOURCE

POINT
"B"

PIPE

POINT "A"
ON EARTH
ABOVE PIPE

POLARIZED
POTENTIAL

COMBINATION OF ANODE-TO-EARTH
RESISTANCE AND PIPE-TO-EARTH
RESISTANCE WHICH IS LESS THAN
THE SUM OF PIPE AND ANODE
RESISTANCES TO REMOTE EARTH.

EQUIVALENT CIRCUIT 1

PIPELINE WITHIN "AREA OF
INFLUENCE" OF GROUND BED

POWER
SOURCE

REMOTE EARTH

POINT
"B"

PIPE

POINT "C"

POLARIZATION
POTENTIAL

RESISTANCE
OF GROUND
BED ANODES
TO REMOTE
EARTH

RESISTANCE
BETWEEN
PIPELINE
AND REMOTE
EARTH

POINT "A"
ON EARTH
ABOVE PIPE

EQUIVALENT CIRCUIT 2

GROUND BED ELECTRICALLY
REMOTE FROM PIPELINE

Figure 5.2   Pipe-to-environment potential change with flow of cathodic protection current.

With the background developed above, a discussion of actual potentials can be undertaken. In Chapter 4, we discussed the concept that if cathodic areas on the pipeline are polarized to the open circuit potential of the anodic areas, macrocell corrosion will cease. As established by various investigators, the most highly anodic areas to be expected on a steel pipeline in most soils and waters will have a potential of around -0.8 V as measured with respect to a CSE contacting the environment immediately adjacent to the anodic area. For usual potential measurements, it is not practical to excavate so that the electrode can be placed at pipe depth. The most common approach is to place the CSE at the ground surface directly above the pipeline. To allow for a drop in potential in the soil between this point and the pipe, and to allow for some latitude in the potential of the most highly anodic areas, the practical value of -0.85 V (CSE) has been adopted as an indication of satisfactory protection. This criterion along with its applications and limitations is discussed in detail in Chapter 4.

Remote vs Close Potential Measurements

Pipeline potential readings usually are referred to either "close" or "remote" electrodes. If neither is designated, "close" electrode will be meant in most cases.

Close Earth

A reading to close electrode usually means an observation made with the reference placed on the ground (or water) surface directly above the pipeline being studied. A reading to remote electrode means the reference is placed in earth that is electrically remote from the pipeline. Often, to permit reproducing similar conditions, the distance and direction will be indicated, as "potential to remote CSE, 100 east" or similar notations. Applications of both types of reading are covered below.

Remote Earth

Under certain testing conditions, it may be desirable to know how far one has to go from a structure before the potential represents an electrically remote distance from the structure being evaluated. Examples are the area of influence around an impressed current ground bed and the area affected by potential gradients around a cathodically protected pipeline. This distance may be determined by a series of readings between the structure being evaluated and a CSE moved away from the structure at specified intervals. When the data are plotted for a cathodically protected pipeline, it might appear as illustrated by Figure 5.3.

The plot taken at an impressed current ground bed would look similar except that potentials would increase in the positive direction instead of negative and the distance to remote earth could be greater.

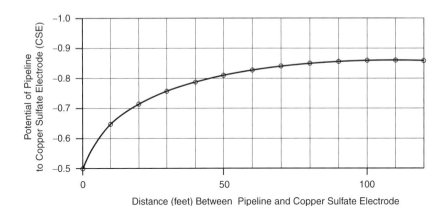

Figure 5.3   Determination of remote earth.

It should be pointed out that the distance to remote earth will not necessarily be the same at all points along a protected line nor will the distance to remote earth necessarily be the same for all similarly sized impressed current ground beds at different locations. Both soil resistivity and soil structure have an effect. In high-resistivity soil areas, the distance to remote tends to be greater. Probably the greatest effect causing extension of the distance to remote earth is observed at areas where pipelines or ground beds are in relatively shallow surface layers of earth overlying material of much higher resistivity (such as rock). In these instances, the current to the pipeline or from the ground bed tends to concentrate in the surface layer rather than come from or flow to the general earth mass. This substantially extends the distance from the structure to electrically remote earth. Awareness of this effect, when working in such areas, is important in considering the possible interference effect of potential gradient fields on other structures.

Over-The-Line Potential Surveys (Close Interval Surveys)

So why are different readings obtained when the reference is placed directly over the line? The readings are affected by corrosion current flowing to or from the pipe. Such currents cause voltage drops in the soil in the immediate vicinity of the pipeline, which are reflected in the readings to a close electrode. Which readings then indicate unfavorable conditions?

In general, when interpreting over-the-line potential survey readings, for pipelines without CP the worst corrosion will be where the potential readings are the most negative, and there will be little or no corrosion at the points of least negative readings.

To illustrate results that can be obtained with an over-the-line potential survey on a well-coated pipeline without CP, Figure 5.4 represents plotted data taken from an

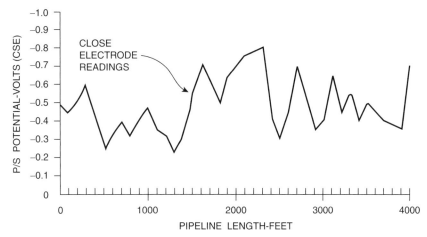

Figure 5.4   Close interval potential survey (w/o CP applied).

actual field survey. The plotted data do not form a smooth curve. Peaks in the plot indicate locations to be suspected as corroding areas. Major peaks mark those areas that require closest attention and coordination with other survey data to be discussed later.

If areas are encountered where stray current electrolysis is a problem, this will be apparent from the potential measurements. Potentials attributable to soil conditions only show little or no variation during measurements made with indicating voltmeters, whereas the effects of a DC transit system, for example, can cause observation of erratic and extreme variations in potential values. In severe cases, the variation can be from several volts positive to several volts negative with respect to the copper sulfate electrode. When such conditions are encountered, electrolysis preventive measures may be needed as discussed in Chapter 11.

To illustrate information that can be obtained with an over-the-line potential survey on a well-coated pipeline with CP, Figure 5.5 represents plotted data taken from an actual field survey. The plotted data again do not form a smooth curve even when taken on a cathodically protected pipeline. Depressions in the plot (least negative potential) indicate locations where CP may not be adequate because of underground contacts to other pipelines or structures or areas of possible coating damage. These areas of potential depressions may require close attention and coordination with other survey data to be discussed later.

Over-the-line potential surveys provide measurement of potentials to a reference electrode directly above the pipe and at frequent intervals along the pipe; survey results can be used to locate the more actively corroding areas (hot spots) on a pipeline not under CP or areas of depressed potentials on cathodically protected pipelines. A detailed discussion can be found in Chapter 16. Three methods that may be used for taking these closely spaced readings are as follows:

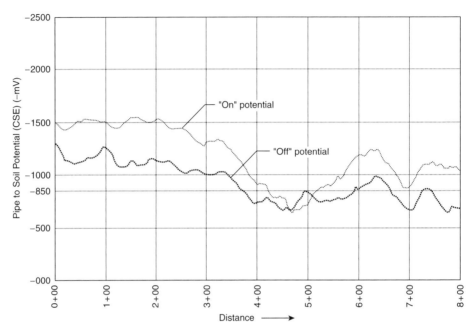

Figure 5.5 Over-the-line survey (with cathodic protection).

Method 1

The principle involved in the over-the-line survey is illustrated in Figure 5.6 which shows readings taken on a continuous basis at 3- to 5-ft intervals along the pipeline. For an all-welded steel pipeline, there would be negligible voltage drop through the pipe between any two points tested (at the usual soil corrosion currents flowing in the pipe). Typically,

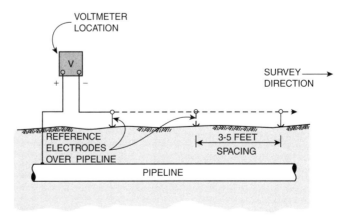

Figure 5.6 Over-the-line potential surveys (Method 1).

a measuring device, with light wire for continuous contact to the pipeline, is used with a data logger to capture data as the survey is being performed. The location of each electrode position is recorded with the observed potential. Different types of over-the-line survey equipment are discussed in Chapter 6.

In areas where traffic conditions, terrain features, or other obstructions do not interfere, long distances can be surveyed on either side of each pipeline connection. The distance is limited only by the length of test conductor available. The resistance of the light-wire test lead should not be sufficient to cause noticeable error in potential measurements made with a suitable high-resistance voltmeter. This is true if spools of light wire conductors 3 to 5 miles long are maintained properly and have no high-resistance connections. For example, 15,000 ft (3 miles) of no. 34 gage light wire would have a resistance of approximately 2,800 ohms. A high-impedence voltmeter or datalogger with a minimum input impedence of 20×10^6 ohms typically reduces any errors from the wire resistance.

Method 2

Another measurement technique involves the use of a pair of CSE in leapfrog fashion, as illustrated in Figure 5.7.

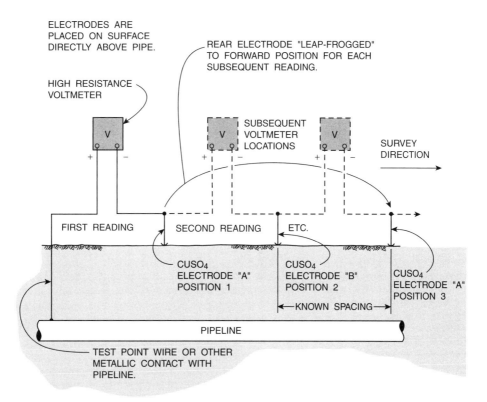

Figure 5.7   Over-the-line potential surveys using two copper sulfate electrodes (Method 2).

Table 5.1   Data Record for Leap Frog Potential Surveys

Position (or Pipe-line Station)	Potential Drop From CuSO$_4$ at Last Position	Polarity of Forward CuSO$_4$	Pipe to CuSO$_4$ Potential
1	—	—	−.625 volt[1]
2	.08	+	−.705
3	.04	+	−.745
4	.075	−	−.670
5	.10	−	−.570

[1]Initial value measured via direct pipeline contact at Position 1.

When using this technique, the survey may be started with a measurement to the pipeline at a connection point (ETS) in the usual manner, as shown at Position 1 in the figure. The value observed and the electrode position are recorded. Leaving this electrode (A) at that location, a second electrode (B) is placed at the next location along the pipeline (Position 2 in the figure), and this potential difference is observed and recorded, together with the polarity of the forward electrode. Electrode A at Position 1 is leapfrogged to Position 3 and the potential between the electrodes is measured as above. The procedure is continued in the same manner along the length of the pipeline.

The actual pipe-to-electrode potential at Position 2 is the observed potential at Position 1 with the potential between Positions 1 and 2 being numerically added to the Position 1 value if the polarity of the forward electrode is (+) or subtracted if it is (−). This is continued for each subsequent reading. The data may be recorded as shown in Table 5.1.

The two-electrode technique avoids the need to string out long leads but does involve greater probability of error, particularly in areas having variable DC stray current. Leapfrogging the electrodes avoids any cumulative error caused by potential difference between electrodes. Potential drops between electrodes must be measured accurately and using a high-impedance voltmeter will typically eliminate that error. An error in observing and recording the data at any one position will be reflected in all the subsequent calculated pipe-to-electrode potentials.

Where this method is used, good practice calls for checking the cumulative pipe-to-electrode potential by direct measurement to a pipeline contact every thousand feet or so and adjusting accordingly. This will guard against unnoticed errors in the data. With careful work, however, this method is quite reliable.

Method 3

This method, often called the side drain technique, measures the potential drops between two copper sulfate electrodes, as shown in Figure 5.8. Electrodes used should be matched

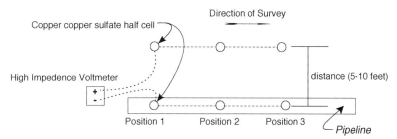

Figure 5.8 Over-the line (Method 3).

(not more than 5 mV difference in electrode potential). Measurements are made on each side of a unprotected pipeline, typically in areas in question, to identify areas of current flow onto and off the pipeline. In Fig 5.8 positive voltage reading would indicate current flow to the pipe. A negative voltage reading would indicate current flow off the pipeline.

This technique is not widely used because it is time-consuming. Direct contact potential measurements as described in Method 1 are easier than the other methods described. Methods 2 and 3 are typically used to qualify specific areas of concern identified using Method 1 survey techniques.

Line Current Measurements

Measurement of pipeline current by the resistance drop method is useful in pipeline survey work. It is also useful in determining the distribution of current along a cathodically protected pipeline and for other applications such as stray current. The procedures outlined typically use permanent test points to contact the pipe.

Permanent Two-Wire Test Points

Where the two-wire test points spanning a known length of pipe are available, currents may be measured by determining the potential drop across the span, selecting the pipe resistance from tables, and calculating the current using Ohm's law. The general arrangement is shown in Figure 5.9.

The procedure may be performed as follows:

1. Measure the circuit resistance of the test leads and pipe span by passing known battery current through the circuit and measuring the resulting voltage drop across the test point terminals. Calculate resistance in ohms by Ohm's law: R (resistance) = V (volts) divided by I (amperes). If the resistance obtained is higher than reasonable for the size and length of test wires, defective leads may be suspected.

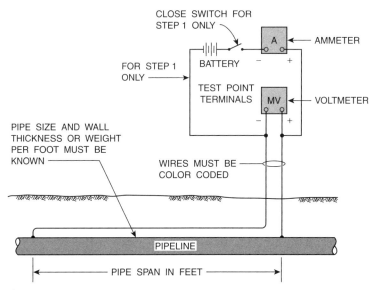

Figure 5.9 Current measurement, 2-wire test point.

2. Measure the voltage drop across the test point terminals caused by the normal current flowing in the pipeline. Usually this will be millivolts or microvolts. Instrument resistance must be known and correction made for the external circuit (measured in Step 1). Note the polarity of the meter connection to the test point terminals and indicate the direction of current flow (+ to −) along the pipeline.
3. Using pipeline resistance tables, determine the resistance of the pipeline span.
4. Calculate the pipeline current flow by Ohm's law. Current in milliamperes = corrected millivolt drop (from Step 2) divided by pipe span resistance in ohms.

Table 5.2 may be used as a general guide to pipeline resistance. Resistivity values for steel typically range between 15 and 23 $\mu\Omega$-cm, depending on the composition of the steel. The average value is ~18 $\mu\Omega$-cm.

Sample determination of current flow on a 200-ft span of 30-in-diameter pipe weighing 118.7 lb/ft (pipeline runs east and west) requires the following measurements and calculations:

Step 1. (Battery current = 1.2 A; voltage drop = 0.108 V; circuit resistance = 0.108/1.2 = 0.09 ohm.

Step 2. Potential drop at test point terminals = 0.16 mV; the west terminal is (+).

Step 3. Resistance of pipeline span (from Table 5.2) = 2.44 × 10^{-6} × 200 = 0.49 milliohm.

Step 4. Current = 0.17 mV/0.49 milliohm = 346 mA; flow is from west to east.

Table 5.2 Steel Pipe Resistance[1]

Pipe Size, Inches	Outside Diameter, Inches	Wall Thickness, Inches	Weight Per Foot, Pounds	Resistance of One Foot[2] in Ohms$\times 10^{-6}$ (Millionths of an Ohm)
2	2.375	0.154	3.65	79.2
4	4.5	0.237	10.8	26.8
6	6.625	0.280	19.0	15.2
8	8.625	0.322	28.6	10.1
10	10.75	0.365	40.5	7.13
12	12.75	0.375	49.6	5.82
14	14.00	0.375	54.6	5.29
16	16.00	0.375	62.6	4.61
18	18.00	0.375	70.6	4.09
20	20.00	0.375	78.6	3.68
22	22.00	0.375	86.6	3.34
24	24.00	0.375	94.6	3.06
26	26.00	0.375	102.6	2.82
28	28.00	0.375	110.6	2.62
30	30.00	0.375	118.7	2.44
32	32.00	0.375	126.6	2.28
34	34.00	0.375	134.6	2.15
36	36.00	0.375	142.6	2.03

[1]Based on steel density of 489 pounds per cubic foot and steel resistivity of 18 microhm-cm as stated in text.

[2]$R = \frac{16.061 \times \text{Resistivity in Microhm-cm}}{\text{Weight per foot}}$ = resistance of one foot of pipe in microhms.

Permanent Four-Wire Test Points

Pipelines having four-wire test points with two color-coded wires at each end of a current-measuring span are best equipped for accurate measurements of pipeline current because each such span can be calibrated accurately. This avoids errors in length of pipe span and pipe resistance that may occur when the two-wire test point is used. The general arrangement for a pipeline current measurement is shown in Figure 5.10.

The test procedure is as follows:

1. Measure the circuit resistance in the current measuring span (between terminals 2 and 3) by using Step 1 for the two-wire test point procedure.
2. Calibrate the span by passing a known amount of battery current between the outside leads (terminals 1 and 4) and measure the change in potential drop across the current measuring span (terminals 2 and 3). Divide the current flow in amperes by the potential drop in millivolts to express the calibration factor in amperes per millivolt. Normally, when the pipeline operating temperature is stable, the calibration factor remains constant and does not need to be recalibrated. However, on pipelines where the temperature of the pipe changes considerably (with accompanying changes in resistance), more frequent calibration may be necessary.

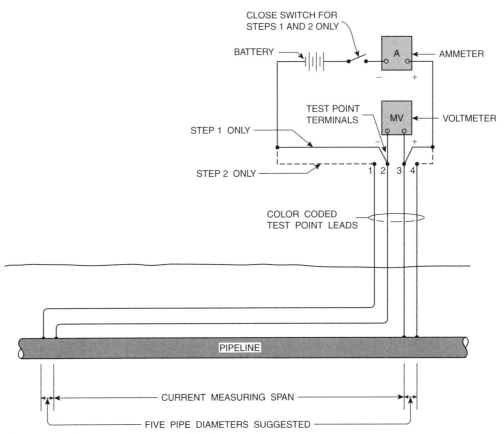

Figure 5.10   Current measurement, 4-wire test point.

3. Measure the potential drop in millivolts across the current-measuring span (terminals 2 and 3) caused by the normal pipeline current. Calculate the current flow by multiplying the measured potential drop by the calibration factor determined in Step 2. Note the direction of current flow.

Sample determination of current flow in the same pipeline section used for the example on two-wire test point current determination requires the following measurements and calculations:

Step 1.   Circuit resistance between terminals 2 and 3 measured as 0.09 ohm.

Step 2.   Ten amperes of battery current passed between terminals 1 and 4. Corrected potential drop, current on $= 5.08$ mV. Corrected potential drop, current off $= 0.17$ mV. Change in potential drop $(\Delta V) = 4.91$ mV. Calibration factor $= 10$ A/4.91 mV $= 2.04$ A/mV.

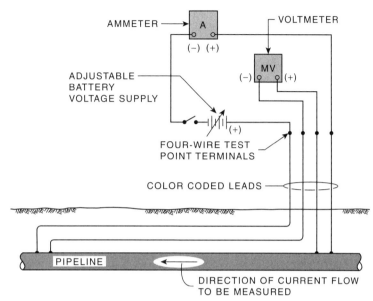

Figure 5.11   Null ammeter circuit.

Step 3. Potential drop across current-measuring span (terminals 2 and 3) = 0.17 mV (corrected) with west end terminal (+). Pipeline current = 0.17 mV × 2.04 A/mV = 0.346 A (346 mA); flow is from west to east.

An alternative method for measuring line current is to use a null ampere test circuit arrangement based on procedures described by Werner.[6] The circuit, illustrated by Figure 5.11, is used with four-wire test points. With a high-impedance voltmeter connected between the inner pair of wires, current from the battery flows between the outer pair of wires in opposition to the measured current flowing in the pipe. As the opposition current is increased, the voltage measured will move towards zero. When the voltage reading is at or very near zero, the subsequent opposition current measured on the ammeter represents the magnitude of current flow in the pipeline span under consideration. Remember the measured opposition current is flowing in the opposite direction of the actual current flow on the pipeline, so be sure to document the actual direction of pipeline current flow (the opposite of that of the opposition current).

Probe Rods

Where necessary, pipeline current may be measured by obtaining the potential drop across a pipe span of measured length. The pipe may be contacted at each end of the span by using pipe-contacting probe rods as described earlier. Otherwise, the test arrangement is generally similar to that illustrated in Figure 5.9. There are, however, several additional steps (to ensure accuracy) to those outlined for the two-wire test point procedure.

The set-up and test procedure may be performed as follows:

Step 1. Locate the pipeline with a pipe locator so that probe rods may be worked into the ground squarely above the pipe.

Step 2. Measure and mark off the current measuring span (such as 100 ft) to an accuracy of ±1 in.

Step 3. Insert the probe rods, working them down to a solid contact with the pipe steel. The rods must be kept vertical so that the span length will not deviate from the measured value.

Step 4. The two leads used to connect the measuring instrument to the probe rods should be connected together first, so the series resistance of the two leads can be measured and the value noted.

Step 5. Connect the two leads to the probe rods and measure the circuit resistance, which includes the test lead resistance and that of the pipe span. This value should be the same, for all practical purposes, as the resistance of the test leads only (measured in Step 4). This is because the resistance of an electrically continuous pipe span is so low compared with that of the test wires that the difference will not be detectable by the usual test procedures (except for long spans of very small pipe). If the resistance is measurably higher, it would be assumed that good contact between probe rods and pipe has not been attained. Work the rods against the pipe until the circuit remains stable. (If the circuit resistance does not drop to the desired value with solid contacts between rods and pipe, it is an indication of a possible extraneous resistance in the pipe span, such as a pipe fitting or mechanical coupling. In this event, current flow cannot be measured accurately and it will be necessary to move the probe rods to another point where they will span solid pipe.)

Step 6. Measure the millivolt drop between the two probe rods and correct the reading for the effect of the external circuit resistance. Note the polarity to determine direction of current flow.

Step 7. Repeat the circuit resistance measurement of Step 5 to be sure that the circuit has remained stable while the test was being made. If not, repeat the procedure.

Step 8. Determine pipe span resistance from Table 5.2 and calculate the current flow by Ohm's law, following the procedure established for two-wire permanent test points.

Line Current Survey Evaluation Methods

If corrosion is taking place on a pipeline, there will be current flow to the line at some points and current flow away from the line at others. For small local cells, often termed "long line," the current may follow the pipe for hundreds or thousands of feet. It is these long-line currents that can be detected in a line current survey.

Because the pipe itself has some resistance to the flow of electric current, there will be a voltage drop in the pipe if current is flowing through this pipe resistance. The voltage drops are usually very small but can be determined by using suitable instrumentation (discussed in Chapter 6). The resistance per foot of steel pipe is not great and becomes progressively smaller as the pipe size and weight per foot increases. Many pipeline companies install permanent test point installations with wires of a known span length, for example, 100 ft. To see how sensitive such a span would be to small values of pipeline current, consider two examples:

1. If the pipeline is an 8-in-diameter line with 0.322-in-thick wall weighs 28.6 lb/ft and is made of 5LX32 steel, the resistance across a 100-ft span would be 9.75×10^{-4} ohms. If the available test instrument is sensitive to a potential as small as 0.02 mV, a current of only 20.5 mA flowing through the span resistance would cause this minimum deflection.
2. A 30-in-diameter line with 0.375-in-thick walls weighs 118.7 lb/ft (also of 5LX32 steel) will have a 100-ft span resistance of $\sim 2.36 \times 10^{-4}$ ohms. With this lower resistance span, a current flow of 84.7 mA through the pipeline will be required to give the assumed minimum deflection of 0.02 mV. Obviously, a given test span length is much less sensitive on large-diameter pipe than on small lines. Using longer span lengths on large pipes (that is increasing the span resistance) will result in increased sensitivity.

On lines without permanently installed test spans, contact bars may be used to establish a span for test purposes. This must be done carefully to avoid error as discussed earlier. This procedure would be necessary, however, to make closely spaced line current measurements (at 500- or 1000-ft intervals, for example) during a line current survey on a bare line.

At each point of measurement in a line current survey, the voltage drop is observed and recorded, together with the polarity of instrument connections to indicate the direction of current flow (plus to minus). Knowing the span resistance of the pipe being surveyed, one may convert the voltage drops to equivalent current flow by application of Ohm's law (voltage drop in millivolts/span resistance in ohms = current flow in milliamperes). The values of current together with the direction of flow then may be plotted vs line length. The results might be generally similar to the plot shown by Figure 5.12.

As illustrated, at one area the current flows from both directions toward a particular point on the line. This must be a point of current discharge and, unless the current is being drained off by a metal contact such as through another structure, corrosion may be expected in that area.

Line current surveys in most cases will be more meaningful for bare lines than for well-coated lines. On coated pipe, current can enter or leave the pipe only through breaks or pinholes in the coating. With current concentrated at these coating defects, current density in terms of milliamperes per square foot of exposed steel usually is greater than on bare pipe. This means that the degree of attack will be greater at coating defects in anodic areas on coated pipe with a greater rate of penetration than would be the case

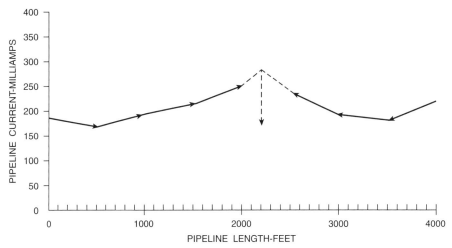

Figure 5.12   Line current survey.

with bare pipe under similar soil conditions. Nevertheless, the total long-line current flow on the coated pipe between anodic and cathodic areas would be much less than on bare pipe (again, under similar soil conditions) because, with reasonably good coating, all but a very small percentage of the pipeline steel is insulated from the surrounding soil.

There are several possibilities of error in making line current surveys. Care must be taken when using probe bars to contact the pipe as mentioned earlier. Unless actual resistance is measured for each test span, changes in pipe size or wall thickness (that is, differences from what may be normal for the line being surveyed) can result in the actual span resistance being substantially different from that calculated from the normal pipe dimensions. Likewise, unless the span resistance is measured, the presence of an unknown mechanical pipe coupling in the test span could introduce enough resistance to make results completely erroneous. Permanently installed test spans are usually put in at the time of pipeline construction, using span length and color-coded wiring in accordance with an established specification. Errors in color coding may result in the current flow being indicated in the wrong direction.

When planning test point installations for new pipeline systems (or when installing them on an existing system), it is good practice to provide current-measuring test spans with two separate wires connected to the pipeline at each end of the span. This permits measuring the actual span resistance, as described earlier.

Soil Resistivity Survey

This indication of a tendency for current to flow becomes more important if something is known about the soil resistivity. High-resistivity soils may offer so much resistance

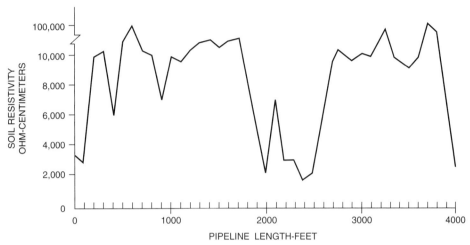

Figure 5.13   Soil resistivity survey.

to current flow that conditions are not as severe as the plotted potential data might lead one to believe. Conversely, severe potential peaks coupled with a relatively low resistivity environment may mean a truly serious condition. Frequent soil resistivity determinations are important when making a detailed survey on a pipe line. In addition to being a valuable aid when interpreting the severity of corrosive areas, a soil resistivity profile is extremely helpful in the later selection of sites for CP installations. Figure 5.13 is a plot of the soil resistivity measurements taken along the same section of pipeline used as a basis for the plots shown in Figures 5.4 and 5.12.

Data plotted in the figure represent average soil resistivity to approximate pipe depth. In this example, a very wide range of soil resistivity is represented. Other cases would not necessarily have such a large difference between maximum and minimum resistivities along a similar length of line.

Along well-coated pipelines, measurements of soil resistivity can be of great assistance in the later selection of CP installations. This may be particularly true to identify areas where soils of suitable low resistivity for such installations.

Instruments used for measuring soil resistivity by the four-pin method are described in Chapter 6. Certain precautions to be observed in using the method are given below, together with suggestions for planning soil resistivity measurements.

In the example shown, resistivity of the soil was measured at ~100-ft intervals along the proposed alignment. Soil resistivity measurements were conducted by the Wenner four-pin method, utilizing a soil resistance meter (see Chapter 6). The Wenner method requires the use of four metal probes or electrodes, driven into the ground along a straight line, equidistant from each other, as shown in Figure 5.14. An alternating current from the soil resistance meter causes current to flow through the soil, between pins C1 and C2. The voltage or potential is then measured between pins P1 and P2. The meter then

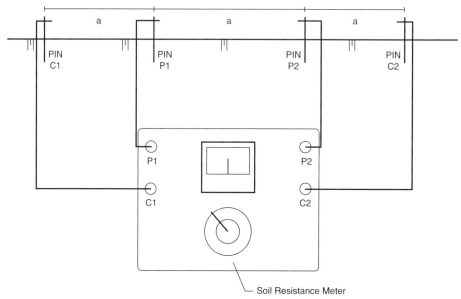

Figure 5.14   Soil resistivity test set-up (Wenner four pin method).

registers a resistance reading. Resistivity of the soil is then computed from the instrument reading, according to the following formula:

$$\rho = 2\pi\, AR$$

where ρ = soil resistivity (ohm-centimeters)

   A = distance between probes (centimeters)

   R = soil resistance (ohms) {instrument reading}

   $\pi = 3.1416$

The resistivity values obtained represent the average resistivity of the soil to a depth equal to the pin spacing. Resistance measurements are typically performed to a depth equal to that of the pipeline being evaluated. Typical probe spacings are in increments of 2.5 ft (76.2 cm).

If the line of soil pins used when making four-pin resistivity measurements is closely parallel to a bare underground pipeline or other metallic structure, the presence of the bare metal may cause the indicated soil resistivity values to be lower than it actually is. Because a portion of the test current will flow along the metallic structure rather than through the soil, measurements along a line closely parallel to pipelines should be avoided. When making soil resistivity measurements along a pipeline, it is good practice to place the line of the pins perpendicular to the pipeline with the nearest pin at least 15 ft from the pipe—further, if space permits.

Table 5.3   Format for Recording Soil Resistivity Measurements

Test Location	Nominal Pin Spacing, Feet	Ohms	Factor	Resistivity in Ohm-cm
No. 1				
Pipeline Station	2.5	4.40	500	2200
1000 + 00. Nearest	5	2.05	1,000	2050
pin 100 ft west of pipe.	7.5	1.26	1,500	1890
Line of tests perpendicular	10	0.96	2,000	1920
to pipe. Clay Moist	12.5	0.78	2,500	1950
	15	0.62	3,000	1860
	50	0.17	10,000	1700
No. 2				
Station 1001 + 00.	2.5	1.30	500	650
Nearest pin 200 ft	5	0.60	1,000	600
east of pipe. Line of	7.5	0.45	1,500	675
tests parallel to pipe.	10	0.36	2,000	720
Edge of swamp. Wet	12.5	0.34	2,500	850
	15	0.33	3,000	990
	25	0.34	5,000	1700

Soil resistivity data taken by the four-pin method should be recorded in tabular form for convenience in calculating resistivities and evaluating results obtained. The tabular arrangement may be as shown in Table 5.3. Where many soil resistivity measurements are to be made, field time will be saved by using printed forms arranged for entering the necessary data.

With experience, much can be learned about the soil structure by inspecting series of readings to increasing depths. The recorded values from four-pin resistivity measurements can be misleading unless it is remembered that the soil resistivity encountered with each additional depth increment is averaged, in the test, with that of all the soil in the layers above. The indicated resistivity to a depth equal to any given pipe spacing is a weighted average of the soils from the surface to that depth. Trends can be illustrated best by inspecting the sets of soil resistivity readings in Table 5.4.

Soil resistivity is an electrical characteristic of the soil/groundwater which affects the ability of corrosion currents to flow through the electrolyte (soil/groundwater). Resistivity is a function of soil moisture and the concentrations of ionic soluble salts and is considered to be most comprehensive indicator of a soil's corrosivity. Typically, the lower the resistivity, the higher will be the corrosivity.

Table 5.5 correlates resistivity values with degree of corrosivity. The interpretation of soil resistivity varies among corrosion engineers. However, this table is a generally accepted guide.

The first set of data in Table 5.4, Set A, represents a uniform soil conditions. The average of the readings shown (~960 ohm-cm) represents the effective resistivity

Table 5.4 Typical Soil Resistivity Readings Using 4 Pin Method

Pin Spacing (Feet)	Soil Resistivity (ohm-cm)			
	Set A	Set B	Set C	Set D
2.5	960	1100	3300	760
5	965	1000	2200	810
7.5	950	1250	1150	1,900
10	955	1500	980	3,800
12.5	960	1610	840	6,900
15	955	1710	780	12,500

that may be used for design purposes for impressed current ground beds or galvanic anodes.

Data Set B represents low-resistivity soils in the first few feet. There may be a layer of somewhat less than 1000 ohm-cm around the 5-ft depth level. Below 5-ft, however, higher-resistivity soils are encountered. Because of the averaging effect mentioned earlier, the actual resistivity at 7.5-ft deep would be higher than the indicated 1250 ohm-cm and might be in the order of 2500 ohm-cm or more. Even if anodes are placed in the lower-resistivity soils, there will be resistance to the flow of current downward into the mass of the earth. If designs are based on the resistivity of the soil in which the anodes are placed, the resistance of the completed installation will be higher than expected. The anodes will perform best if placed in the lower resistance soil. The effective resistivity used for design purposes should reflect the higher resistivity of the underlying areas. In this instance, where increase is gradual, using horizontal anodes in the low-resistivity area and a figure of effective resistivity of ~2500 ohm-cm should result in a conservative design.

Data Set C represents an excellent location for anode location even though the surface soils have relatively high resistivity. It would appear from this set of data that anodes

Table 5.5 Soil Resistivity vs. Degree of Corrosivity

Soil resistivity (ohm-cm)	Degree of corrosivity
0–500	Very corrosive
500–1,000	Corrosive
1,000–2,000	Moderately corrosive
2,000–10,000	Mildly corrosive
Above 10,000	Negligible

Reference: *NACE Corrosion Basics.*

located >5-ft deep, would be in low-resistivity soil of ~800 ohm-cm, such a figure being conservative for design purposes. A lowering resistivity trend with depth, as illustrated by this set of data, can be relied upon to give excellent ground bed performance.

Data Set D is the least favorable of these sample sets of data. Low-resistivity soil is present at the surface but the upward trend of resistivity with depth is immediate and rapid. At the 7.5-ft depth, for example, the resistivity could be tens of thousands of ohm-centimeters. One such situation could occur where a shallow swampy area overlies solid rock. Current discharged from anodes installed at such a location will be forced to flow for relatively long distances close to the surface before electrically remote earth is reached. As a result, potential gradients forming the area of influence around an impressed current ground bed can extend much farther than those surrounding a similarly sized ground bed operating at the same voltage in more favorable locations such as those represented by data Sets A and C.

One mathematical procedure, known as the Barnes method, is based on calculating the resistivity of the soil in each incremental layer of soil. This is done by using the data from the four-pin soil resistivity test but extending the calculations by determining the conductivity of each incremental layer and converting this conductivity to resistivity. Applying the procedure to the Set B soil resistivities (Table 5.6) provides a demonstration of the method.

The Barnes method of analysis is not infallible because its accuracy requires soil layers to be of uniform thickness and parallel to the surface. In cases, where this is true, each added layer of earth must increase the total conductivity from the surface to the bottom of the added layer, no matter what the resistivity of the added layer may be. If, as

Table 5.6 Calculation of Soil Resistivity by Layers

4-PIN DATA, SET B[1]				BARNES PROCEDURE					
								Layer Resistivity	
Spacing Feet	R_1 Ohms	Factor	Resistivity Ohm-Cm	Mhos[2] $1/R_1$	Mhos[3] $\Delta 1/R_1$	R_2 Ohms $1/\Delta 1/R_1$	Factor[4]	Ohm-cm	and Layer Depth, Feet
2.5	2.2	500	1100	0.455	—	—	—	1100	0–2.5
5.0	1.0	1000	1000	1.0	.545	1.84	500	920	2.5–5.0
7.5	0.833	1500	1250	1.2	.20	5.0	500	2500	5.0–7.5
10.0	0.75	2000	1500	1.33	.13	7.7	500	3850	7.5–10
12.5	0.645	2500	1610	1.55	.22	4.55	500	2275	10–12.5
15.0	0.57	3000	1710	1.75	.20	5.0	500	2500	12.5–15

[1]From Table 5.4
[2]This is the conductivity in mhos (reciprocal of resistance) to the indicated depth.
[3]This is the increase in conductivity caused by the added layer of earth.
[4]The factor used here is for nominal 2.5 foot layer increments. If other layer thickness are used, the factor must be changed accordingly (191.5 × layer thickness in feet).

in the sample calculations above, the conductivity (the column headed $1/R_1$) continues to increase with depth, conditions appear to approach the ideal closely enough to make the method usable. Decreases in the conductivity at any point in a series are an indication that soil layers are too distorted to permit use of the method for analysis of data at that depth. For example, if the Barnes method procedure is applied to soil data Set D, results cannot be calculated by this method below the 5-ft level. One inference from this type of data is that the low resistivities observed near the surface indicate the presence of a limited pocket of favorable soil in an area of soil having predominantly very high resistivity.

In some areas, experience will show that soil resistivities may change markedly within short distances. A sufficient number of four-pin tests should be made in a ground bed construction area, for example, to be sure that the best soil conditions have been located. For ground beds of considerable length (as may be the case with impressed current beds), four-pin tests should be taken at intervals along the route of the proposed line of ground bed anodes. If driven rod tests or borings are made to assist in arriving at an effective soil resistivity for design purposes, such tests should be made in enough locations to ascertain the variation in effective soil resistivity along the proposed line of anodes.

Soil Chemical Analysis

If soil samples are not measured "on location" but are collected for later measurement, they should be kept in air-tight containers to preserve the normal moisture content. In some instances, abnormally dry surface soils may be moistened with distilled water to obtain their resistivity under wet conditions.

A wide variety of soluble salts are typically found in soils. Two soils having the same resistivity may have significantly different corrosion characteristics, depending on the specific ions available. The major constituents that accelerate corrosion are chlorides, sulfates, and the acidity (pH) of the soil. Calcium and magnesium tend to form insoluble oxide and bicarbonate precipitates in basic environments, which can create a protective layer over the metal surface and reduce the corrosion. In contrast, the chloride ion tends to break down otherwise protective surface deposits and can result in corrosion and corrosion pitting of buried metallic structures. Bicarbonates are not typically detrimental to buried metallic. However, high concentrations of bicarbonates found in soils/groundwater tend to lower the resistivity without the resulting increase in corrosion activity.

Soil samples should be taken at the depth of the pipeline in areas where soil resistivity data may indicate corrosive conditions. Samples should be sent to a qualified laboratory to perform the analysis in accordance with standard practices.

Table 5.7 correlates the effect of chlorides, sulfates, and pH on the corrosion of buried steel or concrete structures. Acidity, as indicated by the pH value, is another aggressive factor of soil/groundwater. The lower the pH (the more acidic the environment), the greater the corrosivity with respect to buried metallic structures. As pH increases to >7

Table 5.7   Effect of Chlorides, Sulfates, and pH on Corrosion of Buried Steel Pipelines

Concentration (ppm)	Degree of corrosivity
Chloride[1]	
>5,000	Severe
1,500–5,000	Considerable
500–1,500	Corrosive
<500	Threshold
Sulfate[1]	
>10,000	Severe
1,500–10,000	Considerable
150–1,500	Positive
0–150	Negligible
pH[2]	
<5.5	Severe
5.5–6.5	Moderate
6.5–7.5	Neutral
>7.5	None (alkaline)

[1]Reference: ACI-318, *Building Code Requirements for Reinforced Concrete* (American Concrete Institute, 1999).
[2]Reference: M. Romanoff, *Underground Corrosion*, 1957.

(the neutral value), conditions become increasingly more alkaline and less corrosive to buried steel structures.

In many areas, soils encountered along a pipeline route will be approximately neutral (pH 7). There may, however, be locations where unusual environmental conditions exist, either alkaline (pH values >7) or acid (pH values <7).

Alkaline conditions do not pose any serious difficulty to steel pipelines because such an environment is not aggressive toward steel. Strongly alkaline conditions can be detrimental to aluminum piping, however. Under some conditions, use of CP may not be able to prevent alkaline attack on aluminum.

Acid conditions around the pipe have the general effect of making it much more difficult to polarize the line to protective potentials (the acid acts as a depolarizing agent) when CP is applied. This increases the current requirements in the area.

Clearly, during a corrosion survey, it would be of value to check the soil pH in areas where there is a possibility of unusual chemical conditions. The results could have considerable effect on the locations selected for CP rectifiers or galvanic anodes. A particularly acid soil condition, for example, would indicate the need for a relatively high current density to maintain CP. This could in turn make it desirable to locate CP installations at or near the area of high current requirement.

CURRENT REQUIREMENT TESTING FOR CATHODIC PROTECTION

Bare Lines

Current Applied Method

The most widely used method for current requirement testing of a pipeline is represented below in Figure 5.15. Basically, direct current is forced to flow from a temporary ground connection to the pipeline section being studied, and determining how much current will be needed to protect that section.

The output of the current source shown in the figure may be adjusted until protective potentials are attained at the ends of the section to be protected. When working with bare line, the current should be allowed to flow steadily, which will permit the line to polarize to some degree, depending on the duration of the test. Full polarization on a bare line may take weeks to achieve; if, however, during the test, the increase in protective potential is plotted versus time at a fixed current output, the curve can be extended to give a rough approximation of the potentials that would be obtained with complete polarization. Current flowing into the protected section from the pipeline on either side may be measured by the voltage drop across a known pipe span as described previously. These two values may then be subtracted from the total current to obtain the net flow into the protected section. Getting the net current in this manner is significant if, when making permanent CP installations, there will be CP units in adjacent areas that would

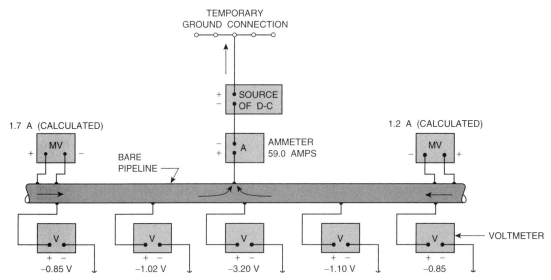

Figure 5.15   Current requirements for CP.

reduce or eliminate the current flow from remote areas into the area being tested as described.

Current requirement tests of the type described do not give more than a reasonable close approximation of current needs. Variations will be caused by such things as ground bed resistance and location with respect to the pipeline, polarization effects (as mentioned above), the amount of line that is protected by each installation, and whether or not adjacent installations will affect the amount of current flowing to the pipeline beyond the area to be protected. Such variables can cause appreciable differences between survey results and the ultimate performance of permanent installations. Interpretation of survey test results on bare lines is seldom simple. Experience is most valuable when developing a final design from field survey data of the nature discussed.

Because bare line current requirements usually are high, substantial currents will be flowing along the pipeline. These, in turn, will cause significant voltage drops in the line, which will limit the length of pipe that may be protected from one point without producing excessive potentials at the point of current drainage. Unless circumstances are unusual, only a few hundred up to a thousand feet or so of bare pipe should be tested at one time. As a general rule, longer pipe lengths can be tested when working with larger-diameter lines because their longitudinal resistance is less. When planning a current requirement test on bare line, the current source needed should have sufficient capacity to supply, as a guide, at least 1-3 mA per square foot of pipe surface plus 25% more. The voltage of the power source must be sufficient to force the needed current through the temporary ground connection used. Storage batteries may be adequate for testing short lengths of small-diameter pipe, whereas a source such as a DC welding generator may be needed for longer lengths of larger-diameter pipe. See Chapter 7 for information on the resistance of ground beds.

Coated Pipelines

When surveying a coated pipeline system, data on the electrical strength of the coating and on current requirements for CP can be taken concurrently. If the coating is in reasonably good condition, current requirements are much smaller than on bare lines. This makes it possible to test many miles of pipeline with one test set-up and a modest power supply. Batteries are usually sufficient.

Although the same coating specification may be used throughout the length of a given pipeline, the effective electrical strength of that coating (in terms of its ability to resist the flow of current) may vary considerably along the route. Variations may be due to the type of terrain, construction difficulties (rocky pipe-laying conditions may result in many more accidentally damaged areas), changes in average soil resistivity, and different degrees of quality of pipeline construction work and inspection. In any event, knowledge of areas where abnormally low coating resistances are prevalent on a given line will assist the corrosion engineer in planning the corrosion control system.

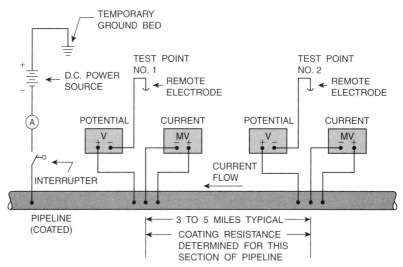

Figure 5.16   Coating resistance and CP current requirement tests.

When making the combined survey on a coated line, a test arrangement may be used as illustrated by Figure 5.16. At the test battery location, a current interrupter (see Chapter 6) is used to automatically switch the current source on and off at a convenient time interval (such as 10 s on and 5 s off). This way the data needed for coating resistance calculations are obtained. At the same time this procedure assures the test engineer at remote locations that the battery installation is still operating properly as long as the potential and line current measurements continue to change in accord with the established on–off cycle.

On a reasonably well-coated pipeline, test data taken at intervals of, typically, 3 to 5 miles will give satisfactory information on the average coating resistance within each section tested. Testing section by section can be continued in each direction from the temporary CP location until the changes in the observed currents and potentials (as the current interrupter switches on and off) are no longer large enough to result in accurate data. The limits of the area that can be maintained above the protected ctiterion of −0.85 V or better will be established at this same time.

Coated pipelines polarize very rapidly. The better the coating, the faster the polarization. This means that conditions stabilize within the first few minutes (and sometimes in a matter of seconds) after the test current is applied.

On coated pipeline systems provided with test points for potential and line current measurement, a survey will proceed rapidly. Data may be taken with reasonable accuracy by a single test engineer. For maximum accuracy, however, two engineers in radio communication can observe data simultaneously at each end of each section tested. This becomes essential if the pipeline under test is affected by stray current. Strays may make it necessary to take a series of simultaneous readings and average them to obtain usable data.

To obtain data for calculations of coating resistance, readings are taken along the pipeline to a copper sulfate electrode with the interrupter on and off, and pipeline current is measured with the interrupter on and off at each end of each line section. From these readings one can determine the change in pipe potential (ΔV) and the change in line current (ΔI) at each end of the test section. The difference of the two ΔI values will be equal to the test battery current collected by the line section when the current interrupter is switched on. The average of the two ΔV values will be the average change in pipeline potential within the test section caused by the battery current collected. The average ΔV in millivolts, divided by the current collected in milliamperes, will give the resistance to earth, in ohms, of the pipeline section tested. From the length and diameter of pipe in the section tested, its total surface area in square feet may be calculated. Multiplying the pipe-section-to-earth resistance by the area in square feet will result in a value of ohms per average square foot, the effective coating resistance for the section tested. Some workers express coating condition in terms of conductivity (in mhos or micromhos). This is simply a matter of conversion. The reciprocal of the resistance per average square foot is the conductivity in mhos. The reciprocal of the resistance per average square foot is the conductivity in mhos. The reciprocal times 10^6 is the conductivity in micromhos.

Here is an example of data and its treatment as described in preceding paragraph. Referring to Figure 5.16, assume that the section between test points 1 and 2 is under test and that this section consists of 15,000 ft of coated pipeline having a total external pipe surface area of 50,070 ft^2. Test data taken at test point 1 are as follows:

$$\text{Pipe to CuSO}_4 = -1.75 \text{ volts, ON and } -0.89 \text{ volts, OFF}$$
$$\Delta V = -0.86 \text{ volt}$$

Pipe span potential drop = +0.98 MV, ON and +0.04 MV, OFF

With span calibrated at 2.30 amps per mV (discussed earlier in this chapter.),

$$\text{Pipeline current} = +2.25 \text{ amps, ON and } +0.09 \text{ amps, OFF}$$
$$\Delta I = 2.16 \text{ amps}$$

Test data taken at test point 2 are

$$\text{Pipe to CuSO}_4 = -1.70 \text{ volts, ON and } -0.88 \text{ volts, OFF}$$
$$\Delta V = -0.82 \text{ volt}$$

Pipe span potential drop = +0.84 MV, ON and −0.02 MV, OFF

With span calibrated at 2.41 amps per MV,

$$\text{Pipeline current} = +2.03 \text{ amps, ON and } -0.05 \text{ amps, OFF}$$

(negative off currents indicate current flow in opposite direction)

$$\Delta I = 2.08 \text{ amps}$$

Calculation of coating resistance is therefore:

$$Average\ \Delta V = (-0.86 + -0.82) \div 2 = -0.84\ volt$$
$$Current\ collected = 2.16 - 2.08 = 0.08\ amp$$
$$Pipe\ to\ earth\ resistance = 0.84\ V \div 0.08\ A = 10.5\ ohms$$
$$Effective\ coating\ resistance = 10.5\ ohms \times 50,070$$
$$= 526,000\ ohms\ for\ an\ average\ square\ foot\ (approx.)$$
$$(ohms\text{-}ft^2)$$

Note that the average soil resistivity has an effect on the effective coating resistance measurement. In part this is because the apparent pipeline resistance to remote earth measure in the procedure described is a combination of the coating resistance and the resistance to remote earth of the pipeline itself. In the example given, if we assume that the test section was in 1000 ohm-cm soil, the resistance to earth of the 15,000 ft of 12-in-diameter line, if bare, would be in the order of 0.0062 ohm. If the average soil resistivity were 100,000 ohm-cm, this resistance would be 0.62 ohm. If the difference, $\sim$0.6 ohm, is added to the 10.5 ohms of pipe-to-earth resistance calculated in the example, the new total of 11.1 ohms, multiplied by the 50,070 ft^2 surface area, would give an indicated effective coating resistance of 606,000 ohms per average square foot.

Actually, however, the resistance to earth of exposed steel at coating defects may have a much greater effect on the apparent coating resistance with variation in soil resistivity. Using the example again, if the coating were perfect (10^{13} ohm-cm resistivity), the resistance of the pipeline section to remote earth would be in the order of 50,000 ohms—whereas the measured value was only 10.5 ohms. Now if we assume that the 10.5 ohms (in 1000 ohm-cm soil) is primarily the resistance to earth at pinholes distributed along the 15,000 ft section, this resistance will vary in approximate proportion to the soil resistivity. The resistance in 100,000 ohm-cm soil, then, would be in the order of $(100,000/1,000) \times 10.5$ or 1050 ohms $\times$ 50,070 ft^2, or 52.5×10^6 ohms for an average square foot (ohms-ft^2). This relationship is not rigorous and depends on the relative size and spacing of coating defects as well as the ratio between the section resistance with perfect coating and that as actually measured (when the ratio is high, as in this case, pinhole resistance prevails). This does, however, demonstrate the effect that soil resistivity can have on apparent coating resistance. In particular, it shows that something must be known about the soil resistivity when evaluating a section of pipeline coating.

The method described for obtaining an approximation of effective coating resistance depends, for accuracy, on the precision with which field data are taken. The potential measurements pose no particular problem (unless erratic stray current effects are present), but the line current measurements are another matter. Unless current-measuring test points of a type that can be calibrated are permanently installed, errors in span length or variations in pipe span resistance may make calculated currents erroneous. Also, as was demonstrated earlier, it may not be possible to detect small currents or current differences that are below the sensitivity range of the millivoltmeter being used. Nevertheless, as long as these limitation are recognized, the procedure is fully practical in establishing relative coating quality from section to section.

An initial coating resistance profile along a new pipeline will serve as a reference to which similar data taken in later years may be compared. Such comparisons reveal information on the long-term performance of the coating. For example, detrimental effects caused by such things as high pipeline operating temperature, areas of abnormal soil stress, areas subject to a high degree of bacterial activity, or any other condition that may affect the coating.

ADDITIONAL CONSIDERATIONS

Microbiologically Influenced Corrosion

Microbiologically influenced corrosion (MIC) is one manifestation of the effect on corrosion by soil bacteria. MIC is discussed in detail in Chapter 14. Certain bacteria, which can exist under anaerobic conditions (absence of oxygen) at the pipeline surface, have the ability to reduce any sulfates present and consume hydrogen in the process. Consumption of hydrogen at the pipe surface acts to depolarize the steel at cathodic areas and permits more rapid consumption of the metal by galvanic corrosion cells. The bacteria, then, do not directly attack the pipe but provide conditions conducive to a more rapid attack by existing corrosion cells, which are normally partially stifled by the development of an insulating polarization film of hydrogen.

The practical effect of anaerobic bacteria activity on the application of CP is an increase in the amount of current required to maintain CP. Some workers have reported that higher-than-normal protective potentials should be used in areas where anaerobic bacteria are active because the open circuit potentials of anodic areas are more negative. An additional 100 mV of protective potential has been suggested (-0.95 V to copper sulfate electrode instead of the usual -0.85 V).

Bellhole Examinations

Sometimes there is nothing that will satisfy the corrosion engineer more than having an actual look at the pipe that has been surveyed by electrical methods. Actually, this is an acceptable and desirable procedure for use in evaluating the relative severity of corrosive areas detected during a survey.

Typical hot-spot corrosive areas found during a corrosion survey on an older bare line may be uncovered and inspected. This will give the corrosion engineer a guide for evaluating other corrosive areas on the line.

Areas where anaerobic corrosion is suspected may be exposed for examination. If anaerobic bacteria are present and active, a layer of black iron sulfide will coat the pipe surface. The deposit would be expected only at coating defects on pipelines having a bonded coating. If this black material is iron sulfide, treating it with a dilute solution of hydrochloric acid will release hydrogen sulfide gas, which is recognized by its characteristic rotten egg odor.

If areas have been found where pipe coatings have unusually low resistance values, bellhole inspections may be in order to trace the causes of coating damage. This may be particularly valuable in connection with older pipeline coatings to determine the nature of deterioration over time as a guide to selection of materials for future coating projects.

EXAMPLES OF CORROSION SURVEYS

Corrosion Survey on a Typical Coated Line

To conduct a corrosion survey on a 100-mi-long, 30-in-diameter pipeline having an very good dielectric coating, what should one know? In the first place, particularly if the line was recently laid, the usual intent is to cathodically protect the line. Accordingly, information to be obtained during the survey will be based on this objective. With this in mind, the following types of data may be procured for such a line:

1. Soil resistivity information at intervals along the line, including locations suitable for CP installations. If at sites where electric power is available, note details of power supply line: company, voltage, pole number, single or three-phase, and so forth.
2. Effective electrical resistance of the coating.
3. Current requirements for CP.
4. Location of unusual environmental conditions along the pipeline route such as acidic areas, sections where severe bacterial attack may be suspected, or any other condition that might tend to result in increased corrosion rates or rapid coating deterioration.
5. Effect of stray current, if any.
6. Tests at crossings with structures of other ownership to see if mutual interference effects may be a problem.
7. Condition of cased crossings at roads and railroads.

All the above types of information can have a direct bearing on the type and design details of the CP system to be developed for the pipeline being surveyed. Only when such information is complete can a protection system be designed for optimum performance from the standpoint of protection coverage, reliability, and economy. Survey methods used to obtain most of the above-listed types of information have been described earlier in this chapter.

At crossings with underground structures of other ownership, tests will be made to make sure that the two systems are electrically insulated from one another. If the foreign system is cathodically protected, the possibility of adverse effect on the line being surveyed is investigated. Likewise, it may be necessary to determine if a CP system on the line being surveyed will affect the foreign structure to a degree requiring corrective action. These effects are a form of stray current and are discussed in greater detail in Chapter 11.

Corrosion Survey on a Typical Bare Line

Bare line surveys are time-consuming and expensive when compared with corrosion surveys on coated pipelines of the same length. Because of this, careful planning is necessary to be sure that all needed information is obtained without extending the scope of the survey beyond the requirements of the pipeline situation involved.

Example No. 1

Assume that a bare line to be surveyed is old and has an extensive leak record. Also, although the line is planned to be in use for only another 10 years, the cost of repairing leaks is becoming prohibitive. In this instance, the line operators might elect to adopt stop-gap measures by applying CP at the worst spots. A field corrosion survey, then, would be confined to those trouble areas where leakage is a problem, as defined by the leak records.

One approach to surveying this pipeline would be to make soil resistivity measurements for the selection of rectifier-powered CP units at each trouble area and to make current-requirement tests to assist in the design of the final installations. This approach would be adopted logically if the leakage areas were relatively few and well defined but large enough to justify the installation of one or more rectifier units in each area.

Another survey approach might be adopted if the leakage areas were frequent and small such that the use of rectifiers might not seem justified. Galvanic anodes might be the better choice. In this event, the corrosion survey would consist of soil resistivity measurements to assist in the selection of size and type of anodes to be used.

Either approach described should be supplemented by sufficient pipeline potential readings to establish whether or not stray current damage is a possibility if there is any reason to suspect an effect from such sources. Locating foreign pipeline rectifiers is also necessary where they are close enough to the line being surveyed to be a possible source of damaging interference. The location of all foreign underground structures should be known in areas where CP installations are to be made, particularly if rectifier units are contemplated.

Example No. 2

Assume that the bare line to be surveyed is relatively new but corrosion has started to become apparent through leak development. Assume further that the line is of a critical nature, requiring corrosion control throughout its length, and that its life is to be extended indefinitely. This could be a line, for example, that was expected to have a short economic life when installed originally (hence laid bare) but was found later to be needed for as long as possible.

For such a line, a complete corrosion survey would be indicated. As a minimum, the survey techniques should include an over-the-line potential survey and a soil resistivity survey, both described earlier in the chapter.

Field survey data accumulated as above will serve as an adequate basis for the design of CP installations.

RECORDING SURVEY DATA

No corrosion survey will be of value unless data are recorded in such form that they can be analyzed properly during and after the survey. This requires planning before the survey starts. When a considerable amount of any one type of data is expected to be taken, time will be saved in the field by having data forms on which to enter the readings. In addition to reducing paper work in the field, such forms will serve as a reminder of readings that should be taken.

An area of particular importance in recording field data is designating where the readings are taken. Location may be identified by pipeline station numbers when maps showing this information are available. If there is no station numbering system, distances from the closest positively identifiable landmark should be recorded. For example, if corrosive areas are found during potential surveys on bare lines, the information will be of value only if the precise location can be found again later when corrective CP is to be installed.

Chapter 6

Instrumentation

Mark Lewis

The corrosion engineer must have a sound basic knowledge of the variety of test instruments used in corrosion work and he or she must know how to use them effectively in the field. Only with such knowledge can engineers obtain reliable and meaningful data. The corrosion engineer will routinely employ not only common electronic multimeters but also very specialized instrumentation.

Section 1 of this chapter includes a discussion of typical equipment used for the various field tests. Section 2 covers the variety of accessories and supplementary equipment that may be needed along with the basic test instruments. Section 3 addresses the care and maintenance of corrosion instrumentation.

EQUIPMENT

This section will examine the operating characteristics and capabilities of instrumentation suitable for corrosion testing. Although typical instrumentation will be illustrated, all available devices cannot be covered. For more thorough coverage of these instruments, as well as others not described, consult the manufacturer's operating instructions, or an instrumentation supplier. Equipment vendors can also offer operating advice, as well as firsthand instruction on the operation of the more specialized instruments.

Voltmeters

Measurement of voltage, such as that between a pipeline and a reference electrode, is probably the most frequently made determination in corrosion testing work. If suitable voltage measuring equipment is not used (or if the right equipment is not used properly), the values obtained may be misleading or completely meaningless.

Voltmeters and Resistance

Because of improvements in measurement technology, electronic voltmeters are manufactured with an enormous variety of capabilities. Many commonly available voltmeters are referred to as *multimeters* because they have the ability to measure multiple electrical values in addition to voltage. The features offered on a given instrument may be tailored to the needs of a particular industry or discipline, or the device may offer a combination of test capabilities common to many applications.

It is important to understand the versatility of these devices as well as their limitations. Certain multimeter functions and features are valuable for corrosion engineering work, while others can be insufficient or unnecessary.

When measuring, for example, the voltage difference between a pipeline and a reference electrode, two important resistance values must be kept in mind. To determine a pipe-to-soil potential value, a voltmeter must measure across an external circuit resistance, which may vary widely from one environment to another. For instance, the resistance of a reference electrode in contact with moist or wet soil will be considerably less than one in contact with dry sand or frozen or oily soil. Therefore, the reference electrode's contact resistance represents a large portion of the overall resistance of the circuit across which a voltage is to be measured.

To compensate for these variations in the measuring circuit, voltmeters *must* be equipped with a high *impedance*, or input resistance. A high external resistance requires a high input resistance to maintain accuracy during measurements. Most conventional multimeters currently produced have an internal impedance of 10 million ohms (10^7 ohms, or 10 megohms), or more. However, some inexpensive voltmeters are available that are not intended for use in the measurement of high resistance circuits, such as those encountered in corrosion testing. The use of a meter with, for example, an internal resistance of only 2×10^3 ohms per volt can cause significant error when used to measure pipe-to-soil potentials.

Measurement of other voltage values, such as rectifier output voltage or voltage drop across a current measuring shunt does not require such a high impedance voltmeter. However, it is prudent to select a voltmeter suitable for every anticipated field test. To determine the input impedance of a particular voltmeter, consult the instrument's technical specifications.

Voltmeter Selection

In addition to high input impedance, it is important to select a voltmeter with the appropriate *range, resolution* and *accuracy*. Many standard voltmeters are available off-the-shelf that are suitable for measuring corrosion-related voltages. Figure 6.1 shows a typical

Figure 6.1 Battery powered multimeter. (Photo courtesy of Farwest Corrosion Control and John Fluke Mfg. Co. Used with permission.)

hand-held battery-powered multimeter. The meter illustrated can measure a maximum of 1,000 volts (both AC and DC) in any of five different ranges and features a basic accuracy of 0.1%. The device has a 10 megohm input resistance, which is suitable for all but the highest resistivity environments. This instrument also has the capability to measure resistance, capacitance, frequency, and both DC and AC current. Digital multimeters such as that illustrated are widely available and produced by many manufacturers.

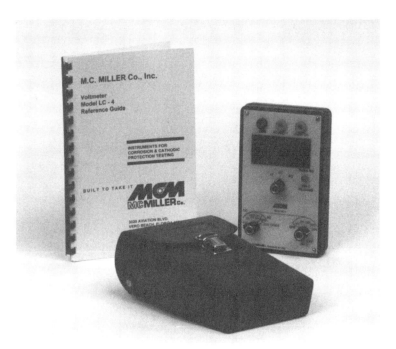

Figure 6.2   Specialized voltmeter with variable input resistance. (Photo courtesy of M. C. Miller Co.)

Figure 6.2 shows a specialized voltmeter which has a selectable input resistance. This meter can be used where very high input resistance is required, such as in extremely high resistivity soils. It is also useful in the verification of structure-to-soil potential data. Changing the resistance-selector switch can validate a particular pipe-to-soil potential measurement. No change in potential while switching between resistance ranges indicates a valid reading. This instrument also incorporates the ability to measure up to 600 volts AC, and resistance values as high as 200 ohms.

When selecting a voltmeter it is important to consider the meter's measuring range and resolution. To measure small voltage increments, such as the voltage across a shunt, a meter should offer an appropriate combination of range and resolution. For instance, when using a 0.001 ohm shunt to measure current to within 0.1 ampere accuracy, a voltmeter with a 0.1 millivolt resolution is necessary. Conversely, if a meter's resolution is 0.1 millivolt, that same shunt will yield an accuracy of $+/-0.1$ amp.

The importance of a meter's resolution becomes apparent when measuring the current output of a galvanic anode using an external shunt. To measure, for instance, 54 millamps flowing through a standard 0.01 ohm shunt, a meter must have a resolution of 0.01 millivolts. If the meter has only 0.1 millivolt resolution, as in the above example, the current will be measured as 50 mA, not 54 mA. The meter shown in Figure 6.2 has a lower range of 0–20 millivolts DC, and a resolution of 0.01 millivolts. This combination is ideal for measurement of direct current through external shunts.

With regard to meter accuracy, many meters offer a $3\frac{1}{2}$ or $4\frac{1}{2}$ digit resolution. This refers to the number of significant digits that will be used to display an accurate voltage value. For cathodic protection measurements, where a voltage of, for instance, minus 0.972 volts is being measured, a more accurate measurement of minus 0.9721 may not be relevant to a field determination of protection. The significance of extreme precision must be viewed in conjunction with the necessity of such accuracy.

The selection of voltmeters should also include an evaluation of cost versus practicality. Many commercially available meters are hand-held, battery-powered, and well suited for field applications, while others are primarily suitable for bench tests or laboratory work. Voltmeters can be purchased with an array of features such as large data storage capacity, oscilloscope display, recording capability and computer interface connections. A voltmeter should be chosen for its applicability to the work at hand, with the proper balance of cost, durability, and accuracy.

Resistivity Test Instruments

The corrosion engineer has many occasions to measure soil resistivity during corrosion surveys, selecting locations for cathodic protection groundbeds and other similar work. These tests may be made with a battery and an individual DC ammeter and voltmeter. For greater speed and convenience in making field determinations, however, there are specialized instruments available that can be read directly.

Soil resistivity field measurements are often made using ASTM[1] G57 or IEEE[2] Standard 81, more commonly known within the corrosion industry as the "Wenner 4-Pin Method". This procedure involves driving four steel pins into the earth in a straight line, equally spaced, with the pin spacing equal to the depth to which knowledge of the average soil resistivity is desired. Soil resistivity is a simple function of the voltage drop between the center pair of pins, with current flowing between the two outside pins.

Meters such as that shown in Figure 6.3 can provide the necessary current supplied to the outer pins, while simultaneously measuring the voltage drop between the center pair of pins. The resistance, in ohms, is then the reading on the dial multiplied by the range switch position. The instrument can measure resistance values between 0.01 ohm and 11×10^5 ohms depending on which multiplier (scale) is selected. The meter also uses alternating current, which overcomes the problem of polarization of the pins, an inherent problem with direct current tests.

The meter shown is Figure 6.3 is also useful for other measurements, such as during anode installation or for measuring the resistance of anode beds and grounding systems. The resistance-to-earth of ground rods can be measured when used in the 3-pin configuration. It is important to remember *not* to measure across energized circuits to avoid damaging the meter. In addition, the resistance of the test leads might be included in the measurement, depending on the test lead configuration.

[1] American Society for Testing and Materials, West Conshohocken, PA.
[2] Institute of Electrical and Electronics Engineers.

Figure 6.3   Soil resistivity meter. (Photo courtesy of Nilsson Electrical Laboratory.)

Recording Instruments

Some cathodic protection measurements are best made in relation to specific periods of time, or distance, to quantify values that change or fluctuate. A number of recording voltmeters are available which can measure and record readings while left unattended, such as during interference testing. The chart recorder shown in Figure 6.4 records voltage values on a continuous basis and prints a graphical copy of the data. Other recording devices, such as that shown in Figure 6.5, operate on an electronic basis and can interface with computers to facilitate data plotting and presentation. The electronic chart recorder shown in Figure 6.5 is very small and compact, allowing it to be inconspicuously located during testing. Such recording devices can measure and plot several parameters simultaneously to enhance data collection and interpretation.

Other recording instruments are used to measure and store pipe-to-soil potentials while traversing a pipeline during an over-the-line type survey. Figure 6.6 shows a data recorder that can store many thousands of data entries, including text comments. When

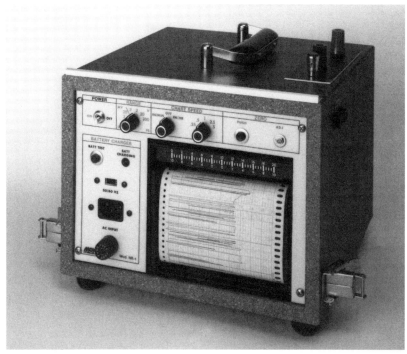

Figure 6.4 Strip-chart recorder. (Photo courtesy of M. C. Miller Co.)

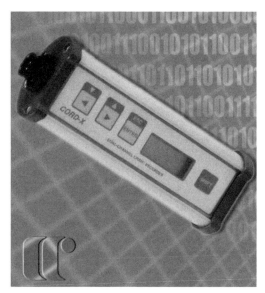

Figure 6.5 Electronic dual-channel recorder. (Photo courtesy of Corrpro Companies, Inc.)

Figure 6.6   Electronic data recorder. (Photo courtesy of Corrpro Companies, Inc.)

used with a distance measuring "chainer," data can be gathered and plotted showing voltage versus distance. Several of the accessories used in the over-the-line survey are illustrated in Section 2 of this chapter.

Wall Thickness and Pit Gages

While the corrosion engineer is primarily concerned with the elimination or reduction of corrosion, sometimes it is necessary to quantify the remaining wall thickness of a pipeline.

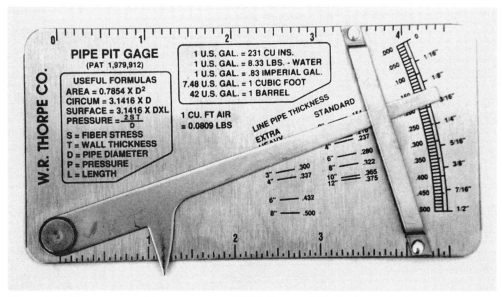

Figure 6.7   Pipe pit gage. (Photo courtesy of KTA Tator and W. R. Thorpe Co.)

The traditional pit gage, as shown in Figure 6.7, is a very handy tool for the measurement of pit depth. These gages are small, reasonably accurate and can be carried easily in a toolbox or briefcase. Care must be taken to use them properly, and to understand their limitations.

For instance, on all but the largest diameter pipes, this instrument must be aligned lengthwise with a pipeline, and must rest on an even surface. On severely pitted or partially coated structures, such a gage may offer only a rough estimation of pit depth, if it cannot be properly aligned. A more accurate pit gage is shown in Figure 6.8. It does not require such a large, flat surface for accurate positioning. However, it is more fragile as well as somewhat more expensive.

Another non-destructive device for gathering corrosion data is the ultrasonic wall thickness gage, such as shown in Figure 6.9. This device, and those similar to it, can accurately measure wall thickness using ultrasonic (sound) waves. They operate by computing the elapsed time between echoes produced when an ultrasonic pulse is passed through a material. By knowing the velocity of sound in that particular material, the thickness is calculated. Other more sophisticated versions offer features such as data storage and data printing capabilities, and display-screens showing the actual waveform and soundpath echo. These devices can detect and characterize flaws within the steel plate itself, and some can measure wall thickness through various coatings. All ultrasonic measuring devices must be periodically calibrated and have certain important limitations to their use. Worn or improperly used transducers, for instance, can give erroneous readings, sometimes twice or three times the actual value. Knowledge of the material being tested is also important, because the speed of sound varies from material to material, and can be altered by temperature, heat treatment, and other material qualities.

Figure 6.8 Dial type pit gage. (Photo courtesy of KTA Tator and the L. S. Starrett Co.)

Current Interrupters

The ability to interrupt cathodic protection current is an important and frequently used technique in cathodic protection testing. A variety of current interrupters are available, most of which offer the benefits of precision timing and the ability to synchronize multiple interrupters. The device shown in Figure 6.10 relies on a quartz crystal for accurate timing and can serve as a master unit to synchronize similar interrupters. Other devices are manufactured with sophisticated timing clocks, which can be programmed to run pre-set timing cycles during the day (when surveys take place), and return to a closed circuit at night (Figure 6.11). This feature saves time because the survey crew does not need to return to the unit each morning for re-installation. It also minimizes structure depolarization because of unnecessary off-cycling.

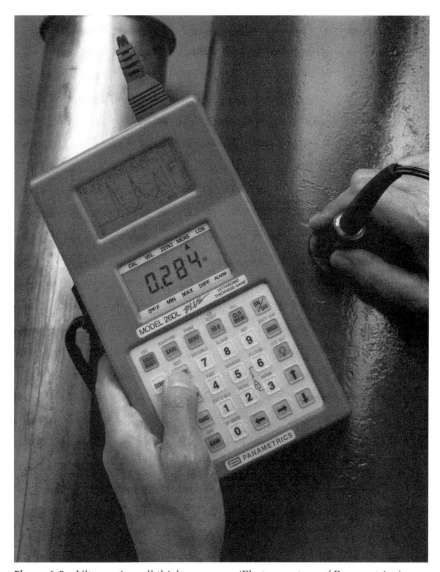

Figure 6.9 Ultrasonic wall thickness gage. (Photo courtesy of Panametrics.)

When using any interrupter it is important to follow the manufacturer's recommendations on the maximum allowable current (either AC or DC) that the instrument can safely handle. It is also important to recognize the amount of drift in the timing of multiple current interrupters. The industry is beginning to overcome this limitation by using the clock transmission from satellites for interrupter timing (Figure 6.12). To incorporate this feature into corrosion testing requires that the interrupter's receiving antenna gathers

Figure 6.10   Quartz crystal controlled current interrupter. (Photo courtesy of Nilsson Electrical Laboratory Inc.)

frequent and accurate satellite communication data. If battery operated, these instruments will require monitoring to replace batteries regularly during extended surveys.

Pulse Generators and Analyzers

The pulse generator is gaining acceptance as an alternative to traditional current interruption. The pulse generator is installed in the cathodic protection power supply and momentarily interrupts the output in a precisely timed pattern. The interruptions are extremely brief and occur in a repetitive cycle. Pulse generators can be installed in multiple rectifiers (or other CP power sources, including galvanic systems) and an "on/off" survey conducted with a portable analyzer.

Figure 6.11   Programmable current interrupter. (Photo courtesy of M. C. Miller Co.)

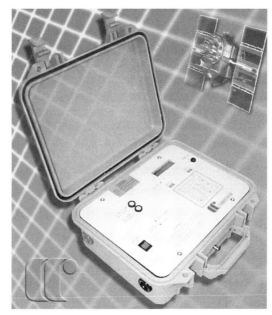

Figure 6.12   Satellite controlled current interrupter. (Photo courtesy of Corrpro Companies, Inc.)

The analyzer recognizes these multiple momentary current interruptions and, using an algorithmic analysis, calculates the overall "off" potential of the protected structure. It is critical to ensure that all pulse generators are *operating*, and that they are each set to a timing cycle that *exactly* corresponds to the algorithm analyzer. These analyzers also have a finite limit to the number of pulse generators that they can recognize, so this must also be taken into consideration when surveying or interpreting survey data. When used correctly they offer the advantage of measuring "off" potentials at every test site, without the installation of numerous specialized test stations. A disadvantage to permanent pulse generator installation is that the pulsing signal may be confusing to the operators of neighboring utilities who happen to see this pattern during surveys of their own structures. To avoid this, permanently installed generators can each be set to steady-state operation.

Pipe and Cable Locators

During the course of corrosion testing, it is sometimes necessary to determine the location of buried items such as the pipeline being worked on, the location of foreign utilities, groundbed cables and other concealed metallic structures. The pipe and cable locator can be a great time-saver in such a case. Pipe and cable locators impress an electrical signal onto the target line, and this permits a hand-held receiver to detect their location. Electrical contact with the metallic structure being located need not be made, although conductive locating is generally much more accurate than inductive. Figure 6.13 (a) and (b) show two commercially available instruments.

The type of signal that is transmitted to the pipe (or cable) can vary from manufacturer to manufacturer, and can even be variable within a single locator. Alteration of the signal frequency allows the operator to select the most appropriate signal for the application. For example, poorly coated pipes, well coated pipes, shorted pipelines, and insulated cables, might each be best located using different frequencies. It is imperative to remember to set both the transmitter and the receiver to *matching* frequencies.

Other locator features can be useful in cathodic protection work. Some transmitters have a clamp accessory that can be clipped around a conductor to induce the signal, such as when tracing a live electrical cable. This technique saves time as well as enhances safety. The clamp can be placed around an electrical conduit leading to a rectifier, for instance, so that unlocking and opening the rectifier enclosure becomes unnecessary. Of course, if the conduit contains multiple conductors, verification of a correct tracing may be necessary.

Advances in locator technology have also enabled a variety of attributes to be incorporated into pipe and cable locators. Depth measurement capability has greatly improved and allows the operator to measure, with increasing confidence, the depth of the target. Other pipe locators have the ability to measure and trace the amount of signal current being conducted by the pipeline or cable (Figure 6.14). These locators can trace the pipeline as well as improve the operator's ability to analyze and evaluate the pipe's current-carrying characteristics. Tools such as these are becoming accepted in locating electrical shorts to distribution networks. By tracing current flow and magnitude, unintended

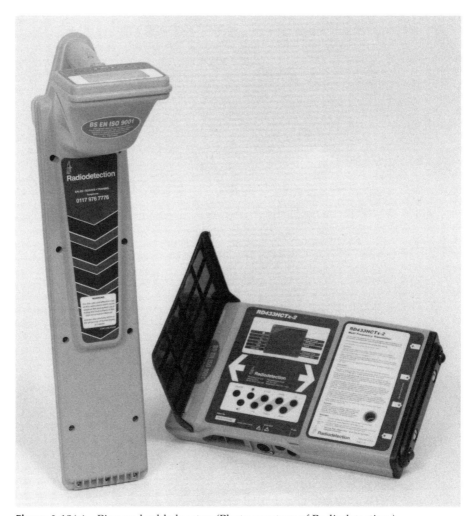

Figure 6.13(a)   Pipe and cable locator. (Photo courtesy of Radiodetection.)

shorts can be rapidly found. Operator experience with pipe locators is valuable in utility operations in general, and particularly effective in cathodic protection administration.

Ammeter Clamps

The measurement of AC or DC current flowing through a pipeline or cable is obviously a useful kind of measurement in cathodic protection work. However, shunts or "current spans" may not exist at a location where a measurement is necessary. If the pipe or cable is made accessible, a portable non-contact ammeter clamp can measure the current magnitude and direction of flow. These devices rely on the relationship between current

Figure 6.13(b)   Pipe and cable locator. (Photo courtesy of Fisher.)

flow in a conductor and the electro-magnetic field that it generates. They use amplifying coils positioned around the pipe or cable such as shown in Figure 6.15. These clamps are quite specialized in that they must fit around the pipe being tested. They are also a tool for which there is no substitution in certain applications. They can be used in interference testing, short locating, fault detection, and to identify bad insulating joints. The proper use of ammeter clamps requires careful attention to coil orientation, magnetic interference, nearby current flow, and polarity interpretation.

Insulator Checkers

Portable, battery-operated instruments that check the integrity of insulators find a very valuable place in cathodic protection and corrosion control.

Devices such as that shown in Figure 6.16 can not only identify shorted flanges, but when tested individually, can detect shorted bolt-sleeve-washer assemblies. They can also test other insulating assemblies, such as dielectric insulating unions. These

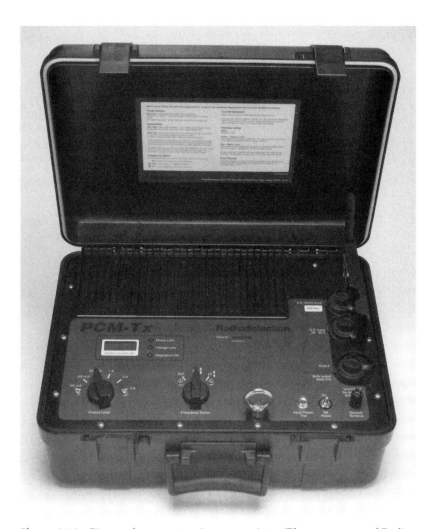

Figure 6.14   Pipe and current tracing transmitter. (Photo courtesy of Radio-detection.)

instruments are affordable and can rapidly test critical insulating devices before they are backfilled.

Test Rectifiers

Current requirement tests, groundbed testing and CP design work require portable power supplies. A common automobile battery may suffice for some of these tests, but an adjustable power supply is more appropriate and more versatile (Figure 6.17). Most rectifier manufacturers offer portable, adjustable power supplies that can be carried into

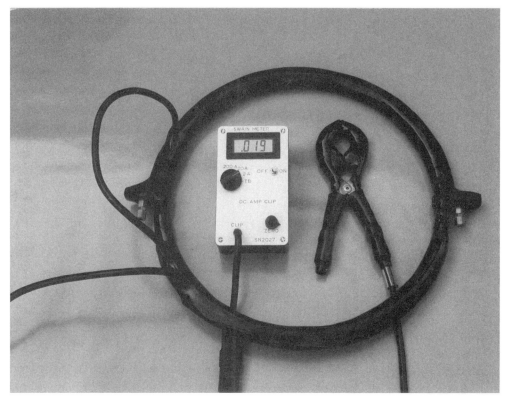

Figure 6.15   Non-contact ammeter clamp. (Photo courtesy of William H. Swain Co.)

the field and used as convenient and temporary rectifiers. Optional features, such as built-in current interrupters or unusual input/output options can be ordered with such equipment.

Portable rectifiers, of course, require an AC power source. Low-current power supplies that are battery powered are also available. They are adjustable, and within the limits of their battery source, are very useful in short-term tests, such as current requirement testing, short-locating, and tests of steel casing-to-pipeline continuity. Figure 6.18 shows one such compact power supply.

Holiday Detectors

Many corrosion engineers might never use a holiday detector because the pipelines they protect have been buried and, perhaps, well protected for many years. However, in new construction and during rehabilitation projects, these instruments are important to corrosion control.

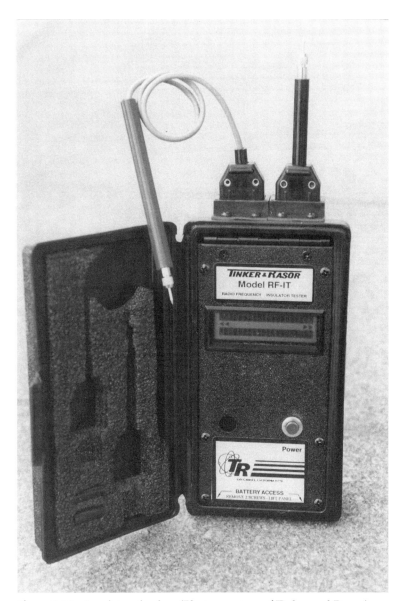

Figure 6.16   Insulator checker. (Photo courtesy of Tinker and Rasor.)

For bonded dielectric coatings, one must ensure that a pipeline, for instance, is installed with a coating of the highest integrity. Scrapes and tears are readily discernible by visual inspection; however, pinholes and small holidays are not. A holiday detector will help to find them by impressing an electrical voltage across the coating. An electrode then passes over the entire coating surface and as it crosses a coating defect, it gives

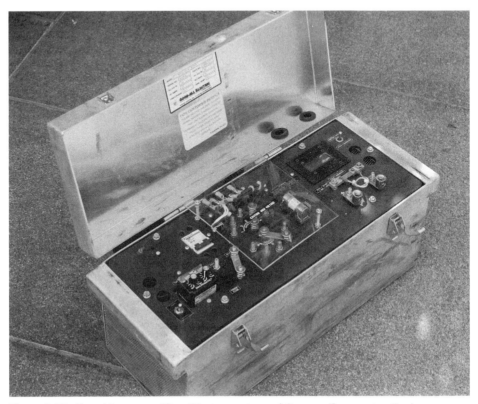

Figure 6.17   Portable test rectifier. (Photo courtesy of Corrpro Companies, Inc.)

off an electrical discharge, or spark, which signals the operator that a holiday has been detected. The operator can then mark the holiday for subsequent repair prior to company acceptance. Holiday detectors must be selected for the thickness and type of coating being tested. Excessive voltage can stress or damage thin coatings if the detector has been set too high. Adherence to the manufacturer's instructions is recommended, including *both* the manufacturer of the coating and the manufacturer of the holiday detector. NACE International also publishes a recommended practice (RP0274) for high voltage holiday detection.

ACCESSORIES

Reference Electrodes and Coupons

Cathodic protection testing depends largely on the proper use and interpretation of pipe-to-electrolyte measurements. These determinations, in turn, rely on reference electrodes.

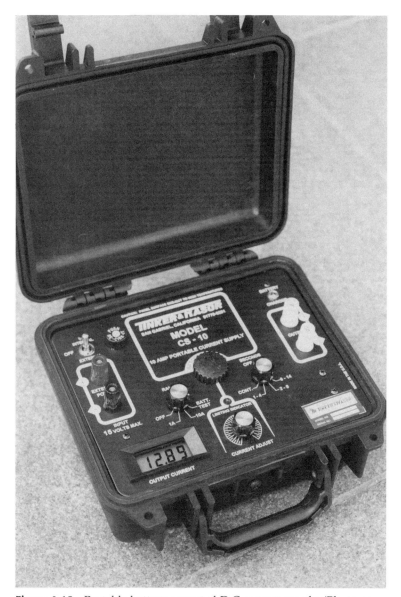

Figure 6.18 Portable battery operated D.C. power supply. (Photo courtesy of Tinker and Rasor.)

Similarly, the use of buried test coupons is another tool in the evaluation of CP's effectiveness.

The type of reference electrode the corrosion technician uses is dictated by the environment in which the electrode is used. Predominantly, copper-copper sulfate

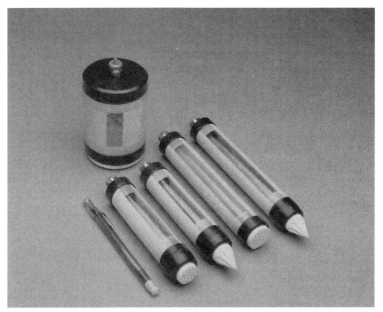

Figure 6.19   Portable copper-copper sulfate reference electrodes. (Photo courtesy of M. C. Miller Co.)

(CSE) electrodes are used, but other types are common and often necessary. Silver-silver chloride and zinc-zinc sulfate are also used in corrosion measurement applications, particularly in high chloride environments such as seawater. All reference electrodes are available in transportable models as well as models manufactured for permanent burial or immersion.

Portable reference electrodes have a variety of configurations as seen in Figure 6.19. Note that some have a large sensing area for use where maximum soil contact is desirable. Other slim models can be used where only a narrow soil access is available, such as in small test holes drilled through pavement. These can also be easily transported in a shirt pocket or briefcase.

The antimony electrode (Figure 6.20) is an accessory that can measure the pH (acidity) of soil or water. It does *not* measure a cathodic protection potential, but can help conduct soil evaluations, and is helpful during forensic work.

Reference cells are also used in permanent installations. These are buried or submerged adjacent to a structure with test leads routed to an accessible test station. Other reference electrode configurations (Figure 6.21) incorporate a test coupon built into the electrode assembly. These devices represent a discreet sample of the subject steel, usually connected within the test station. The coupon simulates a bare portion of, or coating holiday in, the steel. This device enables the corrosion engineer to determine the amount of protection being afforded the structure. The devices can also be disconnected (or interrupted) from the CP system to evaluate the polarization level.

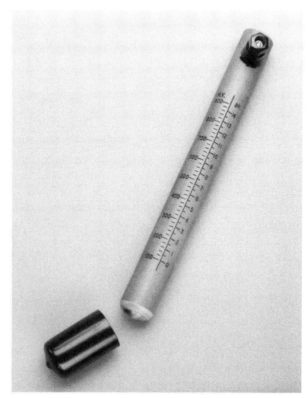

Figure 6.20 The antimony electrode for measurement of pH. (Photo courtesy of Agra.)

Figure 6.21 Reference cell equipped with a test coupon. (Photo courtesy of Borin Manufacturing.)

When using test coupons, it is important to use an alloy identical to that of the protected structure. Following coupon installation, it will take some time to stabilize the coupon at a level representative of the true corrosion activity.

Reference electrodes should always be selected for compatibility with the environment in which they will be used. Copper sulfate electrodes are easily contaminated by saline or brackish environments that have high levels of ionic chlorides. If a portable reference electrode is suspected of contamination, it should be cleaned and re-filled with fresh solution. Reliance on a single electrode for field work is never advisable, for it precludes both cell-to-cell comparison, and the redundancy of having a spare cell on hand. Reference electrodes require maintenance to ensure accuracy, and must be periodically "re-charged". They should also be periodically checked against a standard to determine if further maintenance is required.

Reference electrodes also can be equipped with accessories to make them more versatile. Waterproof adapters can be fitted onto the cell, which attaches it to a long, well-insulated and waterproof wire and makes the electrode submersible. Electrode extensions can also be fabricated or purchased for over-the-line walking type surveys on land.

Meter Accessories

Meter manufacturers as well as corrosion specialty suppliers offer many accessories to be used with corrosion test equipment. Wire reels, for instance, are indispensable for many test applications. They can be configured in many ways, dependent upon wire gage and length of cable. Figure 6.22 shows several of those available. The integrity of the insulation must be maintained for accuracy, as 'skinned' insulation can compromise many measurements if the copper wire becomes shorted to other structures, or to earth.

Meter manufacturers also offer a variety of test leads, carrying cases, and complementary accessories, such as temperature probes. These usually plug directly into the meter and will accommodate the variety of conditions encountered by a corrosion technician. Insulated leads and test clips are always recommended, especially if higher current or voltage applications are encountered. Custom-made leads and connectors can also be fabricated to suit a particular situation.

Portable shunts are available, some, such as in Figure 6.23, can plug directly into the voltmeter and allow current measurement to be made at any cable connection point. As with any permanently installed shunt, portable shunts must be used with careful observation of rating and capacity.

Resistance Accessories

Several complementary accessories are available for use with a resistivity meter. Soil pins can be purchased, and should be selected for the degree of service to which they will be subjected. A corrosion engineer with only an occasional need to measure soil resistivity might suffice with the use of large screwdrivers, or other improvised temporary

Figure 6.22 Wire reels. (Photo courtesy of M. C. Miller Co.)

Figure 6.23 Portable shunt. (Photo courtesy of Agra.)

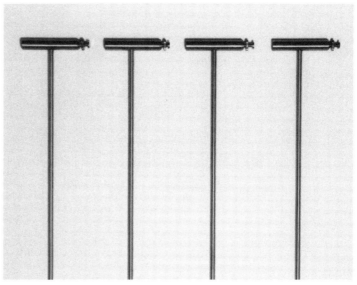

Figure 6.24   Soil resistivity pins. (Photo courtesy of M. C. Miller Co.)

electrodes. Alternatively, a substantial amount of survey work, or work in highly compacted soil, might justify the purchase of more durable electrodes. Long stainless steel pins equipped with handles suitable for repeated hammering are available if needed (Figure 6.24).

If multiple soil-depth resistivity measurements are to be taken, a convenient selector box can be used. It enables the technician to install a long series of properly spaced pins into the ground, and then gather data for many soil depths without returning to reposition the pins. This is done by switching the selector box to connect the correct 4-pin array to the resistance meter.

The soil box is a valuable accessory used in conjunction with a standard resistivity meter. Soil boxes are designed for connection to the potential and current terminals of these meters, usually with only a multiplication factor to remember (Figure 6.25). However, the soil box can permit the disadvantages of improper sample handling, compaction, and moisture preservation. Nevertheless, the soil box offers substantial information about the corrosivity of a particular soil, and can be valuable when combined with laboratory soil work.

Close Interval Survey Accessories

A number of accessories have been developed to gather multiple pipe-to-soil potentials in relation to distance. These include wire carrying and measuring backpacks, reference electrode extensions, and numerous other devices to make the long pipeline survey

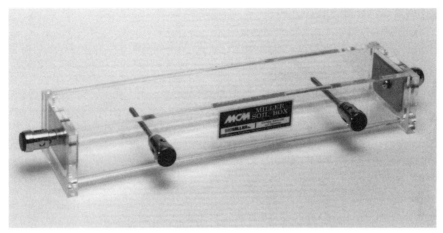

Figure 6.25   Soil resistivity box. (Photo courtesy of M. C. Miller Co.)

accurate and efficient (Figure 6.26). Many of these systems are designed to work in conjunction with proprietary software and plotting programs. Close interval survey equipment may also include related current interruption equipment that can be integrated into the survey to gather "on" and "off" data.

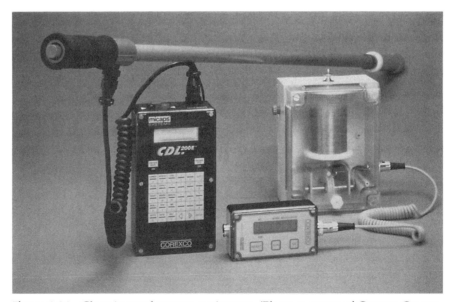

Figure 6.26   Close interval survey equipment. (Photo courtesy of Corrpro Companies, Inc.)

CARE AND MAINTENANCE

Correct handling and maintenance of corrosion test equipment used in the field will pay dividends in ensuring the reliability of the instruments and the procurement of accurate test data. The following suggestions are given as a guide.

Probably the greatest cause of damage to sensitive test equipment is inadequate protection during transportation. When carrying equipment in cars or trucks, sensitive instrumentation should be protected from road shock and should be secured so that the various items of equipment will not slide about and knock against each other. In addition, electronic instrumentation should be protected from moisture and road dust. The corrosion engineer must also decide which instruments are needed on a routine basis, and which are better left in storage and carried into the field as necessary. Deploying every imaginable instrument into the field may be impressive; however, it brings a greater obligation to proper equipment care and maintenance.

Long-term reliability of corrosion test equipment also involves documentation and record keeping.

Meter serial numbers, warranties, instruction manuals, and purchase records should be kept in an orderly fashion so that repair or replacement can be done as necessary with minimal interruption to productivity.

Calibration records should also be kept, particularly when survey work involves legal or regulatory issues. Oftentimes calibration must be traceable to the National Institute of Standards and Technology (NIST[3]), and such documentation should be maintained. Evidence of traceability for a particular instrument is available from the instrument manufacturer, although certain limitations and fees are usually involved.

Portable instruments rely on batteries that are inexpensive and easily replaced, but easily overlooked. The corrosion technician should carry spares for each type of battery used. Consideration should be given to the use of rechargeable batteries for instruments using larger, frequently drained batteries (Figure 6.27). Meters used infrequently should have the batteries removed to prevent leakage and subsequent damage to the instrument components.

Copper sulfate reference electrodes should be kept clean and uncontaminated. The copper sulfate solution must be a *saturated solution*; that is, crystals are visible in the solution at ambient temperature after sufficient time is allowed to reach solution equilibrium. The copper rod may be cleaned when it becomes encrusted or if it is suspected that the copper sulfate solution is contaminated. The rod can be sanded with fine, nonmetallic sandpaper. The use of metal-containing sandpaper will embed foreign metallic particles in the copper rod and can compromise accuracy. Disposal of used copper sulfate solution is also now regulated in some areas because of its potential for environmental impact. Consult with local regulations before disposing copper sulfate solution.

Reference cells stored in or subject to freezing conditions can be filled with anti-freeze solution. These must be periodically refreshed, just as with ordinary electrodes. Electrode tips may occasionally require replacement, particularly if they are routinely used in close interval survey work.

[3] National Institute of Standards and Technology, Gaithersburg, Maryland.

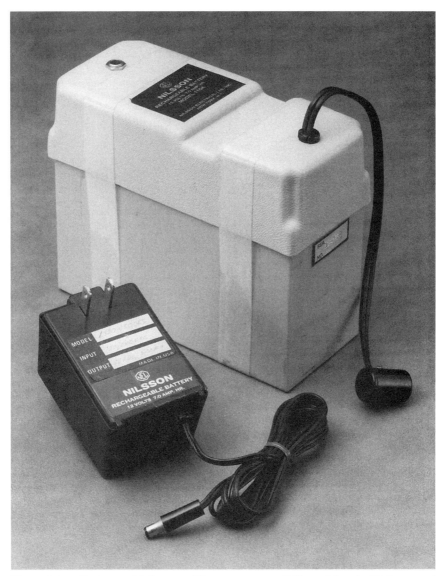

Figure 6.27   Rechargeable battery. (Photo courtesy of Nilsson Electrical Laboratory.)

Always remember that test equipment should be handled and maintained in top working condition. This is essential for optimum results when conducting field tests and surveys. Even the most sophisticated instrumentation is of no value if used incorrectly or improperly maintained.

Chapter

Ground Bed Design

Ronald L. Bianchetti and Steve McKim

This chapter will provide a guideline for design of anode ground beds and serve as a nucleus for the development of design procedures for the pipeline corrosion engineer.

LOCATING GROUND BED SITES

Previous chapters (3, 4 and 5) have provided basic considerations involved in deciding approximately where cathodic protection (CP) current will be needed and how much will be required. Once these decisions have been made, specific installation sites for ground beds may be selected and proper designs prepared.

In selecting ground bed sites, the most important consideration from a design standpoint is determination of effective soil resistivity. The discussion on measurement and analysis of soil resistivity in Chapter 5 serves as a guide. Other considerations that must be taken into account when selecting a site include the following:

- Are other underground metallic structures within the area of influence surrounding the ground bed? If so, they may pick up current from the ground bed and create a stray current interference problem that will require corrective measures if the site is used. This is important when planning impressed current ground beds.
- Is the proposed site on or off the pipeline right-of-way? If off (as is apt to be the case with impressed current ground beds), can right-of-way be procured? Check with the pipeline right-of-way department on this.
- If a rectifier-powered impressed current system is to be installed, is there a power line present? If not, is a power line extension from the nearest source practicable?
- Is the site reasonably accessible for construction and maintenance purposes?
- Are there plans for building construction (new pipelines, highway development, or other similar work) that will make the site untenable in the near future?

In most cases, locations for galvanic anode installations are easier to select than those for impressed current ground beds because they usually can be placed within the pipeline right-of-way, are independent of power sources, and are relatively free of interference with foreign underground structures. Impressed current ground beds may be located at certain sites by compromise rather than other sites with more favorable soil resistivity.

DESIGNING THE GROUND BED

Once ground bed locations have been selected for either impressed current or galvanic anode systems and the effective soil resistivities for design purposes have been determined, the design process can proceed. Designs are reasonably simple when design charts are available, and many companies utilize such charts. These charts are typically based on the type of anode and construction to be employed. Determining effective soil resistivity is prerequisite to all decisions before designing the system. Because of all of the variables involved, it should be recognized that the design calculations for completed ground bed resistance may not be highly precise. The design engineer can consider the design successful if the final completed ground bed resistance is consistently within 10% of design calculations.

Impressed Current Ground Beds

Design charts for impressed current ground beds should be based on the types of anode construction adopted by the corrosion engineer for his pipeline system. Typical construction sketches will be shown to illustrate principles involved, but others may be used if found more suitable for specific pipeline conditions.

Figure 7.1 illustrates one form of vertical anode installation. The figure includes the essential features only. The carbonaceous backfill surrounding the anode, when well tamped, serves two functions:

- Being of a very low resistivity, it has the effect of increasing the anode size with resulting reduction in resistance to earth, and
- Most of the current is transmitted to the backfill from the anode by direct contact so that the greater part of material consumption should take place at the outer edges of the backfill column.

Since a positive potential (voltage) is impressed on the entire ground bed assembly, it is absolutely essential that all header cable insulation, anode pigtail wire insulation, the connection between anode and pigtail (a manufacturer's function) and insulation of connections between pigtails and a header cable or cable runs to a test or junction be completely intact and moistureproof. If this is not maintained, current will be discharged through insulation imperfections, causing wires to corrode and sever in a relatively short period of time, thus losing connections to all or part of the ground bed. Connections between header cable and anode pigtail must be of permanent low resistance. This may

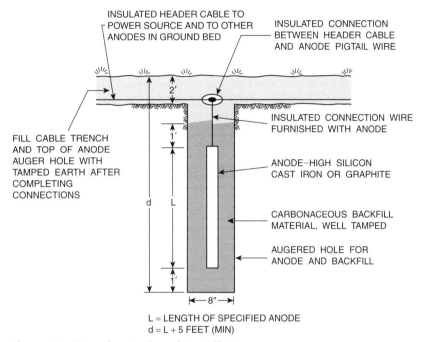

INSULATED HEADER CABLE TO
POWER SOURCE AND TO OTHER
ANODES IN GROUND BED

INSULATED CONNECTION
BETWEEN HEADER CABLE
AND ANODE PIGTAIL WIRE

FILL CABLE TRENCH
AND TOP OF ANODE
AUGER HOLE WITH
TAMPED EARTH AFTER
COMPLETING
CONNECTIONS

INSULATED CONNECTION WIRE
FURNISHED WITH ANODE

ANODE–HIGH SILICON
CAST IRON OR GRAPHITE

CARBONACEOUS BACKFILL
MATERIAL, WELL TAMPED

AUGERED HOLE FOR
ANODE AND BACKFILL

2′

1′

d   L

1′

|←— 8″ —→|

L = LENGTH OF SPECIFIED ANODE
d = L + 5 FEET (MIN)

Figure 7.1   Typical vertical anode installation.

be accomplished by methods such as thermite welding, soldering, or high compression crimp-type connections.

The number of vertical anodes required to attain a required ground bed resistance can be determined by using the typical chart in Figure 7.2. The figure is based on all anodes being along a straight line, the most favorable ground bed configuration in most instances. This chart is for use with the type of anode installation illustrated by Figure 7.1. Similar graphs can be prepared for anode-backfill combinations of other dimensions. Curves on these graphs were developed using the following formulas and procedures.

Total resistance of each anode to earth consists of the resistance of the anode to the carbonaceous backfill plus the resistance to earth of the backfill column itself. Resistance of the anode to backfill is obtained by using the following equation.

$$R_v = \frac{0.00521\rho}{L}\left(2.3\log\frac{8L}{d} - 1\right) \tag{1}$$

where:

R_v = resistance of vertical anode to earth in (ohms)
ρ = resistivity of backfill material (or earth) in (ohm-cm)
L = length of anode in (feet)
d = diameter of anode in (feet)

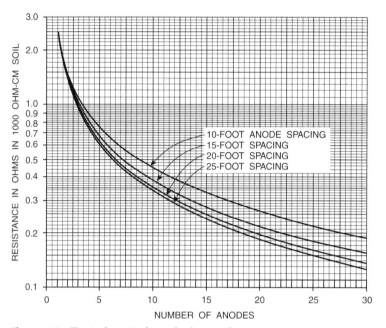

Figure 7.2 Typical vertical anode design chart.

Using a value of 50 ohm-cm for the resistivity of the carbonaceous backfill material, resistances are calculated for the backfill column and the anode (7 ft × 8 in and 5 ft × 2 in respectively in this case). The difference between the two figures is the resistance from the anode to the outer edges of the backfill column. For the anode construction shown in Figure 7.1, this was calculated to be 0.106 ohm.

Resistance of several anodes in parallel can be calculated by the following equation:

$$R_v = \frac{0.00521\rho}{NL}\left(2.3\log\frac{8L}{d} - 1 + \frac{2L}{S}(2.3\log 0.656N)\right) \tag{2}$$

where:

R_v = resistance of vertical anode to earth in (ohms)
ρ = resistivity of backfill material (or earth) in (ohm-cm)
L = length of anode in (feet)
d = diameter of anode in (feet)
N = number of anodes in parallel
S = anode spacing in (feet)

The dimensions of the backfill column (7 ft × 8 in in this case) are used in applying the formula. Curves for 10, 15, 20 and 25-ft anode spacing are included in the Figure 7.2. The curves do not include the anode internal resistance (anode to backfill). The resistance for any number of anodes in parallel from the curves must be added to the internal resistance of one anode divided by the number of anodes in parallel. The effect of this internal resistance becomes less as the number of anodes is increased.

Curves of Figure 7.2 are for anodes in 1000-ohm-cm soil. The resistance for the selected number of anodes from the curves varies directly with the resistivity. For example, if a combination of anodes has a resistance of 0.40 ohm in 1000-ohm-cm soil (as indicated by the curves) but the soil resistivity for design purposes at the installation site selected is 2400 ohm-cm, the ground bed resistance for the same number of anodes is $0.40 \times 2400/1000 = 0.96$ ohms, plus the internal resistance. For a second example, assume the soil resistivity for design purposes was 750 ohm-cm, the resistance of the same anode combination would be $0.40 \times 750/1000 = 0.30$ ohm plus the internal resistance.

Extending this analysis, assume that a ground bed installation site has been selected where the effective soil resistivity for design purposes has been determined to be 2800 ohm-cm. Assume that the nearest ground bed anode will be 300 ft from the pipeline and that No. 4 copper connecting cable will be used. Also assume that the ground bed is to discharge 20 A at 24 V applied from a rectifier.

Before using the chart, the maximum permissible resistance of the anodes must be determined. This is necessary because, in addition to resistance to earth of the anodes, other considerations must be analyzed to determine the total circuit resistance. These include the following:

- Back voltage between ground bed and pipeline,
- Resistance to earth of the pipeline at the ground bed location, and
- Resistance of cable from the pipeline to power source and from the power source to and along the anodes comprising the ground bed.

The *back voltage* is that which exists between the anodes and pipeline in opposition to the applied voltage. For ground bed anodes with carbonaceous backfill, this will be, usually, in the order of 2 V. Some areas of unusual soil composition may result in higher back voltages but the 2-V figure is used commonly for design purposes unless experience in a specific area dictates otherwise. In practice, the back voltage at a working ground bed is determined by measuring the voltage between ground bed and pipeline (across the positive and negative rectifier terminals) immediately after switching the rectifier power OFF. The ground bed will always be positive to the pipeline. If the back voltage is 2 V, it means it will require 2 V of the rectifier source voltage to overcome the back voltage before current can flow through the ground bed.

Resistance to earth of the pipeline depends on the quality of the pipeline coating. The better the coating, the higher the effective resistances at the ground bed location. In the example being used, if current requirement tests made at (or in the vicinity of) the selected ground bed location had indicated that 20 A of applied current would cause a change in pipeline voltage (ΔV) of -1.5 V to a remote copper sulfate electrode (CSE), the effective pipeline resistance would be 1.5/20 or 0.075 ohm.

Cable resistance is the additive resistance of the cable from the pipeline via the power source to the first anode of the ground bed (assuming that the line of ground bed anodes is perpendicular to the pipeline), plus effective resistance of the header cable along the line of anodes or individual anode cables. This effective header cable resistance is less than that of the full length of the ground bed because all current does not flow the full length of the ground bed but is diminished as each anode connected drains off its share of current. Although subject to variations with differences in individual anode resistance and possibly other factors, it is practical to use the resistance of one half of the ground bed header cable resistance as the effective header cable resistance. Table 7.1 includes data on resistance of copper conductors in the sizes commonly used in pipeline corrosion engineering work.

With the above discussion in mind, the design of the vertical anode ground bed for the example proposed can be estimated as follows:

- Maximum power source voltage will be 24 minus 2 V back voltage or 22 V.
- For 20 A current output, circuit resistance can not exceed 1.10 ohm. This is determined by using Ohm's law (Voltage (V) divided by Current (I) = Resistance (R), 22 V divided by 20 A or 1.10 ohm.)
- Deductions from the circuit resistance must be made for the pipe-to-earth resistance (0.075 ohm in this example), and the resistance of the cable from the rectifier to the first anode. In this example use the resistance of 330 ft of No. 4 cable (300 ft distance given, plus 10% slack) that equals 0.082 ohms. The total resistance is determined by adding the resistance to earth of the anodes plus the effective resistance of the ground bed header cable, a variable, (0.075 + 0.082 = 0.157 ohms). These resistances are deducted from the total circuit resistance allowance (1.10 ohm − 0.157 ohm = 0.94 ohm).
- Make an assumption of the allowance to be made for the header cable resistance. As a first try, assume that the anode resistance alone should be 0.90 ohm.
- Convert the 0.90-ohm anode resistance to a 1000 ohm-cm base to permit using the design chart. Because effective soil resistivity for design purposes for the example is 2800 ohm-cm, the converted resistance is $0.90 \times (1000/2800) = 0.321$ ohm.
- Using the chart of Figure 8.2, the indicated number of anodes at 20-ft spacing would be at slightly over 11. For design purposes use 12 anodes. (The number of anodes at other spacing would be determined in similar fashion.)
- Header cable length for 12 anodes would be 11 spaces at 20 ft or 220 ft. Effective resistance would be approximately 110 ft of No. 4 cable or 0.0285 ohm. For design use 0.029 ohm.
- Total anode plus header cable resistance for 12 anodes would then be $((0.308$ ohm (from the chart) $\times (2800/1000)) +$ internal resistance $(0.106/12 = .009) + 0.029 = 0.90$ ohm which is within the desired value of 0.94 ohm.
- Following the same procedure for 11 anodes, total resistance would be approximately 0.96 ohm, which is higher than the desired value, indicating that 12 anodes would be the minimum number to be used at the 20-ft spacing.

Table 7.1   Resistance of Copper Conductors

General Use	Conductor Size (Awg)	Resistance of Stranded Copper Conductors in Ohms per Foot Times 10^{-3} at 25°C[1]
Impressed Current Ground Beds	4/0	0.0509
	3/0	0.0642
	2/0	0.0811
	1/0	0.102
	1	0.129
	2	0.162
	4	0.259
	6	0.410
Galvanic Anode Installations	8	0.654
	10	1.04
Pipeline Test Points	12	1.65
	14	2.62
Instrument Test Leads	16	4.18
	18	6.66
	20	10.6
	22	17.0

Correction Factors for Other Temperature Follow:

Temperature C = F	Multiply Resistance at 25°C by:
−10 14	0.862
−5 23	0.882
0 32	0.901
5 41	0.921
10 50	0.941
15 59	0.961
20 68	0.980
30 86	1.020
35 95	1.040
40 104	1.059

[1]25°C = 77°F

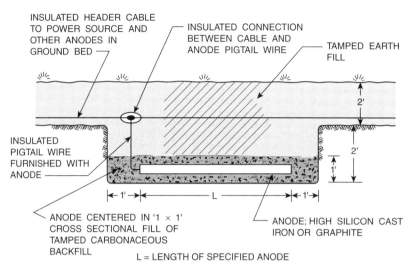

Figure 7.3   Typical horizontal anode installation.

Another important consideration in selecting the number of anodes is desired anode life. This is discussed in detail in the Chapters 8 and 9 on ground bed materials. If the minimum number of anodes that will give a satisfactory low ground bed resistance will not result in adequate life, the number of anodes would have to be increased accordingly. Although, as a general principle, vertical ground bed anodes are preferable to horizontal anodes, it may be necessary to use horizontal construction because of unfavorable soil conditions at depths reached by vertical anodes. A typical method of installing horizontal anodes is shown in Figure 7.3.

Figure 7.4 includes design charts that may be used for determining the resistance of horizontal anodes in parallel. These charts are based on the type of construction shown in Figure 7.3 with all anodes placed along a straight line.

The same general procedure is followed in determining the resistance from the anode to the outer edges of the backfill as was used in Figure 7.2 except that the applicable formula (also derived from H. B. Dwight equations) is the following:

$$R_h = \frac{0.00521\rho}{L} \left(2.3 \log \frac{4L^2 + 4L\{S^2 + L^2\}^{1/2}}{dS} + \frac{S}{L} - \frac{\{S^2 + L^2\}^{1/2}}{L} - 1 \right) \tag{3}$$

where

R_h = resistance of horizontal anode to earth in (ohms)
ρ = resistivity of backfill material (or earth) in (ohm-cm)
L = length of anode in (feet)
d = diameter of anode in (feet)
S = twice depth of anode in (feet)

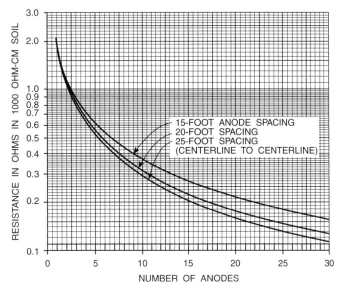

Figure 7.4 Typical horizontal anode bed design chart.

Using this procedure, the resistance in 1000 ohm-cm soil of one horizontal anode installed per Figure 7.3 is approximately 2.22 ohms (including 0.136 ohm internal resistance). No specific formula applicable to horizontal anodes in parallel is known. The curves of Figure 7.4 were obtained by dividing the resistance of 1 anode (excluding internal resistance) by the number of anodes in parallel and applying paralleling factors obtained from the curves of Figure 7.2. To the values obtained from the curves must be added an amount equal to the internal resistance of 1 anode divided by the number of anodes in parallel. To allow for the reduced distance between nearest portions of horizontal anodes at a given spacing compared to that for vertical anodes at the same spacing, paralleling factors for 15 ft horizontal anode spacing were taken from the curve for 10 ft vertical anode spacing, and so forth. This is not at all rigorous but will serve as a reasonable guide.

As an example, the paralleling factor for 20 vertical anodes at 15-ft spacing (from Figure 7.2) is 0.218 ohm. The resistance of one anode calculated from Eq 3 is 2.56 ohm. Paralleling factor = 0.218/(2.56/20) = 1.70. Using this factor for 20 horizontal anodes at 20 ft spacing, the parallel resistance would be 2.08 ohm (resistance of one horizontal anode excluding internal resistance) divided by 20 and multiplied by the factor.

$(2.08/20) \times 1.70 = 0.177$ ohm (see Figure 7.4).

Another approach to horizontal ground bed construction involves the use of a continuous strip of carbonaceous backfill with anodes located at intervals within the strip. Construction would be similar to that shown in Figure 7.3 except that the carbonaceous

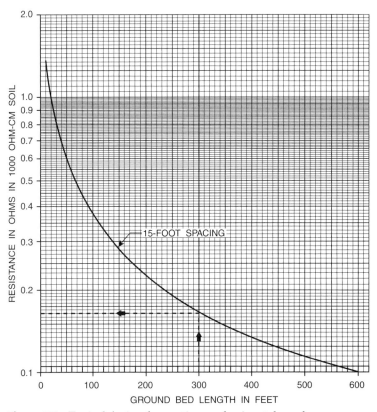

Figure 7.5 Typical design for continuous horizontal anode.

backfill layer is continuous throughout the length of the ground bed. Figure 7.5 is a design curve for determining the resistance of a continuous horizontal ground bed with anodes on 15-ft centers with the carbonaceous backfill strip starting 5 ft before the end of the first anode and ending 5 ft after the end of the last anode.

The curve in Figure 7.5 is based on the formula for a horizontal anode given earlier plus an allowance for longitudinal resistance of the carbonaceous backfill. This curve is based on carbonaceous backfill having 50-ohm-cm resistivity, a conservative value because a good quality backfill, well tamped, should have less than this amount. In using this curve, as with the other design charts, effective soil resistivity must be known with reasonable accuracy.

Galvanic Anode Ground Beds

The design of galvanic anode ground beds involves procedures similar to those used for impressed current ground beds. Design charts, however, differ somewhat with anode

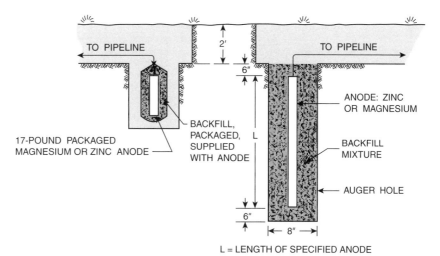

Figure 7.6 Typical galvanic anode installation.

dimensions and backfill used with them. Galvanic anodes (see Chapter 9) use special backfill having resistivities in the order of 50 ohm-cm. Calculations for design charts in this chapter, however, are based on a conservative figure of 300 ohm-cm. Using procedures described previously earlier in this chapter under Impressed Current Ground Beds, similar charts may be developed based on lower resistivity backfill mixtures. Figure 7.6 illustrates two typical types of galvanic anode installation.

The following is a calculation procedure similar to those used for impressed current anodes. The resistance to earth of a 17-lb packaged anode (at the left of Figure 7.6) is approximately 7.17 ohms in 1000-ohm-cm soil. Resistance to earth of the longer anodes (at the right of the figure) will range from 3.48 ohms for a 1.4-in × 1.4-in cross section anode to 3.38 ohms for a 2-in × 2-in cross-section anode in 1000-ohm-cm soil. As stated above, these figures are based on 300 ohm-cm chemical backfill resistivity. Comparable figures using 50-ohm-cm backfill (which reduces the internal resistance between anode and outer edge of backfill column) would be 6.36, 2.94 and 2.92 ohms respectively.

For vertical galvanic anodes in parallel, design curves are provided in Figure 7.7. The curves shown are for 17-lb magnesium anodes at 15-ft spacing and for 5-ft long zinc or magnesium anodes at 15-ft spacing. Similar curves for other spacing may be calculated by procedures described earlier.

Seventeen-pound anodes, being short, need not be installed horizontally except in specific circumstances. Longer anodes may require horizontal installation at locations where soil conditions are not favorable for the more usual vertical configuration. Figure 7.8 includes a design curve that may be used as a guide in determining the parallel resistance of 5-ft horizontal anodes centered in a 6-ft. length of 8-in × 8-in cross section clay-gypsum backfill in a 4-ft deep trench with 15-ft spacing, center to center, between anodes.

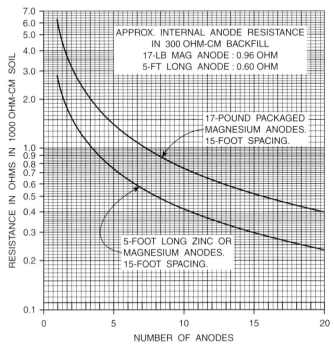

Figure 7.7 Typical design charts for vertical galvanic anodes.

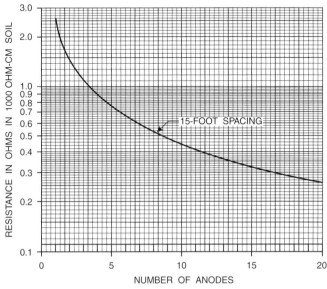

Figure 7.8 Typical design chart for horizontal galvanic anodes.

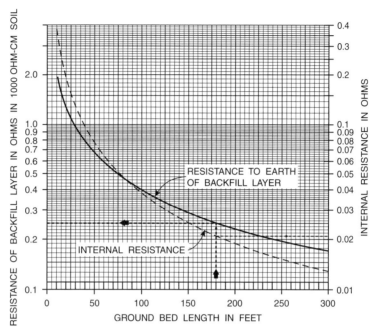

Figure 7.9 Typical design chart for horizontal continuous galvanic anode.

Typically little can be gained by installing individual galvanic anodes in a continuous horizontal layer of backfill as described for impressed current ground bed installations. Longitudinal resistance of the higher resistivity backfill tends to prevent good current distribution along such a bed. If, however, continuous strip anodes are used (available in both zinc and magnesium), this type of backfill construction becomes practical. The design curve in Figure 7.9 may be used as a guide for continuous anode strips centered in a continuous horizontal layer of clay-gypsum backfill, 8-in × 8-in cross section, in a 4-ft deep trench.

As an example of galvanic anode ground bed design, assume a requirement involving the installation of vertical 2 × 2 × 60-in magnesium anodes (see Figure 7.6) in 800-ohm-cm soil to furnish 0.5 A of protective current with the pipeline polarized to −1.0 V to CSE. Assume that anodes will be installed on 15-ft centers, that the nearest anode will be 20 ft from the pipeline, and that No. 8 copper wire will be used for the header cable. Assume that effective resistance between pipeline and earth at the installation site is 0.4 ohm.

The driving voltage available to force current from the magnesium anodes through the circuit resistance will be the polarized open circuit potential of the magnesium used less the polarized pipeline potential. Assume magnesium open circuit potential of standard magnesium (Chapter 9) at −1.55 V to copper sulfate. The driving potential in this case, then, will be $1.55 - 1.00 - 0.10$ (anode polarization) $= 0.45$ V. Maximum permissible current resistance to provide 0.5 A output will be 0.45 V/0.5 A = 0.90 ohm.

From the 0.90 ohm circuit resistance, subtract the effective pipe-to-earth resistance (0.4 ohm in this case) and the resistance of No. 8 wire from pipe to first anode (0.02 ohm used in this case to allow for 35 ft which will permit slack and test point connections). The total circuit resistance is $0.90 - (0.4 + 0.02) = 0.48$ ohm for anode-to-earth resistance plus effective header cable resistance. Using the design curve of (Figure 7.7), convert the 0.48 ohm to a 1000 ohm-cm soil resistivity base.

$0.48 \times (1000/800) = 0.60$ ohm.

Using the curve for 60 in anodes at 15-ft spacing from Figure 7.7, seven anodes in parallel would be selected for the first attempt. Assuming 7 anodes, the resistance would be 0.55 ohm (from the curve) $\times (800/1000)$ (to convert to the 800 ohm-cm soil resistivity at the installation site) $+ (0.60/7)$ (the internal anode resistance) $+ 0.030$ ohm (the resistance of 45 ft of No. 8 wire, half the header cable length). This equals 0.556 ohm, which is too high. By increasing the number of anodes by trial and error, it is found that 9 anodes will be the minimum number that will meet the requirements of the example. The resistance, by the above procedure, will be $(0.45 \times (800/1000)) + (0.60/9) + 0.039 = 0.466$ ohm which is within the 0.48 ohm requirement. The above calculations were made using the higher resistivity chemical backfill. Using the lower resistivity (50 ohm-cm) backfill, the internal anode resistance would be lower and the anode bed resistance lower.

A similar approach to that detailed above would be used for design problems in which other galvanic anode design charts included herein are employed to arrive at a desired value of anode bed resistance. The useful life to be expected must be considered also. See Chapter 9 for data on selection of galvanic anode materials, sizes, and life calculations.

DISTRIBUTED ANODE SYSTEMS

Distributed anodes, either impressed current or galvanic, should be considered when it is necessary to protect a limited area of pipeline. Typically, such systems are used on sections of bare pipeline or coated pipeline in congested areas where electrical shielding precludes effective protection with remote ground bed installations.

The principle of protection received from distributed anode or close anode systems is that the length of pipeline protected by a single close anode depends on changing the potential of the earth around the pipeline rather than changing the potential of the pipeline with respect to earth. The amount of earth potential change (and hence the length of pipe that can be protected from a single anode) is a function of voltage impressed on the anode rather than the amount of current discharged by the anode.

Distributed Impressed Current Anodes

When designing distributed anode systems using an impressed current anode system, effective soil resistivity along the section of pipeline to be protected should be known.

(See Chapter 5.) With this information, resistance of individual anodes can be calculated using procedures described earlier in this chapter. The voltage to be impressed is selected and anode spacing is calculated using the following principles. Existing potentials to earth must be known along the section to be protected, so the earth potential change needed to attain a minimum potential of -0.85 V (pipe-to-close CSE) can be determined at the midpoint between anodes. The parallel resistance of all anodes is calculated. With allowances for header cable resistance and back voltage between pipeline and anodes, voltage and current requirements of the power source may be calculated.

It should be noted if relatively long distances are covered by distributed anodes fed from one power source, voltage attenuation resulting from potential drop in the header cable (current flowing through the cable resistance) will result in reduced voltage to the more remote anodes than that impressed on those close to the power source. This should be checked during the design phase. If the difference is significant, closer spacing between the more remote anodes may be required to attain the same level of protection between anodes along the distributed anode system.

An important consideration in determining spacing between distributed anodes is the additive effect of earth potential changes at midpoints between adjacent anodes. If, for example, the earth potential change at the midpoint between two anodes is 0.1 V from one anode with design voltage impressed on it and is 0.1 V from the second anode, the total earth potential change will be 0.2 V at the midpoint. This should be considered when planning spacing between anodes.

Distributed Galvanic Anodes

When protecting a section of line with distributed galvanic anodes by the earth potential change method, anodes must be close together. Wide spacing is not effective, contrary to what is true with impressed current anodes, because anode voltage is a function of the anode material (i.e. magnesium or zinc). Placing galvanic anodes at individual hot spots (using procedures described in Chapter 5) is a form of distributed anode system used effectively on bare lines or pipelines that experience random leaks over time.

DESIGN AND INSTALLATION OF DEEP ANODE CATHODIC PROTECTION SYSTEMS

Steve McKim

In the past quarter century, deep anode cathodic protection (CP) systems have become an industry standard. While such installations can be very useful under most conditions, they are not applicable to all situations. This section discusses design considerations that may be used as a guide during planning and construction. Local restrictions may influence installation of certain deep anode configurations, and communications with the local authorities for further information is always advisable.

DEFINITION

A deep anode system is an impressed current CP arrangement in which the anodes are located in wholly, or partially, electrically remote earth extending down vertically from the surface in a hole drilled for the purpose, or an existing hole. This achieves the same result obtained by locating anodes electrically remote laterally from the structure, and near the surface as described earlier in this chapter.

USES AND BENEFITS

Deep anodes provide effective CP to facilities as diverse as underground pipelines, storage tanks, refineries, power plants, treatment plants, pile structures, and well casings in areas where surface soil resistivities are either very high or, if reasonably low, are shallow and overlie high resistivity material. These conditions require large surface anodes too far from the structure to obtain reasonably low resistance electrically remote from the structure.

Deep earth formations must, however, have low enough resistivity to permit construction of a deep anode that radiates the volume of current at a reasonable necessary impressed voltage. In deep formations with low resistivity compared to surface soils, excellent current distribution along the structure is expected. Even where surface soils are entirely satisfactory for surface anode design, deep anodes can be useful in congested areas where surface anodes are difficult to locate so that they will be remote electrically from foreign structures as well as from the structure being protected.

Because remote earth is obtained vertically, the deep anode can be placed within the structure right-of-way, which is difficult with conventional surface-type remote anodes. As discussed earlier in this chapter, these remote earth properties provide optimum current distribution along the protected structure and minimize voltage gradient variation. These benefits allow installation of high output systems near foreign utilities and structures with fewer negative side effects associated with surface anode systems, such as interference with foreign structures, hydrogen embrittlement of susceptible steels, and cathodic coating degradation.

Installing systems at greater intervals reduces the overall cost of CP. The compact installation means less foreign utility damage during installation and less chance of subsequent system damage from other construction activities. Fewer systems mean fewer locations to coordinate rectifier power and negotiate easement rights, fewer rectifiers to maintain and less interference to investigate, correct, and monitor.

Installing multiple anodes in one carbon column achieves maximum anode current discharge balance. The high level of carbon compaction in deep anodes provides maximum electronic current discharge, thereby increasing anode life. The high probability for ground water provides the lowest possible circuit resistance. Properly installed venting systems minimize the risk of gas blockage and allow for anode irrigation with potable water. Inherently low circuit resistance of these anode systems minimizes the costs of AC power consumption. Note that many of the benefits of deep anodes are reduced substantially if the designer attempts to install too few systems at too great intervals. In areas with foreign underground structures, the maximum recommended current output is 30 A.

DESIGN CONSIDERATIONS

Figure 7.10, represents a typical deep anode installation.

Standard features include nonmetallic vent pipe, active column consisting of multiple anodes placed between 5 and 20 ft apart and backfilled with coke breeze (carbon), and an inactive column consisting of nonconductive backfill and sanitary well seal.

Other early deep anode configurations proved successful, although their use has diminished in recent years. These configurations included carbon steel pipe or heavy steel rails in place of fabricated anodes. Another less common deep anode configuration utilizes multiple anodes attached to a single header cable instead of individual cables from each anode. Looping the anode header cable back to the rectifier from each end will increase design reliability.

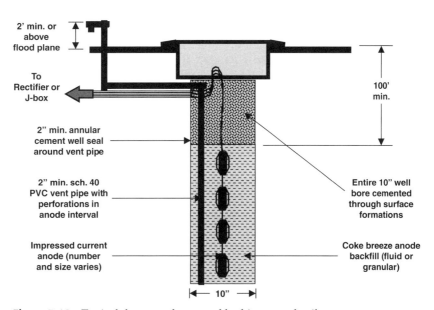

Figure 7.10   Typical deep anode ground bed in normal soil strata.

Soil Resistivity

Resistivity of deep formations may be determined by several techniques. Information gained from existing nearby deep anodes is most valuable. Histories of current output readings from individual anodes can indicate relative resistivity of downhole formations. Histories of rectifier outputs can indicate total anode bed resistance values. Existing soil logs may be available from nearby water wells or monitoring wells. This information can provide clues to the relative resistivity of downhole formations.

The four-pin method of measuring soil resistivity may be used in some instances. Techniques described in Chapter 5 are applicable. After determining surface soil resistivities in the usual manner, deep formation resistivities may be measured with, first, pin spacing of 50 ft and then with spacing increased progressively by 50-ft increments until it is felt that the location has been explored satisfactorily. Relatively thin strata of either high or low resistivity may be missed, but average conditions will be determined. Measurements may be made to depths of several hundred feet but resistance values obtained will be so low that the DC method will have to be used in most cases. The measured change in voltage between potential pins will be small, requiring high impedance electronic circuitry. Data analysis can be achieved as outlined in Chapter 5.

Obviously, when using the four-pin test to measure at greater depths, the soil pins will be spread over a wide area (1500 ft, for example, from first to last pin for a reading to a depth of 500 ft). This requires a large clear area. For accurate results, the pins must remain clear of all underground structures (pipelines, cables, pole line grounds, etc.) that could pick up or discharge a portion of the test current and upset the geometry of the test. Due to the free space requirements, four-pin measurements to sufficient depth are usually impractical in urban areas.

If existing wells can be found in the area being investigated and if the length of casing and/or tubing is known, resistance of such structures may be measured to remote earth. From this, the effective soil resistivity may be estimated to a depth equal to the length of casing and/or tubing. This is done by application of the Dwight formula for a single vertical anode and solving for soil resistivity. Other methods of measuring deep soil resistivity, such as electromagnetic conductivity, are cited by Morgan in CP, second edition, NACE, 1993. Opportunities for application of these methods may be infrequent.

Probably the most effective method of proving a location is to drill a small pilot hole to a depth of the proposed deep well. If natural water is not encountered, the hole must be filled with potable water to measure the downhole resistance. A single anode is lowered down the hole with a long attached wire connected to the structure in series with a battery (or other DC power source) and an ammeter (shunt). By measuring the current output of power source voltage at intervals as the test anode is lowered, a profile of current output with depth can be developed. This profile will reveal the best permanent anode locations opposite the more highly conductive earth layers, as indicated by the highest current outputs from the test anode. If the pilot hole proves satisfactory, it may be drilled out to full size for a permanent deep anode installation. Applying test anode resistance and dimensions to the Dwight formula at favorable anode locations may determine effective soil resistivity. Averaging the values obtained through that part of the hole where anodes could be installed would give a figure that may be used for designing the permanent installation.

Upon developing a figure for effective soil resistivity, the resistance for a permanent system may be based on the resistance of a single vertical anode, using the Dwight formula. As a last resort in areas of varying soil resistivities, it may be advantageous to install the deep anode before sizing the rectifier. This will allow actual resistance measurement and accurate rectifier ratings.

Well Dimensions

Common deep anode depths range from 50 ft to 500 ft. Prominant geologic formations near the proposed location may control final depth. Deeper installations may provide more remote earth and allow larger coverage, they also allow for more anodes, which will increase system life. Local regulatory authorities may constrain the design philosophy, so early contact is recommended.

Most anodes have a nominal diameter of 10 in, which is achieved with a standard $9\frac{7}{8}$ in rotary drill bit. This diameter provides the most cost-effective combination of system life, installation cost, and operation expense. Other common drill bit diameters used for deep anodes are 6 in, $7\frac{7}{8}$ in, $8\frac{3}{4}$ in, $10\frac{5}{8}$ in and $12\frac{1}{4}$ in. Smaller diameters reduce initial installation cost; however, they also shorten system life by reducing the bulk mass of carbon available for consumption. Smaller diameters also raise overall circuit resistance, which increases rectifier power consumption costs. Larger diameter wells reverse these effects, but cost of construction increases exponentially. Diameters larger than $9\frac{7}{8}$ in become quite costly in hard formations. Applications of Dwight equations indicate a more efficient reduction in anode resistance by increasing the length of active anode column rather than by increasing the diameter of active column.

VENT PIPES

All deep anode installations should include a method of venting produced gases to the atmosphere. Lack of ventilation can lead to gas blockage of anodes and eventual system failure. Ventilation is normally accomplished by installing nonmetallic pipe with a diameter between 1 in and 2 in. The vent pipe is perforated throughout the active column and solid through the inactive column. Standard perforations range from 0.006 in wide slots to $\frac{1}{4}$ in diameter holes and are commonly placed every 6 in of pipe length. To prevent plugging with inactive column backfill, perforations should end even with top anode.

Schedule 40 PVC is the most common material used for vent pipe. Schedule 80 is only required when head pressure from deep cement well seals could cause pipe collapse. Upper end of vent pipe should be terminated so produced gases are allowed to dissipate naturally to the atmosphere. Termination should be above any flood plain elevation. Vent pipe installation should be designed to allow for eventual well destruction. Destruction procedure could be regulated by local regulatory authorities and may include filling vent pipe with nonporous materials.

Anode Suspension Systems

The standard method of installation is to lower each anode by its attached wire, suspend it at the desired depth, and tie it off at the surface. This technique allows adjustment of anode position to low resistance soil formations and also provides a ready method to test for proper carbon backfill settlement by pulling on suspended anode wires.

Some installations have separate suspension systems to hold anodes and eliminate stress on the attached wires using ropes, steel pipe, or the vent pipe. Anode suspension systems are usually not required when following proper loading procedures. Use of $1\frac{1}{2}$-in diameter steel pipe is the most common suspension system. However, it requires dielectric unions between anodes to allow resistance logging during backfill. Another disadvantage of using a metallic support material is its eventual corrosion due to contact with the anode circuit. This may complicate eventual well destruction.

Use of PVC vent pipe for suspension eliminates need for dielectric unions but is extremely dangerous during installation. PVC vent pipe suspension is not recommended because of the dangers associated with vent pipe joint separation during loading. Separation will lead to downhole free-fall of anodes, which could result in injury to the installation crew.

Anode Centering Devices

Anode centralizers may be installed to ensure that carbon backfill surrounds each anode. Centralizers should be designed to prevent damage to anode wires during installation and allow anode movement in the well without snagging on downhole formations or other anode assemblies.

Carbon Backfill

High quality calcined petroleum coke is recommended for all deep anode installations. Granular carbon sinks readily in fresh water and is normally poured directly from the bag into the well. Fluid coke is comprised of fine carbon particles that compact tightly around anodes. Because of small particle size, fluid coke should be pumped from the

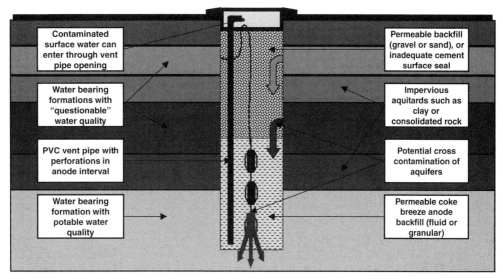

Figure 7.11   Typical deep anode ground bed without surface seal.

bottom up using a pipe installed for this purpose. Fluid coke should normally be allowed to settle overnight and sounded prior to installation of inactive column.

Inactive Column and Well Seals

To eliminate anode current leakage up the inactive column, the upper section of deep anodes should be backfilled with nonconductive materials. Materials include PVC casing, sand, gravel, and cement. Sand bridges easily during installation and is not recommended. Depth of inactive column will depend on current distribution requirements. Pea gravel backfill above the active column will increase the probability for ground water recharge. However, long columns of porous backfill can lead to commingling of aquifers with differing water qualities.

All deep anodes should include a nonporous sanitary well seal in upper section of inactive column. Depth of seal should be 50 ft minimum and could be in excess of 100 ft. Seal materials include cement, concrete, and specially formulated bentonite. Depth may be dictated by local regulatory agency.

Conductor casings may be required to prevent caving of surface formations during installation. Steel casing should be removed from inactive column within 50 ft of active column. PVC casings can be left in inactive column, but should be cemented into place to provide sanitary well seal. Top of casings must be sealed to prevent surface runoff that could lead to contamination of downhole aquifers. Size well diameter to provide 2-in minimum annular space around outside diameter of casing for proper seal placement.

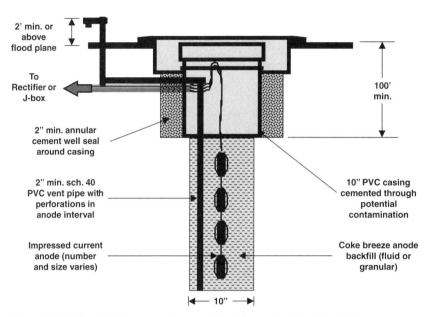

2' min. or above flood plane

To Rectifier or J-box

2" min. annular cement well seal around casing

2" min. sch. 40 PVC vent pipe with perforations in anode interval

Impressed current anode (number and size varies)

100' min.

10" PVC casing cemented through potential contamination

Coke breeze anode backfill (fluid or granular)

|← 10" →|

Figure 7.12   Typical deep anode ground bed in contaminated soil strata.

In potentially contaminated formations, surface casing should be cemented into place before drilling active column. This should eliminate cross contamination during installation and operation of anode system.

INSTALLATION CONSIDERATIONS

Deep anodes are normally drilled with truck-mounted rotary drilling equipment. Typical equipment circulates water-based drilling mud to maintain well integrity and remove downhole cuttings. Compressed air circulation systems may be advantageous in limited situations where downhole formations allow their use. Installation procedures are critical, so use only fully qualified drillers.

Loading Procedures

As previously mentioned, deep anodes are ordinarily drilled with direct mud rotary equipment. After reaching desired depth, downhole mud slurry must be thinned to nearly the viscosity of fresh water to allow proper carbon settlement around anodes. Thinning is performed by pumping potable water from the bottom up through mud circulation system until it returns to surface in well bore. Accurate well thinning is critical to system installation.

Drillers familiar with proper thinning procedures are essential. Higher downhole fluid viscosities provide more resistance to caving of formations, but slow carbon settlement. Lower viscosities speed carbon settlement, but can lead to caving of downhole formations. Caving formations can bridge in well bore or settle around anodes. These conditions prevent carbon settlement around anodes, which will significantly decrease system performance and life.

After thinning, drill pipe is removed from well to allow system loading. Vent pipe is usually lowered first and tied into position. Anodes are lowered by their attached wire to the desired elevation and tied off at the surface. After anodes are placed at desired elevations, carbon backfill is poured or pumped downhole. Anode resistance logging before, during, and after carbon backfill provides proof of proper carbon settlement. Settlement of top-loaded granular carbons normally occurs within 1 hr. Settlement of pumped fluid carbons normally takes 6 to 12 hr. Total settlement should occur before backfill of inactive column.

Site Layout

Deep anode installation equipment usually includes portable rotary drill rig, mud circulation system, water truck, drill mud and cuttings containment system, material trailer, and support equipment.

Drill rig masts are normally between 20 ft and 40 ft high. Safe and legal clearance from overhead power lines and other obstructions is mandatory.

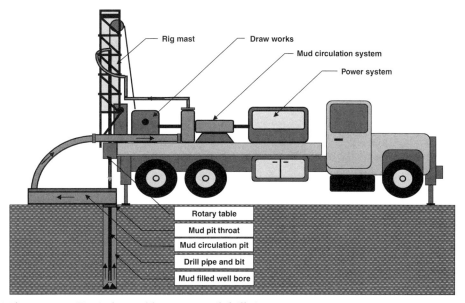

Figure 7.13   Typical portable rotary mud drill rig.

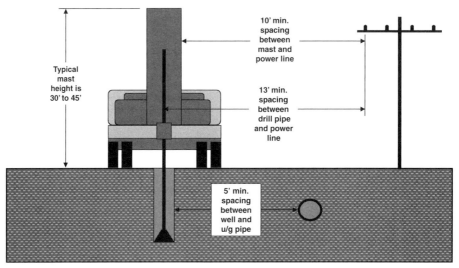

Figure 7.14   Minimum drill rig clearance dimensions.

Drill rigs are also between 20 ft and 40 ft long. Anode location must provide enough space to safely place required equipment.

Rig must be near level during drilling. Slope of anode location cannot exceed limits of drill rig leveling equipment.

Containment of drill cuttings and circulation fluid must also be considered when choosing anode locations.

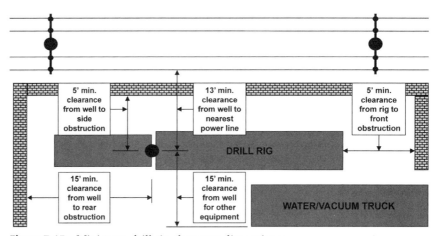

Figure 7.15   Minimum drill rig clearance dimensions.

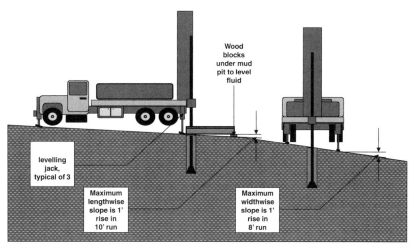

Figure 7.16 Maximum drill rig site slope dimensions.

REFERENCES

Derived from equations in "Calculation of Resistance to Ground", by H.B. Dwight. Electrical Engineering, p. 1319 (1936) December.

Derived from equations in the book by Erling D. Sunde. "Earth Conduction Effects in Transmission Systems." D. Van Nostrand Co., Inc. (1949).

Impressed Current Cathodic Protection

Ronald L. Bianchetti

Rectifiers are used more than any other source of impressed current power. Areas discussed include rectifier types, rectifier selection, specification requirements, and typical installation details. Various types of impressed current anodes and components that make up an impressed current system are also presented.

RECTIFIER TYPES

Cathodic protection (CP) rectifiers have the following major components. These typically include a transformer to step down AC line voltage to low voltage AC on the secondary with a tap arrangement to permit selecting a range of voltage, a rectifying element (usually full wave silicon diodes for rectification), and a housing for outdoor mounting. These components are supplemented by an AC circuit breaker and DC output meters. Both single-phase and three-phase units are in common use. Figure 8.1, illustrates diagrammatically single-phase and three-phase units of the full-wave bridge-connected type.

Where electrical storm activity is prevalent, it is advisable to provide protection against lightning damage.

- Lightning surges may occur from the electric distribution line (the more probable) and/or
- Surges coming from the pipeline (both from lightning and AC ground fault)

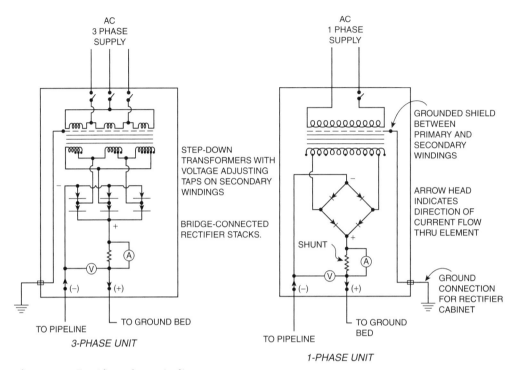

Figure 8.1   Rectifier schematic diagrams.

Specifying rectifiers having transformers with an electrical shield between primary and secondary transformer windings may provide some protection from lightning surges. Such a shield (shown in the figure), when grounded properly, intercepts the high voltage peak surge of a lightning pulse and carries it to ground. Otherwise, it can break down a rectifying element and may burn out the element. Low voltage lightning arrestors can also be placed across rectifier terminals and may provide protection from lightning surges from the pipeline. Neither type of protection, however, is effective against a direct strike to the rectifier itself.

Rectifier manufacturers produce units for CP applications with a wide range of outputs. Data are available in the supply catalogs of CP equipment. Three general housing types are available. Ventilated housings that provide for convection air cooling are used for most pipeline applications. Where highly corrosive atmospheres exist (marine or industrial, for example), the equipment may be oil-immersed in a tank-type housing. For locations subject to hazards and explosives an explosion proof housing is available for oil-immersed units. Figure 8.2 illustrates the appearance of typical air-cooled and oil-immersed units.

 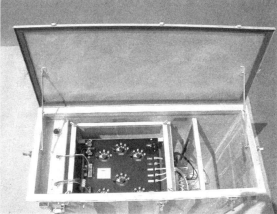

Figure 8.2   Typical rectifiers: (left) air cooled unit; (right) oil immersed unit. (Courtesy of Universal Rectifier, Inc.)

Rectifying elements typically used in units today are silicon diodes. A silicon diode has high resistance to current flow in one direction and low resistance in the other. This characteristic makes rectification possible. The diagrams of Figure 8.1 show that for a given direction of current flow in the transformer secondary winding, the current can flow on only one route through the rectifying element (in the direction of the arrow heads). This flow is out the positive terminal to the ground bed and back from the pipeline connection to the negative terminal. When the direction of current flow in the transformer secondary reverses (this occurs 120 times at normal 60-cycle AC power frequency), the current will take a different route through the rectifying element but will still flow out at the positive terminal and back at the negative terminal. The result is direct current (DC).

A rectifying diode is rated by the manufacturer for specific maximum current flow at a given ambient temperature and for maximum inverse voltage (the voltage impressed across the element in the high resistance direction). Diodes are assembled into stacks or assemblies with series-parallel combinations to attain the over-all DC voltage and current rating needed for the rectifier produced. In older rectifiers, the rectifying elements were selenium stacks or discs, but modern rectifiers use mainly diodes as rectifying elements. Rectifying elements have been continuously improved over the years in operating characteristics and efficiency. The rectifier user is advised to review developments in this field and replace older rectifying elements with improved stacks when justified by the improved characteristics and efficiency of newer ones.

Cathodic protection rectifiers may be equipped with filters in the DC output which smooth out the ripple in the rectified DC and permit higher over-all efficiency. These filters are practical where savings in power cost justify the additional investment.

Under certain circumstances, "constant potential" rectifiers are useful on pipeline systems. Such rectifiers are designed to maintain a constant protective potential on the pipeline at the rectifier location, which changes to match pipeline current requirements. Applications include areas subject to stray current from transit systems or in mining operations where potential variations are not beyond the corrective capacity of this type of unit. Use with ground beds subject to wide seasonal variations in resistance (wet to dry) is also included.

Constant potential rectifiers (see Figure 8.3) differ from more conventional rectifiers (which require manual adjustment of transformer taps to change output) in that a sensing circuit that maintains continual checks on the pipe-to-soil potential changes the output current automatically. Typically, this can be accomplished by burying a permanent reference electrode at the point where constant pipe-to-soil potential is to be maintained.

Once the rectifier is adjusted for the desired pipe-to-soil potential, any increase in absolute value of this potential serves (through the electronic controller) to increase the reactor reactance. This cuts the output current back until a balance at the preset potential is regained. Likewise, any decrease in absolute value of this potential between pipeline and reference electrode will cause the rectifier output current to increase automatically until balance is regained.

SELECTION OF RECTIFIER SIZE

Rectifier size (output rating) will depend primarily on the current requirement at the installation site and the output voltage required to force the current through the pipeline to ground bed circuit resistance. Current requirement tests, or other design procedures, determine the amperage. Circuit resistance is determined by the ground bed design as discussed in Chapter 7.

The output voltage rating should be sized 15 to 25% over the design-calculated value to allow for any change in ground bed resistance. This permits maintaining full rated output when ground bed resistance goes up as the anodes deteriorate with age. Final output ratings for current and voltage can then be coordinated with standard output ratings defined on the rectifier name plate or manufacturer's catalogue data.

Initial rectifier current ratings can give some understanding of future system requirements as outlined in the following examples. For example, the current needed to protect a section of bare line is not likely to increase with time, the rectifier may be sized to meet the existing design current requirements. On the other hand, a newly laid well-coated pipeline may initially require only a small amount of current, but as the coating stabilizes with time (or deteriorates from soil stress, temperature effect, etc), it may require several times the initial current. In these cases, it is practical to install rectifiers having maximum current capacity several times greater than the initial requirement. Coated lines that have been in the ground for a long enough time to become well stabilized do not tend to require as much reserve capacity. No firm rules can be established, however,

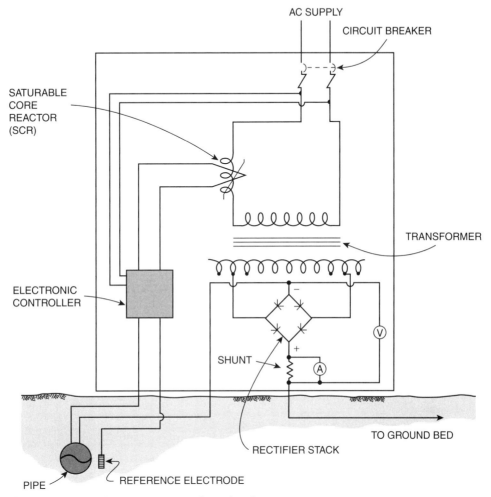

Figure 8.3 Typical constant potential rectifier diagram.

because variables such as length of pipe section protected, coating used, changes in soil conditions, probable temperature effects, and other conditions will apply in each case. Experience with conditions on the pipeline corrosion engineer's own system will help to make proper current rating determination.

When time permits, some pipeline corrosion engineers design and install impressed current ground beds before deciding on the rectifier rating. Following this procedure, it is possible to measure the installed circuit resistance and make new current requirement tests using the completed ground bed. Rectifier voltage and current ratings may be selected with full assurance that the installation will work as planned. Although results are positive, this procedure does require more time and involves additional expense for repeat visits by the construction crews to make rectifier installations. However, when ground bed designs can be prepared with reasonable accuracy, this procedure is not necessary.

In determining power costs, the corrosion engineer should recognize that the smaller rectifiers along the pipeline (well coated pipelines particularly) may draw so little power that the costs do not exceed the power company's minimum billing (where applicable). In such instances, relative efficiency of the rectifier may have little bearing on economic choice.

Although rectifiers operating on three-phase power are more efficient than single-phase units, three-phase power may be available at relatively few locations along a pipeline. Where it is available, the choice between single-phase and three-phase units should be based on a relative cost study. Results of this study can be expected to favor three-phase units for large installations.

The use of filters for improvement in efficiency should be considered only when they will reduce the net annual cost of the complete installation. The savings will be a result of a reduction in power cost. Applicable power rates must be determined when making cost comparisons. Rectifier manufacturers who furnish filters for their equipment should provide data on efficiency improvement.

RECTIFIER SPECIFICATIONS

After deciding on the size and type of rectifier to be used, ordering specifications must include at least the following information in order to ensure obtaining the correct unit when purchasing from the standard lines of rectifier manufacturers.

1. AC input: Voltage, single or three phase and frequency. For example: 120/240 V, single phase, 60 cycles. (The expression 120/240 means that the unit may be field connected for operation on either 120 or 240 V AC).
2. Maximum DC output in amperes and volts.
3. Air-cooled, oil-immersed, or oil-immersed and explosion-proof.
4. Pole mounting, wall mounting, or floor (pad) mounting.
5. Silicon type rectifying element and either full wave bridge or full wave center tap.
6. Maximum ambient operating temperature.
7. Protective equipment: Circuit breaker in AC input. Shielded transformer winding. Lightning arrestors, etc.
8. Instruments: Voltmeter and ammeter with accuracy (such as 2 percent of full scale).
9. Provisions for external current shunt terminals and potential terminals for periodic check of rectifier instruments should be specified.
10. Case construction such as anodized aluminum, galvanized, coated steel or small arms proof.

When standard units do not meet needed requirements, it is necessary to specify additional provisions. These may include an output filter for efficiency improvement, additional positive terminals (for leads from individual deep-well ground bed anodes for example), additional negative terminals where current is to be drained from more than one pipeline, additional current measuring shunts, lightning arrester or other special protective equipment, special housing finish and/or design, and other special features as required. Special provisions such as those above may be supported by an accompanying drawing where necessary to clarify requirements.

Some users of large numbers of CP rectifiers prepare standard detail specifications, which include minimum requirements for all components of rectifier assemblies. These are used to make equipment uniform instead of ordering units from a manufacturer's standard line. Unless the number of units ordered is substantial, this can involve extra cost because manufacturers may have to modify their standard production techniques to meet the specifications.

RECTIFIER EFFICIENCY

In addition to the type of rectifying elements used and whether or not an output filter is used, rectifier efficiency is affected by the percentage of current or voltage loading. The effect is illustrated by Figure 8.4, which shows typical efficiency curves for units operated (1) at full current but reduced voltage and (2) at full voltage but reduced current.

Curves shown are for illustration only and should not be used for calculations. If calculations are required, use the curves applying to the equipment being considered. The curves in the figure show that efficiency suffers most when units are operated at a small percentage of the rated voltage.

The actual overall efficiency of an operating rectifier unit may be determined as follows:

$$Efficiency\ in\ percent = \frac{DC\ power\ output}{AC\ power\ input} \times 100$$

The DC power output is the output current multiplied by the output voltage. The AC power input may be measured by a wattmeter. If the rectifier has a kilowatt-hour meter (provided by the power company) measuring the power taken by one rectifier only, use it to measure the power input. If the meter is marked with a meter constant, measure the number of seconds for the meter disc to make one revolution. The power consumption is then (3600 s/h/s for one disc revolution) x meter constant = watts input. The meter constant is usually shown on the face of the kilowatt-hour meter.

Simply measuring the AC input voltage and current and multiplying them to get the AC power input neglects power factor and will not be accurate. If, however, it is impossible to measure the true power input, using the input current and voltage will yield a reasonable approximation. If this is done, subsequent efficiency measurements

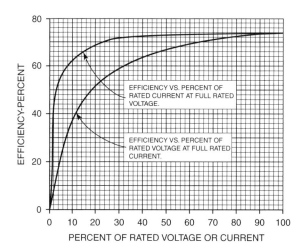

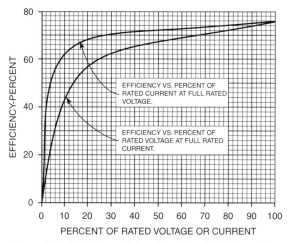

Figure 8.4 Rectifier efficiencies. Top: Selenium – Typical overall efficiency curves for custom line air cooled selenium bridge connected rectified unit rated at 60 V, 60 amp full load DC output. 230-V, single phase, AC input. Bottom: Silicon – Typical overall efficiency curves for custom line air-cooled silicon bridge connected rectifier unit rated at 40 V, 34 amp full load DC output. 230 V, single phase AC input. (Courtesy of Universal Rectifier, Inc.)

should be made in the same manner in order to detect any deterioration of efficiency ones a period of time.

RECTIFIER INSTALLATION DETAILS

Various standards for rectifier installation are used by operating pipeline companies. Installation practices differ depending on local conditions and individual preferences. There is no universal standard in effect. Rectifier installation sketches are shown below, which may be adapted as necessary to meet the user's requirements.

Figure 8.5 illustrates a method for installing a pole-mounted CP rectifier. Most instances of air-cooled rectifiers are pole mounted, as shown in the figure.

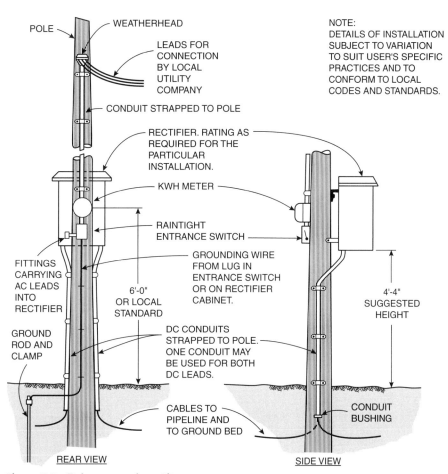

Figure 8.5   Pole mounted rectifier.

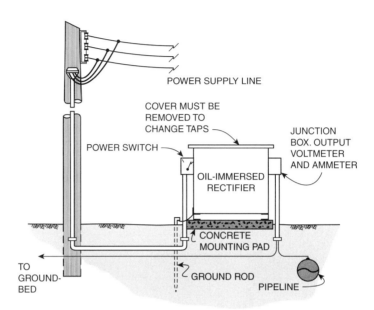

Figure 8.6   Pad mounted rectifier.

Figure 8.6 shows the use of a concrete pad for mounting air-cooled (pedestal type), oil-filled and explosion-proof rectifiers. Neither of these figures represents an attempt to standardize rectifier installation practices. They are included only to serve as a guide to those who may be preparing installation standards that apply to their own specific system requirements.

GROUND BED MATERIALS FOR IMPRESSED CURRENT SYSTEMS

This section includes guidance on the selection of materials for use with impressed current ground beds.

Anode Types

Materials currently popular for use as anode material include graphite, high silicon cast iron, mixed metal oxide, platinum, and steel.

Graphite anodes may be obtained in various sizes (Figure 8.7), although 3-in. diameters by 60-in. rods are most commonly used for pipeline ground beds. These anodes are typically supplied by the manufacturers with insulated copper leads usually high molecular weight polyethylene (HMW/PE). Standard lead length and size usually is

Graphite
Solid Rod Anodes

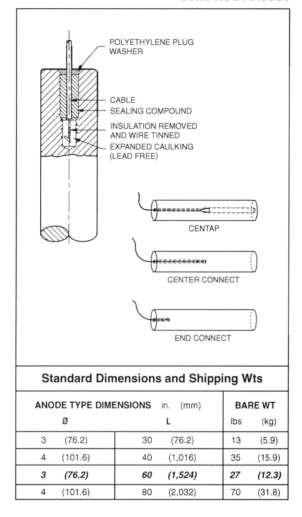

Standard Dimensions and Shipping Wts

ANODE TYPE DIMENSIONS	in.	(mm)	BARE WT	
Ø		L	lbs	(kg)
3 (76.2)	30	(76.2)	13	(5.9)
4 (101.6)	40	(1,016)	35	(15.9)
3 (76.2)	*60*	*(1,524)*	*27*	*(12.3)*
4 (101.6)	80	(2,032)	70	(31.8)

CHEMICAL COMPOSITION

Element	Content %
Carbon	99.80
Ash	0.20

Figure 8.7 Graphite anodes typical sizes and chemical composition. (Corrpro Companies Inc.)

20 ft of No. 8 HMW/PE insulated wire. Leads of any length may be special ordered. Larger wire sizes are available within limits established by the manufacturer. Catalogs for CP material give full details on available sizes and ordering information. The "specially treated" graphite anodes (NA treated) are impregnated with linseed oil to prevent interparticle attack and sloughing off of active material under adverse conditions. The additional cost for treated anodes is justified.

Graphite is brittle so anodes of this material should be handled accordingly. The connection between insulated anode lead and the anode proper is mechanical, and insulating material protects it from moisture penetration. Anode caps are designed to safeguard against early deterioration of the connection end. Caps may be cast in place or may be in the form of a prefabricated heat shrink cap.

When anodes are backfilled with carbonaceous backfill material, they are usually rated at a current output up to one ampere per square foot (1 A/ft^2). A 3-in. by 60-in. anode would have a maximum output of approximately four amperes. This must be taken into account when designing ground beds, as outlined in Chapter 7.

Graphite anodes are consumed at no more than two pounds per ampere per year when discharging current into an electrolyte. When used with carbonaceous backfill by direct electrical contact, most of the material consumed is backfill material rather than the anode itself.

High silicon cast iron anodes normally contain between 14 and 15% silicon plus lesser quantities of other alloying elements. Chemical composition and other information is shown in Table 8.1.

Silicon alloy behaves differently from ordinary cast iron when discharging current. Ordinary cast iron loses approximately 20 lbs of its iron content per ampere per year. High silicon cast iron, on the other hand, loses material at a much lower rate. Typical reported rates are as shown in Table 8.1 for ground bed applications in soil.

High silicon cast iron anodes also have insulated leads as does graphite. The material is somewhat brittle and must be handled with care. They are available in various sizes and available from suppliers of CP material. A common size used in impressed current ground beds is 2-in. diameter by 60-in. length. They are used commonly with carbonaceous backfill, which absorbs most of the consumption resulting from current discharge. Tables 8.2 and 8.3 show sizes and output of rated operating current of high silicon iron anodes.

Mixed-metal oxide anodes are available in a variety of sizes and shapes. Mixed metal oxide coated titanium anodes are based on electrode technology developed in the early 1960s for production of chlorine and caustic soda. Usually the mixed metal oxide films are thermally applied to precious metal such as titanium or niobium cores. These oxide coatings have excellent conductivity, are resistant to acidic environments, are chemically stable, and have relatively low consumption rates. Table 8.4, shows sizes and rated operating current outputs of solid rod anodes in mixed metal for ground bed installations. Table 8.5, shows sizes and rated operating current outputs of tubular mixed metal anodes for ground bed installations. Ground bed installation in soils usually specifies that the anode be prepackaged in a canister with carbonaceous backfill material. Standard lead wire is 10-ft of No. 8 HMW/PE; however, any length and type of cable including Kynar^{TM},

Table 8.1 High Silicon Cast Iron Typical Types and Chemical Composition. (Corrpro Companies Inc.)

Durichlor 51 Tubular
Cast Iron Anodes

HIGH SILICON CAST IRON STANDARD ANODES DURICHLOR 51 ANODE

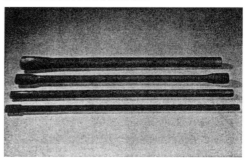

CHEMICAL COMPOSITON

Element	Content %
C	0.70 - 1.10
Mn	1.50 Max
Si	14.20 - 14.75
Cr	3.25 - 5.00
Mo	0.20 Max
Cu	0.50 Max
Iron	Remainder

ANODE MATERIAL	TYPICAL ANODE CURRENT DENSITY (AMPS/FT^2)	NOMINAL CONSUMPTION RATE (PER AMP.YR)
	IN SOIL OR FRESH WATER	
DURICHLOR 51		
No Backfill	0.25 - 0.5	0.25 LB
Coke Backfill	0.5 - 1.0	0.1 - 0.25 LB

Halar^{TM}, and PVC can be specified. Mixed metal oxide anodes can also be configured for use in deep well anode beds.

Platinum and platinized-niobium anodes are available in a variety of sizes and shapes. Platinum anodes are available in wire and rod configurations and in different

Table 8.2 Standard High Silicon Cast Iron Anodes. (Corrpro Companies Inc.)

D-51 STANDARD ANODES
(Continued)

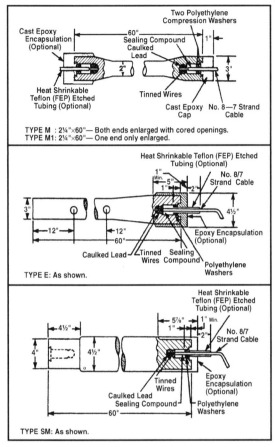

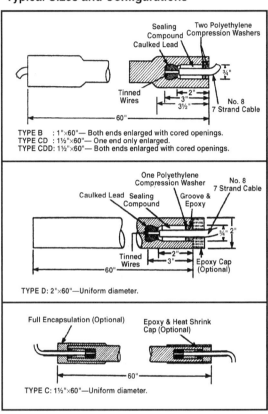

Typical Sizes and Configurations

TYPE	SIZE In (mm)		APPROXIMATE WEIGHT EACH lbs (kg)	AREA ft²(m²)	GENERAL APPLICATION	SPECIAL FEATURES
B	1×60	(25×1524)	12 (5.4)	1.4 (.13)	Fresh water tanks.	Each end enlarged to $1^1/_2$ in. (38 mm) dia. with cored opening for joining.
C	$1^1/_2 \times 60$	(38×1524)	25 (11.4)	2.0 (.19)	Open box coolers requiring lengths greater than 5 feet.	Uniform $1^1/_2$ in. (38 mm) dia. with cored opening both ends for joining.
CD	$1^1/_2 \times 60$	(38×1524)	26 (11.8)	2.0 (.19)	Ground bed with backfill.	One end only enlarged to 2 in. (51 mm) dia. with cored opening for cable connection.
CDD	$1^1/_2 \times 60$	(38×1524)	26 (11.8)	2.0 (.19)	Ground bed with backfill permits joining in series.	Each end enlarged to 2 in. (51 mm) dia. with cored opening for cable connection.
D	2×60	(51×1524)	44 (20.0)	2.6 (.24)	Ground bed without backfill.	Uniform 2 in. (51 mm) dia. with cable connections on one end only.
M	$2^1/_4 \times 60$	(57×1524)	63 (28.6)	2.9 (.28)	Mild saline or deep well without backfill.	Each end enlarged to 3 in. (76 mm) with cored opening for joining.
M1	$2^1/_4 \times 60$	(57×1524)	65 (29.5)	2.9 (.27)	Mild saline or deep well without backfill.	Same as type M but cored opening on one end only for cable connection.
E	3×60	(76×1524)	110 (49.9)	4.0 (.37)	Severe ground, deep well or sea water without backfill.	One end only enlarged to 4 in. (102 mm) dia. with cored opening for cable connection.
EWO	3×60	(76×1524)	110 (49.9)	4.0 (.37)	Severe ground, deep well or sea water without backfill.	One end only enlarged to 4 in. (102 mm) dia. with cored opening for cable connection.
SM	$4^1/_2 \times 60$	(114×1524)	220 (99.9)	5.5 (.51)	Sea water with high current discharge per anode.	Uniform $4^1/_2$ in. (114 mm) dia. with cored opening each end. Permits two cable connections, if required.

Table 8.3 Tubular High Silicon Cast Iron Anodes. (Corrpro Companies Inc.)

DURICHLOR 51 TYPE TA TUBULAR ANODES

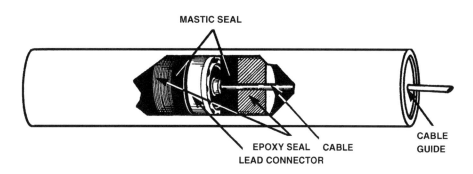

MASTIC SEAL

EPOXY SEAL CABLE LEAD CONNECTOR

CABLE GUIDE

ANODE TYPE	NOMINAL SIZE In (mm)	LENGTH In (mm)	WEIGHT Lbs (kg)	AREA-SQ. FEET (m²)	NOMINAL DISCHARGE-AMPS	GENERAL APPLICATIONS	SPECIAL FEATURES
TA1	$2^{21}/_{32} \times 42$ (67 × 1067)	42 (1067)	31 (14.1)	2.4 (.22)	1.5-2.0	Fresh water tanks, deep ground beds, or standard ground beds.	Center connection, in series on continuous cable or one lead only.
TA2	$2^{3}/_{16} \times 84$ (56 × 2133)	84 (2133)	46 (20.9)	4.0 (.37)	3.0-4.0	Fresh water tanks, deep ground beds, or standard ground beds.	Center connection, in series on continuous cable or one lead only.
TA3	$2^{21}/_{32} \times 84$ (67 × 2133)	84 (2133)	63 (28.6)	4.9 (.46)	3.5-5.0	Deep ground beds or standard ground beds.	Center connection, in series on continuous cable or one lead only.
TA4	$3^{3}/_{4} \times 84$ (95 × 2133)	84 (2133)	85 (38.6)	6.9 (.64)	6.0-7.0	Severe ground, deep well without backfill or sea water.	Center connection and tubular design gives greater surface area.
TA5	$4^{3}/_{4} \times 84$ (121 × 2133)	84 (2133)	110 (49.9)	8.7 (.81)	6-8.5	Severe ground, deep well without backfill or sea water.	Center connection eliminates loss due to "end effect."
TA6	$6^{11}/_{16} \times 78$ (170 × 1981)	78 (1981)	260 (118)	11.4 (1.06)	11-15	Seawater with high current discharge per anode or severe ground bed.	Center connection and tubular design gives longer life.
TA2A	$2^{3}/_{16} \times 42$ (56 × 1067)	42 (1067)	23 (10.4)	2.0 (.19)	1.5-2.0	Fresh water tanks, deep ground beds, or standard ground beds.	Center connection, in series on continuous cable or one lead only.
TA5A	$4^{3}/_{4} \times 84$ (121 × 2133)	84 (2133)	175 (79.4)	8.7 (.81)	9-10	Seawater with high current discharge per anode or severe ground bed.	Center connection and tubular design gives longer life.
TAB	$2^{3}/_{16} \times 24$ (56 × 609)	24 (609)	13 (5.9)	1.1 (.10)	0.5-1.0	Fresh water tanks, distributed systems in ground trenches.	Lightweight flexible assembly with continuous cable.
TABB	$2^{21}/_{32} \times 24$ (67 × 609)	24 (609)	18 (8.2)	1.4 (.13)	0.5-1.0	Fresh water tanks, distributed systems in ground trenches.	Lightweight flexible assembly with continuous cable.
TACD	$2^{3}/_{16} \times 60$ (56 × 1524)	60 (1524)	32 (14.5)	2.8 (.26)	2.5-3.0	Fresh water tanks, deep ground beds, or standard ground beds.	Center connection, in series on continuous cable or one lead only.
TAD	$2^{21}/_{32} \times 60$ (67 × 1524)	60 (1524)	45 (20.4)	3.5 (.32)	2.5-3.5	Fresh water tanks, deep ground beds, or standard ground beds.	Center connection, in series on continuous cable or one lead only.
TAE	$4^{3}/_{4} \times 60$ (121 × 1524)	60 (1524)	125 (56.7)	6.2 (.58)	6-8	Severe ground, deep well without backfill or sea water.	Center connection eliminates loss due to "end effect."
TAJA	$4^{3}/_{4} \times 24$ (121 × 609)	24 (609)	31 (14.1)	2.5 (.23)	1.5-2.0	Fresh water tanks, deep ground beds, or standard ground beds.	Center connection, in series on continuous cable or one lead only.
TAJ	$4^{3}/_{4} \times 60$ (121 × 1524)	60 (1524)	78 (35.4)	6.2 (.58)	5.0-6.0	Severe ground, deep well without backfill or sea water.	Center connection and tubular design gives greater surface area.
TAM	$3^{3}/_{4} \times 60$ (95 × 1524)	60 (1524)	60 (27.2)	4.9 (.46)	3.5-5.0	Deep ground beds or standard ground beds.	Center connection, in series on continuous cable or one lead only.
TAG	$2^{21}/_{32} \times 8$ (67 × 203)	8 (203)	6 (2.7)	0.47 (.05)	0.55	Elevated fresh water tank. Underground cables in ducts.	Center connection, in series on continuous cable or one lead only.
TAFW	$2^{3}/_{16} \times 8$ (56 × 203)	8 (203)	4.3 (1.9)	0.38 (.04)	0.40	Elevated fresh water tank.	Lightweight flexible assembly with continuous cable.
TAFWA	$2^{3}/_{16} \times 12$ (56 × 304)	12 (304)	6.5 (2.9)	0.57 (.06)	0.60	Elevated fresh water tank. Underground cables in ducts.	Center connection, in series on continuous cable or one lead only.

Table 8.4   Typical Sizes and Rated Operating Current Data. Solid Mixed Metal Oxide Anodes. (Corrpro Companies Inc.)

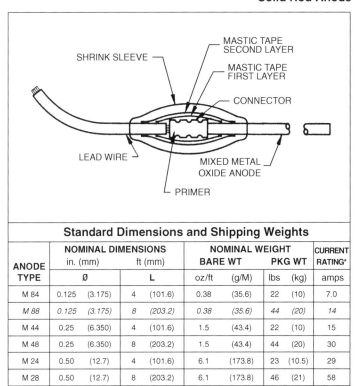

Mixed Metal Oxide
Solid Rod Anode

Standard Dimensions and Shipping Weights

| ANODE TYPE | NOMINAL DIMENSIONS | | | | NOMINAL WEIGHT | | | | CURRENT RATING* |
| | in. (mm) | | ft (mm) | | BARE WT | | PKG WT | | |
	Ø		L		oz/ft	(g/M)	lbs	(kg)	amps
M 84	0.125	(3.175)	4	(101.6)	0.38	(35.6)	22	(10)	7.0
M 88	0.125	(3.175)	8	(203.2)	0.38	(35.6)	44	(20)	14
M 44	0.25	(6.350)	4	(101.6)	1.5	(43.4)	22	(10)	15
M 48	0.25	(6.350)	8	(203.2)	1.5	(43.4)	44	(20)	30
M 24	0.50	(12.7)	4	(101.6)	6.1	(173.8)	23	(10.5)	29
M 28	0.50	(12.7)	8	(203.2)	6.1	(173.8)	46	(21)	58

Based on 15 year design life and XE coating in saltwater

platinum coating thickness. Table 8.6 shows typical chemical composition of platinum anodes.

Typically the anode is composed of a copper core surrounded by a niobium substrate with the platinum metallurgically bonded to the niobium substrate. The consumption of the platinum coating is extremely low (40 to 80 mg/A-year). To achieve the desired design life of the anode the platinum coating thickness can be varied. Typical platinum coating thicknesses are 25, 50 and 100 micro-in. Typical practice for ground bed installation in soils is to specify the anode in a prepackage canister with carbonaceous backfill material. Standard lead wire is 10-ft of No. 8 HMW/PE, however any length and type of cable including Kynar, Halar and PVC can be specified. Platinum anodes can also be configured for use in deep well anode beds.

Table 8.5   Sizes and Rated Operating Current Data Tubular. Mixed Metal Oxide Anodes. (Corrpro Companies Inc.)

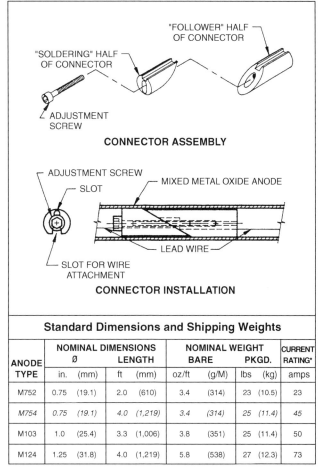

Mixed Metal Oxide
Tubular Anodes

Standard Dimensions and Shipping Weights

ANODE TYPE	NOMINAL DIMENSIONS Ø		LENGTH		NOMINAL WEIGHT BARE		PKGD.		CURRENT RATING*
	in.	(mm)	ft	(mm)	oz/ft	(g/M)	lbs	(kg)	amps
M752	0.75	(19.1)	2.0	(610)	3.4	(314)	23	(10.5)	23
M754	0.75	(19.1)	4.0	(1,219)	3.4	(314)	25	(11.4)	45
M103	1.0	(25.4)	3.3	(1,006)	3.8	(351)	25	(11.4)	50
M124	1.25	(31.8)	4.0	(1,219)	5.8	(538)	27	(12.3)	73

*Based on 15 year design life in saltwater

Table 8.6   Chemical Composition of Platinum Anodes

Element	Content % of Diameter
Copper	79.5
Niobium	19.5
Platinum	Less than 1%

Table 8.7   Chemical Composition of Petroleum and
Metallurgical Coke Backfill

Element	Content %
Petroleum Coke Backfill	
Fixed Carbon	99.77
Ash	0.1
Moisture	0.0
Volatile Matter	0.0
Metallurgical Grade	
Fixed Carbon	85.89
Ash	8–10
Moisture	6–9
Sulfur	0.8
Volatile Matter	0.5

Backfill Materials

The term "carbonaceous backfill" used earlier describes the backfill surrounding ground bed anodes. There are three common materials that fit this description: Coal coke breeze, calcined petroleum coke breeze, and natural or man-made graphite particles. Chemical composition for petroleum coke backfill and metallurgical grade coke backfill are listed in Table 8.7.

All are basically carbon in a low resistivity form. "Breeze" is a loose term indicating a finely divided material. Originally it referred to the fine screenings left over after coal coke was graded for sale as fuel. For backfill purposes, however, specific particle sizes may be obtained.

Carbonaceous backfill serves two purposes when surrounding impressed current anodes:

- To increase the size of the anode to obtain lower resistance to earth and
- To bear the consumption resulting from current discharge.

The latter function requires good electrical contact between the anode and backfill particles. To accomplish this, the backfill must be tamped solidly around the core. Occasionally, subsurface soil conditions may not allow adequate contact pressure, or may relax with time, so that much of the current will discharge directly from anode to electrolyte. This tends to reduce anode life.

Consumption rate of the backfill should not exceed two pounds per ampere per year. In the absence of specific information on the unit weight of the material used, weights may be estimated by using the tabulation in Table 8.8. The suppliers can provide specific information on coke breeze material.

Coke breeze should be procured by specification. Size and resistivity are important. Some users specify, as an example, that maximum particle size shall not exceed 3/8 in.,

Table 8.8 Weights of Carbonaceous Backfill

Material	Lb/Ft^3
Coal coke breeze.	40 to 50
Calcined petroleum coke breeze. . .	45 to 70
Natural graphite particles.	70 to 80
Crushed man-made graphite.	70

that not more than 10% dust shall be included and that resistivity shall not exceed 50 ohm-cm. Petroleum coke must be calcined (heat treated) to remove all other petroleum products; otherwise its resistivity will be too high.

Natural or manufactured graphite both have low resistivity. Although natural graphite is available in flake form, flakes are not desirable for ground bed used where gas must be vented, because the interleaving flakes may block discharge. This applies particularly to deep-well ground beds. Natural graphite may be obtained in granular form (less expensive than flake graphite) and would involve less possibility of gas blocking difficulties.

Deep-well anode ground beds have reported good results when a calcined petroleum coke in the form of rounded granules or beads is used. With material of this type, there will be little interlocking of particles to block passage of gas.

Cable Types

All underground cable, which is a part of an impressed current ground bed, is at a positive potential with respect to ground. If not perfectly insulated, the cable will discharge current and corrode in two, thus cutting off the current from all or part of the ground bed. Thus first quality insulation must be used on all anode leads and ground bed header cables.

Insulation should have at least a 600-V rating and be suitable for direct burial. Wire with a high molecular weight polyethylene (HMW/PE) insulation is widely used for ground bed construction. This has been effective in most cases. Polyethylene may be used with or without a protective jacket. Where chlorine gas may be generated due to ground bed operation or severe chemical environments may be encountered, a protective jacket of KYNAR™ or HALAR™ may be necessary.

Cable should be inspected carefully during installation to be absolutely sure that there are no scars or cuts which may present problems later. Any scars or cuts in the insulation must be encapsulated with a heat shrink sleeve. Select only backfill free of sharp stones or other harmful materials to contact the ground bed cable.

Catalog information on cable suited for ground bed construction is available through manufacturers and through suppliers of CP material.

Selecting cable size has both a practical and an economic aspect. From the practical standpoint, the cable should be large enough to carry the intended current (see the

National Electric Code for tables of current rating) and to withstand mechanical stresses encountered during ground bed construction. Cable smaller than No. 8, for impressed current anode cable is not adequate. Anodes should never be installed by the cable. Similarly, cable that is unusually large may cause handling and connection problems during construction. From the economic standpoint, select a cable size based on a comparison of cable cost with current carrying ability and the cost of power loss from cable resistance when current flows through it.

Connections

Electrical connections between anode leads and header cable are a critical part of impressed current ground bed construction. Anode leads must be connected to the header cable by a method that will have permanently low resistance. The connection, once made, must be insulated so that it will be waterproof to present current leakage and cable corrosion.

Acceptable connection methods for copper wire include soft soldering, powder welding (thermite), hard (silver) soldering, phos-copper brazing, compression (crimp type) couplings, and split-bolt couplings. The first four methods result in complete joining of the metals and have permanent low resistance. Mechanical methods, if used properly, also will give low resistance connections, which will remain low if subsequent joint insulation excludes moisture and air completely so that no corrosion films may form within the joint to introduce resistance. When using joining methods involving the use of a torch, cable insulation adjacent to the connection should be protected against heat damage. Any heat damage should be removed prior to insulating the connection.

Joints should be insulated with materials and methods that will equal, at least, the electrical strength of original cable insulation. The work must be done carefully so that insulation covers all exposed metal and overlaps cable insulation by at least 1 in. Where jacketed cable is used, the jacket should be removed from about the first $\frac{1}{2}$ in. to expose the basic cable insulation, and then the applied joint insulation will adhere to both cable insulation and jacket material.

Acceptable joint insulation includes cast epoxy resin insulation and various tapes. There are several manufacturers of cast joint for CP uses. These materials use a containment mold designed to surround the joint to be coated. Then the mold is filled with a catalyzed resin which sets quickly to form a solid cast around the joint and overlapping wire insulation. Properly made, the poured material fills all crevices of the joint to exclude moisture and air. Such connections are recommended particularly for mechanical joints but are used also with other types. Satisfactory taped joint insulation can be achieved with top quality high voltage rubber splicing compound covering the joint metal and overlapping the wire insulation. This is followed by two half-lapped layers of rubber tape followed by two half-lapped layers of plastic tape. Sharp points or corners should be removed from joints to be taped. If they cannot be rounded sufficiently to prevent tape rupture or puncture, they may be padded with electrical putty. Details of joining and insulating materials may be obtained from the catalogs of CP material suppliers. The splice connections are usually the weakest link in a ground bed installation.

Cathodic Protection with Galvanic Anodes

Ronald L. Bianchetti

Discussion of the common types of galvanic (sacrificial) anode materials including performance characteristics, typical applications, and installation details are outlined below.

TYPES OF GALVANIC ANODES FOR PIPELINE USE

The two galvanic anode metals commonly used for buried pipelines are magnesium and zinc. Appearance of typical anodes is shown in Figures 9.1 and 9.2. Aluminum has a theoretical energy content (in terms of ampere-hours per pound) which exceeds that of magnesium and zinc but so far, aluminum has not proved practical for earth-buried installations because of problems associated with keeping it electrically active with good efficiency characteristics. Aluminum anodes are primarily used for marine applications but this specialized application will not be considered here.

HOW GALVANIC ANODES WORK

The use of galvanic anodes for cathodic protection (CP) is a simple application of the dissimilar metal corrosion cell discussed in Chapter 1. Where a steel pipeline is electrically connected to a metal higher in the electromotive force series and both are in a common conductive electrolyte such as the earth, the more active metal is corroded and discharges current in the process. Magnesium and zinc are such metals. If the amount

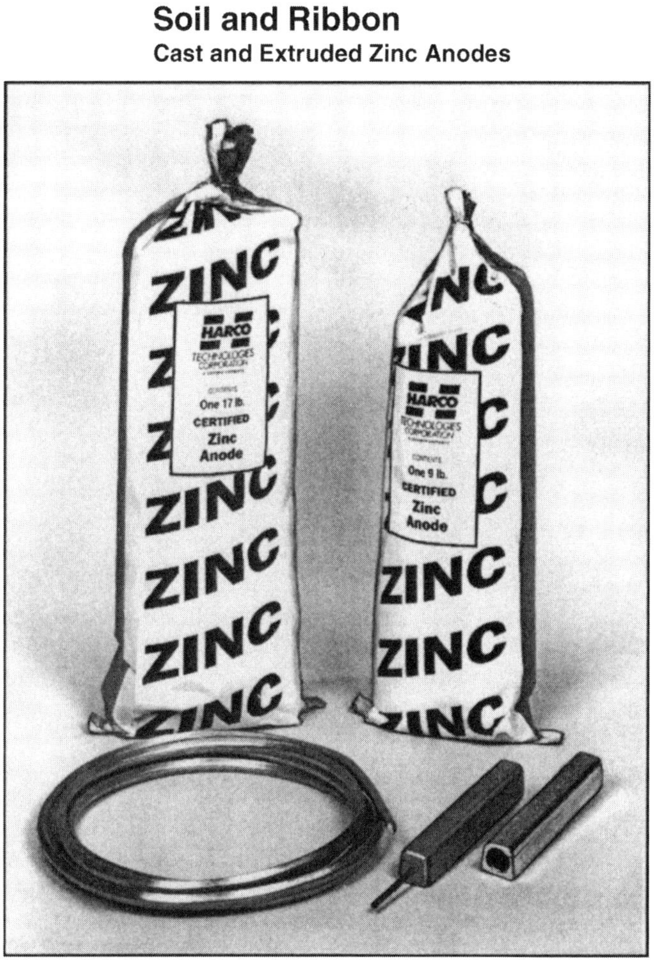
Soil and Ribbon
Cast and Extruded Zinc Anodes
ZINC
HARCO
One 17 lb.
CERTIFIED
Zinc
Anode

Figure 9.1 Typical zinc anodes. (Corrpro Companies Inc.)

of current needed for a given CP application is known, anode systems can be designed using sufficient anode material to produce the desired current output continuously over a desired number of years.

The corrosive nature of the underground environment may cause self-corrosion of the anode material. Electrical currents produced by this self-corrosion do not result in producing CP current. The ratio of metal expended in producing *useful* CP current to total metal expended is termed 'anode efficiency'. This is an important characteristic, which will be discussed in more detail in the following sections.

Cast Magnesium Anodes

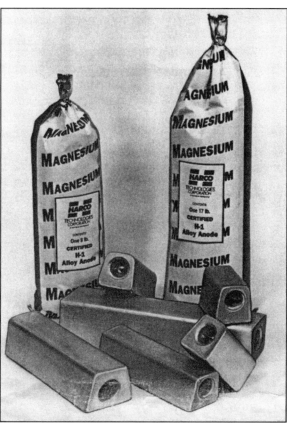

Figure 9.2   Typical magnesium anodes. (Corrpro Companies Inc.)

GALVANIC ANODE APPLICATIONS

For pipeline CP applications, galvanic anodes are generally used in cases where relatively small amounts of current are required (typically less than 1 A) and areas where soil resistivity is low enough (typically less than 10,000 ohm-cm) to permit obtaining the desired current with a reasonable number of anodes. If large amounts of current are needed (typically greater than 1 A) impressed current systems tend to be more economical. If there is a question as to which current source to use, an economic analysis should be undertaken, unless local conditions dictate otherwise. Chapter 15 provides the basis for performing economic analyses.

Short increments of well-coated pipe will have moderate current requirements for protection. These current requirements can be met with galvanic anodes where soil resistivity conditions are suitable.

Some operators follow a practice of installing galvanic anodes at each location where a leak is repaired (hot spot protection) rather than installing a complete CP system. Such practices may be encountered on bare or very poorly coated systems where complete CP may not be feasible from an economic standpoint.

On well-coated pipelines with impressed current CP systems, there may be isolated points where additional current may be needed in relatively small amounts. These requirements can be met with galvanic anodes. Typical applications include poorly or incompletely coated buried valve installations, shorted casings which cannot be cleared, isolated sections where pipeline coating has been badly damaged and areas where electrical shielding may impair effective current distribution from remotely located impressed current systems.

Galvanic anodes may be used in some instances to correct stray current interference conditions at pipeline crossings where the interference arises from impressed current CP systems. This application is discussed further in Chapter 11.

Galvanic anodes (usually zinc) may also be used for electrical grounding applications at pipeline pumping stations and across insulating joints. Zinc anodes as ground rods serve as effective electrical grounds and at the same time provide a measure of CP.

Pipelines may pass through areas where there are many other underground metallic structures under conditions that make it difficult to install impressed current systems without creating stray current interference problems (see Chapter 11). Galvanic anodes may be an economical choice for a CP current source under such conditions.

CHARACTERISTICS OF MAGNESIUM AND ZINC ANODES

Magnesium is the most widely used material for galvanic anodes. Typical characteristics are given in Table 9.1. Magnesium anodes are available in various shapes and weights from the manufacturers. Some of the sizes available, suitable for use in soil, are listed in Table 9.2.

Zinc anodes are available in a number of sizes for use in earth anode beds. Typical characteristics of zinc used as an anode material are given in Table 9.3. These are long slender shapes to achieve low resistances to earth and practical current output at the usual low driving voltage between anode and protected structure. Some sizes available as standard commercial items are shown in Table 9.4. Nonstandard sizes may be obtained on special order.

Packaged magnesium and zinc anodes (anode and backfill furnished as a complete unit ready for installation) are standard with most suppliers.

Table 9.1   Characteristics of Magnesium Anodes

Specific Gravity. 1.94

Pounds per Cubic Foot 121

Theoretical Amp Hours per Pound 1000

Theoretical Pounds per Amp per Year 8.7

Current Efficiency - Percent . . . . .50[2]

Actual Amp Hours per Pound . . . . .500[2]

Actual Pounds per Amp per Year. . . . . .17.4[2]

Solution Potential - Volts to CSE

    Standard H-1 Alloy. . . . .−1.50 to −1.55[3]

    High Potential Alloy. . . . .−1.75 to −1.77[4]

Driving Potential to Pipeline

Polarized to −0.90 Volt to $CuSO_4$

    Standard Alloy - Volts . . . . 0.55[5]

    High Potential Alloy - Volts . . . . 0.80[5]

[1] Anodes installed in suitable chemical backfill.

[2] Current efficiency varies with current density. Efficiency given (which results in actual amp hr per pound and actual pounds per amp per year shown) is at approximately 30 milliamps per sq ft of anode surface. Efficiencies are higher at higher current densities, lower at lower current densities.

[3] Alloy with nominal composition % 6 Al, 3 Zn, 0.2 Mn and balance Mg.

[4] Proprietary alloy–manganese principal alloying element.

[5] Driving potentials allow for anode polarization in service of approximately 0.10 volt which reduces the solution potential by this amount. Driving potential in volts for pipeline polarized to any specific potential (P) in volts = solution potential of magnesium type used minus 0.10 volts minus P.

**STANDARD H-1 ALLOY
CHEMICAL COMPOSITION**

Weight Content %			
Element	**Grade A**	**Grade B**	**Grade C**
Al	5.3 - 6.7	5.3 - 6.7	5.0 - 7.0
Mn	0.15 min	0.15 min	0.15 min
Zn	2.5 - 3.5	2.5 - 3.5	2.0 - 4.0
Si	0.10 max	0.30 max	0.30 max
Cu	0.02 max	0.05 max	0.10 max
Ni	0.002 max	0.003 max	0.003 max
Fe	0.003 max	0.003 max	0.003 max
Other	0.30 max	0.30 max	0.30 max
Magnesium	Remainder	Remainder	Remainder

**HIGH POTENTIAL ALLOY
CHEMICAL COMPOSITION**

Element	**Weight Content %**
Al	0.010
Mn	0.50 to 1.30
Cu	0.02 Max
Ni	0.001 Max
Fe	0.03 Max
Other	0.05 each or 0.3 Max Total
Magnesium	Remainder

Table 9.2   Magnesium Anode Types (Corrpro Companies Inc.)

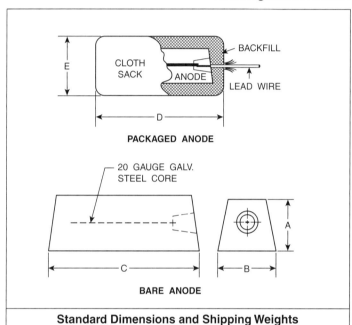

High Potential
Cast Magnesium Anodes

Standard Dimensions and Shipping Weights

ANODE TYPE	NOMINAL DIMENSIONS in (mm)					NOMINAL WT. lbs (kg)	
	"A"	"B"	"C"	"D"	"E"	BARE	PKGD.
3 lb	3 (76)	3 (76)	4.5 (114)	6.5 (165)	6 (152)	3 (1.4)	9 (4.1)
5 lb	3 (76)	3 (76)	7.5 (191)	13.5 (343)	6 (152)	5 (2.3)	14 (6.4)
9 lb	2 (51)	2 (51)	27 (686)	31 (787)	5 (127)	9 (4.1)	36 (16.3)
9 lb	3 (76)	3 (76)	13.5 (343)	17 (432)	6 (152)	9 (4.1)	24 (10.9)
17 lb	2 (51)	2 (51)	51 (1295)	55 (1397)	5 (127)	17 (7.7)	61 (27.7)
17 lb	*3 (76)*	*3 (76)*	*25.5 (648)*	*30 (762)*	*6 (152)*	*17 (7.7)*	*42 (19.1)*
20 lb	2 (51)	2 (51)	60 (1524)	62.5 (1588)	5 (127)	20 (9.1)	70 (31.8)
32 lb	3 (76)	3 (76)	45 (1143)	61 (1549)	6 (152)	32 (14.5)	90 (40.8)
32 lb	5 (127)	5 (127)	21 (533)	30 (762)	8 (203)	32 (14.5)	70 (31.8)
40 lb	3 (76)	3 (76)	60 (1524)	64 (1626)	6 (152)	40 (18.1)	105 (47.6)
48 lb	5 (127)	5 (127)	31 (787)	34 (864)	8 (203)	48 (21.8)	96 (43.6)
60 lb	4 (102)	4 (102)	60 (1524)	64 (1626)	6.75 (171)	60 (27.2)	130 (59.0)

Table 9.2 (*Continued*)

H-1 Alloy
Cast Magnesium Anodes

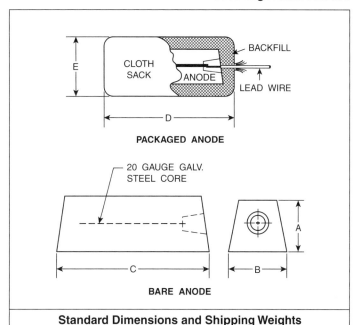

PACKAGED ANODE

BARE ANODE

Standard Dimensions and Shipping Weights

ANODE TYPE	NOMINAL DIMENSIONS in (mm)					NOMINAL WT. lbs (kg)	
	"A"	"B"	"C"	"D"	"E"	BARE	PKGD.
1 lb	2.9 (74)	–	3 (76)	6 (152)	6 (152)	1 (0.45)	3.5 (1.6)
3 lb	3 (76)	3 (76)	4.5 (114)	6.5 (165)	6 (152)	3 (1.4)	9 (4.1)
5 lb	3 (76)	3 (76)	7.5 (191)	13.5 (343)	6 (152)	5 (2.3)	14 (6.4)
9 lb	3 (76)	3 (76)	13.5 (343)	17 (432)	6 (152)	9 (4.1)	24 (10.9)
17 lb	*4 (102)*	*4 (102)*	*17 (432)*	*19 (483)*	*6.5 (165)*	*17 (7.7)*	*42 (19.1)*
32 lb	5 (127)	5 (127)	21 (533)	30 (762)	8 (203)	32 (14.5)	70 (31.8)
50 lb	8 (203)	–	15 (381)	18 (457)	10 (254)	50 (22.7)	110 (49.9)

Table 9.3   Characteristics of Zinc Anodes

Specific Gravity	7
Pounds per Cubic Foot	440
Theoretical Amp Hours per Pound	372[2]
Theoretical Pounds per Amp per Year	23.5
Current Efficiency - Percent	90[3]
Actual Amp Hours per Pound	335
Actual Pounds per Amp per Year	26
Solution Potential - Volts to CSE	−1.1
Driving Potential to Pipeline Polarized to −0.90 Volt to $CuSO_4$	0.2[4]

[1] Anodes installed in suitable chemical backfill.

[2] Zinc used for soil anodes should be high purity zinc such as "Special High Grade" classification which is at least 99.99 percent pure zinc.

[3] Current efficiency of zinc is reasonably constant from low to very high current outputs in terms of milliamperes per sq ft of anode surface. This applies when the high purity anode grade zinc is used. The 90 percent efficiency is conservative.

[4] Zinc not subject to significant anodic polarization when used in suitable backfill. Driving potential is zinc solution potential minus polarized potential of protected structure.

CHEMICAL COMPOSITION

Element	Weight Content %	
	MIL-A-18001 (ASTM B-418 Type I)	ASTM B-418 Type II
Al	0.1 - 0.5	0.005 max
Cd	0.02 - 0.07	0.003 max
Fe	0.005 max	0.0014 max
Pb	0.006 max	0.003 max
Cu	0.005 max	0.002 max
Zinc	Remainder	Remainder

ANODE BACKFILL

For reliable operation in earth installations, both zinc and magnesium anodes are used with a chemical backfill to surround the anode completely. There are several reasons for using chemical backfill. Typical data on chemical backfill are shown in Table 9.5.

With the anode surrounded with a uniform material of known composition, anode current is more efficient. If the soil contacts the anode directly, variations in soil composition can set up local corrosion on the anode resulting in nonuniform consumption of the anode.

By isolating the anode material from the native soil, the backfill material greatly reduces the possibility of adverse effect on anode performance. In the presence of

Table 9.4 Zinc Anode Types

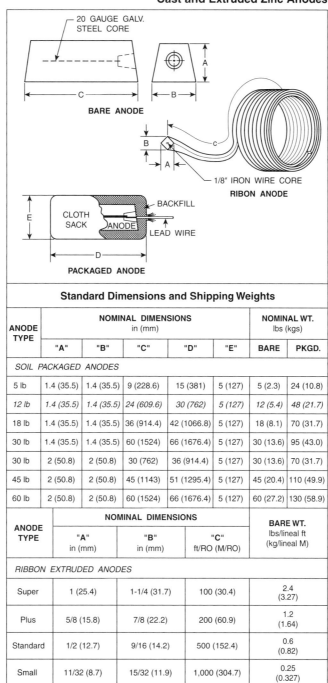

Soil and Ribbon
Cast and Extruded Zinc Anodes

20 GAUGE GALV. STEEL CORE

BARE ANODE

A

B

C

1/8" IRON WIRE CORE

RIBON ANODE

CLOTH SACK

ANODE

BACKFILL

LEAD WIRE

E

D

PACKAGED ANODE

Standard Dimensions and Shipping Weights

ANODE TYPE	NOMINAL DIMENSIONS in (mm)					NOMINAL WT. lbs (kgs)	
	"A"	"B"	"C"	"D"	"E"	BARE	PKGD.
SOIL PACKAGED ANODES							
5 lb	1.4 (35.5)	1.4 (35.5)	9 (228.6)	15 (381)	5 (127)	5 (2.3)	24 (10.8)
12 lb	*1.4 (35.5)*	*1.4 (35.5)*	*24 (609.6)*	*30 (762)*	*5 (127)*	*12 (5.4)*	*48 (21.7)*
18 lb	1.4 (35.5)	1.4 (35.5)	36 (914.4)	42 (1066.8)	5 (127)	18 (8.1)	70 (31.7)
30 lb	1.4 (35.5)	1.4 (35.5)	60 (1524)	66 (1676.4)	5 (127)	30 (13.6)	95 (43.0)
30 lb	2 (50.8)	2 (50.8)	30 (762)	36 (914.4)	5 (127)	30 (13.6)	70 (31.7)
45 lb	2 (50.8)	2 (50.8)	45 (1143)	51 (1295.4)	5 (127)	45 (20.4)	110 (49.9)
60 lb	2 (50.8)	2 (50.8)	60 (1524)	66 (1676.4)	5 (127)	60 (27.2)	130 (58.9)

ANODE TYPE	NOMINAL DIMENSIONS			BARE WT. lbs/lineal ft (kg/lineal M)
	"A" in (mm)	"B" in (mm)	"C" ft/RO (M/RO)	
RIBBON EXTRUDED ANODES				
Super	1 (25.4)	1-1/4 (31.7)	100 (30.4)	2.4 (3.27)
Plus	5/8 (15.8)	7/8 (22.2)	200 (60.9)	1.2 (1.64)
Standard	1/2 (12.7)	9/16 (14.2)	500 (152.4)	0.6 (0.82)
Small	11/32 (8.7)	15/32 (11.9)	1,000 (304.7)	0.25 (0.327)

* The Standard anode model is also available in 1000 and 3600 foot rolls.

Table 9.5   Backfill data for Magnesium and Zinc Anodes

	Gypsum (CaSO$_4$)%		Bentonite Clay %	Sodium Sulfate %	Approx Resistivity in ohm-cm
	Hydrated	Molding Plaster (Plaster of Paris)			
(A)	50	–	50	–	250
(B)	75	–	20	5	50

1. Backfill mix (A) commonly used with zinc anodes.
2. Backfill mix (B), with low resistivity, is useful in high soil resistivity areas to reduce the anode resistance to earth.

phosphates, carbonates and bicarbonates, zinc anodes can develop passive films and cease to produce useful amounts of current. Carbonates and bicarbonates will influence magnesium the same way. Chlorides tend to increase self-corrosion of magnesium and reduce its current efficiency.

Chemical backfills can be helpful in absorbing soil moisture to keep the environment immediately surrounding the anode continuously moist. Anode backfill is of low resistivity and when anodes are installed in soils having a resistivity higher than that of the backfill, the backfill column has the effect of increasing the anode size. This results in a lower resistance to remote earth than would be the case if the bare anode were buried directly in the soil. This effect is discussed in Chapter 7.

CALCULATING ANODE LIFE

If current output of a galvanic anode of any given weight is known, its approximate useful life can be calculated. This calculation is based on the theoretical ampere-hour per pound of the anode material, its current efficiency, and a utilization factor. The utilization factor may be taken as 85%—meaning that when the anode is 85% consumed, it will require replacement because there is insufficient anode material remaining to maintain a reasonable percentage of its original current output.

For magnesium, anode life may be determined by the following expression (efficiency and utilization factor expressed as decimals).

Magnesium Anode

$$\text{Life (years)} = \frac{0.116 \times \text{Anode Weight (pounds)} \times \text{Efficiency} \times \text{Utilization Factor}}{\text{Design Current (amperes)}}.$$

For zinc anodes, anode life may be determined in similar manner by the following expression:

Zinc Anode

$$\text{Life (years)} = \frac{0.0424 \times \text{Anode Weight (pounds)} \times \text{Efficiency} \times \text{Utilization Factor}}{\text{Design Current (amperes)}}.$$

As an example, assume that a 32-lb magnesium anode is producing 0.1 A at 50% efficiency and that a 30-lb zinc anode is producing 0.1 A at 90% efficiency. Compare the expected operating lives at the 0.1 A output.

$$\text{Magnesium Anode Life (years)} = \frac{0.116 \times 32 \times 0.50 \times 0.85}{0.1} = 15.8 \text{ yr,}$$

$$\text{Zinc Anode Life (years)} = \frac{0.0424 \times 30 \times 0.90 \times 0.85}{0.1} = 9.7 \text{ yr.}$$

These calculations reflect the difference in theoretical ampere hours per pound characteristic of the two materials. Although anode costs may fluctuate with the metal market, zinc is typically less expensive than magnesium. Graphical design information has been developed for typical anode types. An example is shown in Figure 9.3.

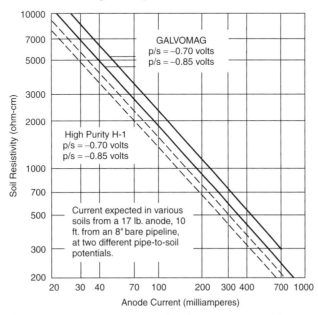

**Current Output of GALVOMAG®
and High Purity H-1 Anodes.**

Figure 9.3 Magnesium anode design curves. (Corrpro Companies Inc.)

DESIGN CONSIDERATIONS

To provide a better understanding of the differences in performance between zinc and magnesium installations it may be helpful to first identify typical types of installation practices. A general rule-of-thumb says that zinc anodes are better used in the lower soil resistivity (below 1500 ohm-cm) and magnesium anodes are better in the higher resistivity soils (between 1500 and 10,000 ohm-cm). This rule is not universal and will depend on the application. This will be illustrated by the examples presented below.

Well-coated pipeline sections typically have low current requirements and will polarize easily to a volt or more. Either zinc or magnesium anodes may provide sufficient current for full protection, but zinc anodes may provide full protection with much less current being wasted. This is illustrated in the following example.

Assume a well-coated section of pipeline having a native or static potential to a copper sulfate reference electrode (CSE) of −0.7 V, an effective resistance-to-earth of 2 ohm at the anode installation site and that 75 mA is necessary to shift the pipeline potential to −0.85 V. Also assume that the soil resistivity at the anode installation site is 1500 ohm-cm.

The installation circuit resistance needed to raise the potential to −0.85 V using zinc anodes is calculated by determining the driving voltage (1.1 V − 0.85 V) or 0.25 V and dividing it by the current requirement. This calculation is performed using Ohm's Law, 0.25 V/0.075 A = 3.3 ohms. The calculated 3.3 ohms minus the effective resistance of the pipeline, estimated at 2 ohms, leaves 1.3 ohms for the resistance of anodes and lead wires. Following the procedures outlined in Chapter 7, it can be calculated that five 1.4 × 1.4 × 60-in zinc anodes (30 lb) surrounded with 50–50 gypsum-bentonite backfill in 8-in diameter holes at 15-ft spacing will have a resistance of 1.21 ohms in the 1500 ohm-cm soil. With 0.03 ohms allowed for lead wire resistance, total resistance is 1.24 ohms which is within the 1.3-ohm design allowance.

The same procedure can be derived for magnesium anodes. The magnesium installation circuit resistance needed to provide the initial 75 mA requirement will be the driving potential (1.55 − 0.85 = 0.70 V) divided by the estimated current requirement of 75 mA, equals 9.33 ohms. Subtracting the 2-ohm pipeline resistance leaves 7.33 ohms for anode-to-earth resistance and lead wire resistance. Using Chapter 7 anode bed resistance procedures, one 2 × 2 × 60-in magnesium anode (20 lb each) with 75% gypsum, 20% bentonite, 5% sodium sulfate backfill in 8-in diameter hole will give 4.80 ohms anode-to-earth resistance in the 1500 ohm-cm soil with 0.01 ohm allowed for lead wire resistance. This totals 4.81 ohms, which is within the 7.33-ohm requirement.

As shown in the previous example, the zinc anode installation number of anodes is much larger. This is not, however, the complete analysis. In most cases, a well-coated pipeline will continue to polarize after initial requirements are met. The pipeline in the zinc anode example may polarize to a potential approaching the −1.1 V open circuit potential of zinc. This will result in the reduced current demand.

Assume a polarized potential of −1.05 volt. The zinc anodes will now have a driving potential of only 0.05 V (1.1 − 1.05 V) and the current output will be 0.05-V/3.24-ohms circuit resistance = 0.0154 A. The magnesium anodes will have a driving potential of 0.35 V (1.55 − 1.2 V) and the current output will be 0.35 V/6.81-ohms circuit resistance = 0.0513 A. These final or stabilized currents can be used to determine the useful lives of the two installations.

The five, 30-lb zinc anodes will have calculated life as follows.

$$\text{Zinc Anode Life (years)} = \frac{0.0424 \times 5(30) \times 0.90 \times 0.85}{0.0154} = 315 \text{ yr.}$$

The single 20-lb magnesium anode will have a calculated life as follows:

$$\text{Magnesium Anode Life (years)} = \frac{0.116 \times 20 \times 0.50 \times 0.85}{0.0513} = 19.2 \text{ yr.}$$

The new calculated design life for each anode is at the efficiencies shown in the formula (90% for zinc, 50% for magnesium). At very low current densities, efficiencies will decrease and actual lives would be less than indicated. This is particularly true for magnesium anodes.

To evaluate these two installations in terms of cost per year of estimated life, the installed cost must be known. Zinc is less expensive than magnesium. Assuming a conservatively high material and installation cost per anode, the five zinc anodes could cost $250 per anode to install or $1,250. The one magnesium anode with installation on the same basis could cost $350. The indicated cost per year for the zinc installation would be $1,250/315 years = $3.96 per year. Similarly, the indicated cost per year for the magnesium installation would be $350/19.2 years = $18.22 per year.

It may appear that the indicated life of 315 years for the zinc installation is beyond reasonable expectations when the usual design life of a pipeline is 20–50 yr. If the cost per year is based on a 20-yr pipeline life, the zinc anode installation cost per year would be $62.50 (although not consumed at the end of this period) while the magnesium cost per year remains at approximately $18. This analysis favors magnesium if the estimated protection current requirements do not change.

If current requirements increase (see the following discussion on regulation), the original zinc installation can continue to provide adequate protection, whereas replacement of the magnesium anode would be required in less than 20 yr. The magnesium anode replacement would require more anodes than were used originally in order to maintain adequate protection. This will bring the cost per year to roughly equivalent figures for zinc and magnesium for the example used in the 1500 ohm-cm soil. Chapter 15 provides more detailed analysis of life cycle cost.

The previous illustration indicates that on a long-term basis, zinc anode installations can be less expensive than magnesium when calculated on a simple cost per year basis. In the example, it was shown that one magnesium anode discharged more than twice as much current as the five zinc anodes. This offers no advantage because zinc fully protects the line while excess current from magnesium is wasted.

Inserting resistance in series in the circuit can control the wasted current from magnesium. In the previous example, current wastage can be eliminated if sufficient resistance could be inserted in series with the magnesium anode to reduce its output to the point that the pipeline would remain protected. That current level would be the same as that obtained from the zinc anode (0.030 A). The driving potential would now be $1.55 - 1.05 = 0.4$ V. Circuit resistance would be 0.4 V/0.030 A = 13 ohms. This value of 13 ohms minus the circuit resistance of the magnesium anode alone, 6.81 ohms (from the example above), leaves 6.52 ohms resistance to be inserted in the circuit. By reducing the current, the magnesium anode indicated life is increased to 33 yr, reducing the cost per year of life to $10.60, which is more in line with the zinc installation. This is further discussed below.

ANODE PERFORMANCE

System Regulation

Regulation as applied to galvanic anode installations is a measure of an installations' ability to adjust output automatically to compensate for changes in the current requirements of the pipeline to which it is attached. In the previous example which compares zinc and magnesium, the assumed pipeline section had an excellent coating, so very little current was required to maintain protection. However, current requirements may increase with time due to coating deterioration, addition of more pipe, or development of a short circuit to another foreign pipeline.

Assuming that this has occurred, the effective resistance of the pipeline to earth at the anode installation site drops from the original 2 ohms to 0.5 ohms. Also assume the minimum current required to maintain a polarized potential of -0.85 V has increased to 130 mA from the original 75 mA. Using figures from the preceding example:

Zinc installation

- Driving potential $= 1.1 - .85 = 0.25$ V
- New circuit resistance $= 1.74$
- Current $= 0.25/1.74 = 0.144$ A (144 mA)
- Indicated life at 144 mA output $= 33.6$ yr

Magnesium installation without current reducing resistor

- Driving potential $= 1.55 - .85 = 0.70$ V
- New circuit resistance $= 5.31$ ohm
- Current $= 0.7/5.31 = 0.188$ A (188 mA)
- Indicated life at 188 mA output $= 8.4$ yr

Magnesium installation with current reducing resistor

- Driving potential = 0.70 V
- New circuit resistance = 24.5 ohms
- Current = 0.7/24.5 = 0.0285 A (28.5 mA)
- Indicated life at 28.5 mA output = 55 yr

In this example, the zinc installation has a greater capability of providing current than the minimum required, indicating that the line will polarize to some value above the −0.85 V minimum protection value and that consequently there will be a better distribution of full protective potentials along the line. The magnesium installation without resistor (which originally discharged more than twice as much current as the zinc and was wasting current) now does not discharge quite enough current to maintain the minimum −0.85 V. The line will assume a potential of something less than −0.85 V. The magnesium installation with a current controlling resistor obviously does not discharge enough current. The size of the resistor would need to be reduced below the calculated 6.5 ohms value from above or the resistor would have to be removed to achieve any substantial degree of protection. This would then reduce the design life of the magnesium anode.

Variations in Soil Resistivity

The relative effect of soil resistivity on anode performance is discussed below. Calculations for zinc and magnesium anodes in soils ranging from low to high resistivity are summarized in Table 9.6. The conditions applicable to Table 9.6 are the same as for the preceding example based on an installation in 1500 ohm-cm soil (the 1500 ohm-cm figures summarize those developed in the example). Specifically, assumptions are the following.

1. That the pipeline section being protected is well coated and that it has an effective resistance to earth of 2 ohms.
2. That 75 mA are required initially to polarize the pipeline to −0.85 V to copper sulfate.
3. That once CP current is applied, the line will continue to polarize to −1.05 V CSE when protected with zinc and to −1.2 V when protected with magnesium.

Anodes of similar sizes were used for both magnesium and zinc for purposes of this comparison. If more than one anode was required, the anode bed resistance was calculated on the basis of 15-ft spacing between anodes.

Although the use of different anode sizes would alter the current output and indicated life, the table does illustrate certain tendencies. These are the following.

1. That zinc anode installations of the smallest size that will meet design current requirements have a substantially longer life than their magnesium anode counterparts.

Table 9.6   Comparison of Zinc and Magnesium Anodes in Varying Resistivities

Soil Resistivity in ohm-cm	Anode Type	Driving Potential in volts with Pipeline Polarized to −0.85 V	Maximum Permissible Circuit Resistance in ohms, for 75 mA	Max Permissible Resistance of Anodes and Leads, in ohms, with 2 ohms Pipe-to-Earth Resistance	Number, Size (in Inches) and Weight (Each) of Anodes Selected	Resistance of Anode Array Selected in ohms	Actual Total Circuit Resistance in ohms	Actual Current in mA with Pipeline Polarized to −1.05 V with zinc or to −1.20 V with Mg	Indicated Anode Life in Years	Max Current, mA, with Pipe-to-Earth Resistance Dropped to 0.50 ohm and with −0.85 V Polarized	Regulation as Ratio of Maximum Current to that Under Initial Conditions	Indicated Anode Life in Years Under Maximum Current Conditions
300	Mag	0.6	8.0	6.0	One 3×3×60 40-Pound	1.44	3.44	72.8	27.2	403	5.55	4.9
	Zinc	0.25	3.3	1.3	Two 1.4×1.4×60 30-Pound	0.76	2.76	18.1	107	198	11.0	9.8
500	Mag	0.6	8.0	6.0	One 3×3×60 40-Pound	2.0	4.0	62.5	31.5	240	3.85	8.2
	Zinc	0.25	3.3	1.3	Two 1.4×1.4×60 30-Pound	1.07	3.07	16.2	120	159.5	9.85	12.2
1500	Mag	0.6	8.0	6.0	One 2×2×60 20-Pound	4.81	6.81	36.6	26.9	113	3.08	8.7
	Zinc	0.25	3.3	1.3	Five 1.4×1.4×60 30-Pound	1.24	3.24	15.4	315	144	9.35	33.6
3000	Mag	0.6	8.0	6.0	Two 2×2×60 20-Pound	4.86	6.86	36.4	55.2	112	3.08	17.6
	Zinc	0.25	3.3	1.3	Eleven 1.4×1.4×60 30-Pound	1.3	3.3	15.2	745	139	9.15	83

2. That as soil resistivity increases, the ratio of number of zinc anodes to the number of magnesium anodes increases. This increases installation costs for zinc at a greater rate than for magnesium.

3. That magnesium anode current outputs are consistently higher than the output of the zinc anodes under design conditions. This represents wasted current from the magnesium anodes because fully adequate protection is obtained from zinc at its lower current output.

4. That if the current demands of the pipeline increase, the magnesium anodes in low resistivity soil will continue to deliver higher currents than zinc anodes. Under lower soil resistivity conditions, more magnesium anode material (using anodes of the size shown) would be needed to obtain equivalent life than would be needed using zinc.

5. That if the current demands of the pipeline increase, zinc anode installations in the higher resistivity soils have a higher current delivery capability than the magnesium installations.

6. That the gains by regulation of zinc installations are consistently better than those from magnesium and that the ratio of the two increases as soil resistivity increases. This characteristic is related closely to observations 4 and 5.

The conclusions that can be reached from the foregoing examples and comparisons include the following.

1. That installations may be designed using either zinc or magnesium over a wide range of soil resistivities.

2. That from an economic standpoint, zinc is most attractive in lower resistivity soils. Using it in soils below 1500 ohm-cm resistivity is a reasonable guide in this respect.

3. That zinc anodes in soils of any resistivity offer the best self-regulating characteristics in terms of continuing to provide sufficient current for adequate protection without excessive current wastage.

GALVANIC ANODE INSTALLATION DETAILS

Galvanic anode installations are simple compared to the usual impressed current installation. The simplest installation is that involving the burying of a single packaged anode at a leak repair location or for distributed anode installations along a pipeline. This is shown by Figure 9.4.

The popular 17-lb, 20-lb, or 32-lb packaged magnesium anodes are used most commonly for this type of application, although packaged zinc anodes may be used in low resistivity soils and heavier packaged magnesium anodes may be used, where conditions warrant, for longer life.

Where several magnesium or zinc anodes are to be installed at a single location, usually on a coated pipeline, the anodes may be connected to a header wire. The header wire should be brought to a test point to permit monitoring, and periodic measurement of output current, for calculation of anode life. This is illustrated by Figure 9.5.

Anodes in a multiple anode bed should be placed in straight line configuration for lowest resistance to earth. The line of anodes may be perpendicular to the pipeline, as shown in the figure, or may be along a line parallel to the pipe. The latter arrangement makes it possible, in many cases, to install a large galvanic anode bed without having to go beyond the limits of the pipeline right-of-way. A parallel line of magnesium anodes

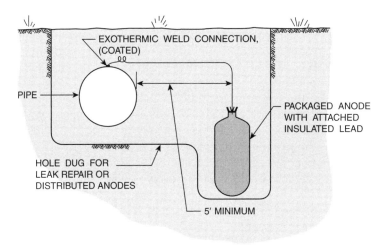

Figure 9.4 Single package anode installation.

should be at least 15 ft away from the pipeline. With zinc, this distance may be reduced to 5 ft or even closer, if little space is available, without affecting significantly the current distribution characteristics of the bed used with coated pipe. Where space is available, however, it is best to allow at least 10 ft between the pipeline and the line of zinc anodes for optimum performance.

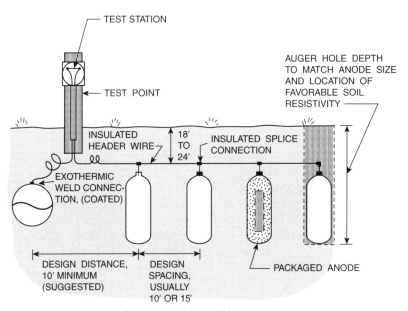

Figure 9.5 Multiple galvanic anode installation.

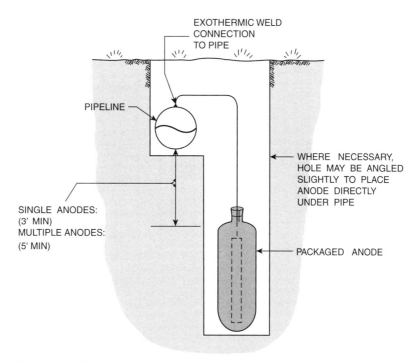

Figure 9.6   Galvanic anode below pipe installation.

Where soil resistivities and augering conditions permit and where space limitations are extremely critical, as may be true in distribution systems, anodes may be placed in auger holes alongside the pipe with the hole being deep enough that reasonable spacing between pipe and anode is obtained. This is illustrated by Figure 9.6.

In this type of installation, very deep auger holes would be required to place multiple anodes as far below the pipe as given above for anodes at lateral distances parallel to the pipe. The recommended depth is shown in the figure. These are justified by the fact that with the anodes deeper in the mass of the earth (and where soil resistivities are favorable) potential gradient effects at the pipeline may be less severe than with anodes closer to the surface and at comparable lateral distances from the pipe. Further advantages of this type of installation are that the anodes, being placed deep, are less subject to seasonal current output variation associated with soil moisture content and there is less connecting wire located where it may be damaged by excavations made for other purposes.

The preceding three illustrations concerned the use of packaged anodes where each anode and its associated backfill material are installed as a single unit. Either zinc or magnesium anodes are available unpackaged. They should, nevertheless, be used with prepared backfill in the usual buried installation. Anodes and backfill may be installed in auger holes as shown in Figure 9.7.

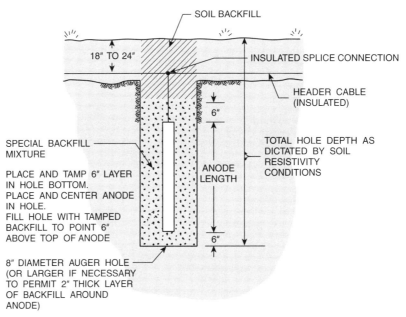

Figure 9.7   Unpackaged galvanic anode installation.

Anodes and backfill installed separately are used more often for multiple anode installations than for single anode installations. The advantage of this type of installation is that the backfill, being installed separately and tamped in place, fills completely all the voids in the auger hole. This minimizes the possibility of the backfill settling away from the anodes and reducing the anodes long-term effectiveness. This possibility is greater when packaged anodes are used because when the backfill container deteriorates, the backfill will settle into voids that may unknowingly have been left around or below the package.

When calculating backfill material requirements, a figure of 70 lbs of backfill material may be used for each cubic foot of space to be filled. This is done by calculating the total volume of the auger hole to be filled with backfill, and then subtracting the volume of the anode. Magnesium anode volume is the anode weight divided by 121 while zinc anode volume is the anode weight divided by 440. A word of caution in calculating hole volume—for example, an 8-in auger, hole will be actually somewhat oversize when completed. An additional 0.5 or 1 in diameter can result in a substantial increase in backfill volume.

As was the case with anodes for impressed current anode beds, galvanic anodes may be installed horizontally where soil resistivity requires it for most effective performance. Either packaged anodes or separate anodes and backfill may be so installed. When placing horizontal packaged anodes in a trench, care must be taken when backfilling to be sure that the earth surrounds the package completely so that no voids exist. Native

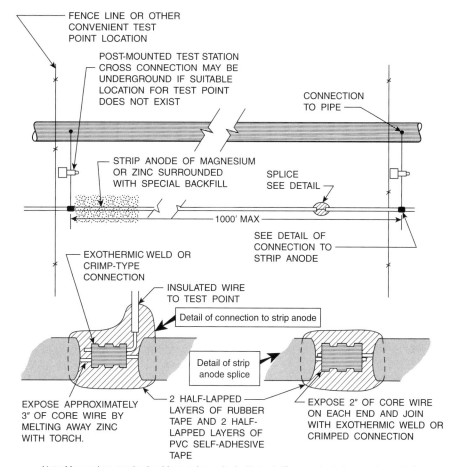

FENCE LINE OR OTHER
CONVENIENT TEST
POINT LOCATION

POST-MOUNTED TEST STATION
CROSS CONNECTION MAY BE
UNDERGROUND IF SUITABLE
LOCATION FOR TEST POINT
DOES NOT EXIST

CONNECTION
TO PIPE

STRIP ANODE OF MAGNESIUM
OR ZINC SURROUNDED
WITH SPECIAL BACKFILL

SPLICE
SEE DETAIL

1000' MAX

SEE DETAIL OF
CONNECTION TO
STRIP ANODE

EXOTHERMIC WELD OR
CRIMP-TYPE
CONNECTION

INSULATED WIRE
TO TEST POINT

Detail of connection to strip anode

Detail of strip
anode splice

EXPOSE APPROXIMATELY
3″ OF CORE WIRE BY
MELTING AWAY ZINC
WITH TORCH.

2 HALF-LAPPED
LAYERS OF RUBBER
TAPE AND 2 HALF-
LAPPED LAYERS OF
PVC SELF-ADHESIVE
TAPE

EXPOSE 2″ OF CORE WIRE
ON EACH END AND JOIN
WITH EXOTHERMIC WELD OR
CRIMPED CONNECTION

Note: Magnesium anode should *never* be melted with torch. Expose steel wire core by carefully
cutting magnesium with knife or sharp object.

Figure 9.8   Continuous galvanic anode installation.

earth then may be used to complete the trench backfill (after making all anode lead connections and insulating them).

In some applications, long strip (ribbon) anodes of either magnesium or zinc may be plowed in parallel to the pipeline along sections of bare or poorly coated line where continuous local protection is required. General features of a strip anode installation are shown by Figure 9.8.

The steel wire core of strip anodes provides continuous longitudinal electrical conductivity even after the anode material is consumed completely in some areas (it will be used up first, in the lower soil resistivity sections). Connections between the pipeline and anode core wire should be made at intervals to complete the protection circuit. If these cross connections can be made at test points located at fence lines or other convenient location, it will be possible to measure current flow periodically and estimate the rate of anode material consumption. Intervals between cross connections should not be too great because there will be some voltage drop in the strip anode, with this voltage drop increasing with time as the strip cross-sectional area is reduced as active material is consumed. Although this effect will vary depending on the soil resistivity and total current being carried by the strip anode, it is suggested that the interval not exceed 1000 ft.

Spacing between the strip anode and pipeline is not critical. To remain clear of the pipe during plowing-in operations, a spacing of at least 5 ft from the near edge of the pipe may be used. The anode strip should be deep enough to be used in continuously moist soil. No less than 2 ft is suggested and greater depths will be necessary in areas where soils are subject to deep drying out during dry periods.

Strip anodes of magnesium or zinc are furnished bare. Using such anodes in earth without a special backfill involves risk of anode passivation and inadequate amounts of current. For most reliable results, the strip anode should be plowed in with suitable special backfill. An adequate allowance, assuming satisfactory dispersion around the anode, is 70 lbs of backfill per 100 ft of strip.

Strip anodes may be used favorably in areas where soil conditions permit the use of tractor-drawn plows fitted to carry trail reels of anode strip and a backfill supply. Rocky or very rough terrain may preclude the use of this type of anode as opening a continuous ditch in the conventional manner would, in most instances, be too costly.

Test points for multiple anode locations may be installed as shown in Figure 9.9.

The shunt in the test point terminal box makes it possible to measure the current from the anodes (using a millivoltmeter as shown) without disturbing the circuit. The common 0.01 ohm shunt does not have enough resistance to have a substantial effect on the anode current output in most cases. If a solid link is used instead of the shunt, however, good practice is to use an ammeter circuit for measuring the anode current or a clamp-on ammeter as discussed in Chapter 6. The separate test wire from the pipeline, as shown in the figure, makes it possible to measure accurately the pipeline potential to a copper sulfate reference electrode. Pipe and anode leads for multiple anode installations may, typically, be No. 8 AWG copper wire with insulation suitable for direct burial insulation. The separate potential test wire should not be smaller than No. 12 AWG insulated wire.

With galvanic anode installations, all wire connected to the anode tends to be protected. This means that if any copper is exposed, it will not tend to corrode and cause severing of the wire as will happen if there is any break in the insulation in wires connected to the positive terminal of the DC power source in an impressed current CP system. Because of this, insulation of underground connections on galvanic anode installation is not as critical but should nevertheless be well done to prevent current loss. Also, if anything other than brazed, soldered or welded connections are used (such as crimp or compression connections), the connection should be waterproofed completely to prevent possible development of resistance within the joint. Probably the most important

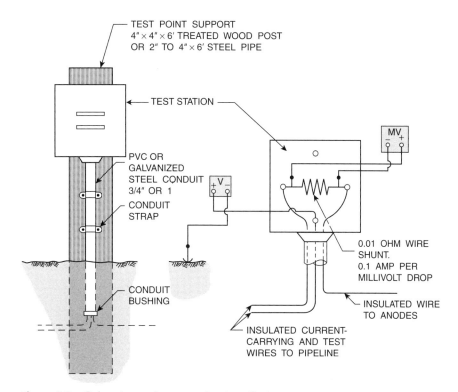

Figure 9.9   Galvanic anode test station installation.

connection in a galvanic anode system from an insulation standpoint is the connection between the pipeline and the copper anode lead. The strong dissimilar metal corrosion cell between steel and copper needs to be thoroughly and permanently waterproofed to prevent any possibility of pipe corrosion immediately adjacent to the connection where the corrosion cell may not be overcome completely by the applied CP. This can occur particularly when bare copper wire lies closely parallel to bare steel such that the wire acts as an electrical shield and prevents protective current from reaching the steel.

When galvanic anode installations are first set up, they may not attain maximum current output for some time. This is because the dry backfill mixture may take up moisture slowly from the surrounding soil. Unless the surrounding soil is very wet, it may be several days or even weeks before maximum output is attained. If dry soil conditions prevail, wetting the soil above the anode after installation will help. The obvious solution of mixing the backfill with water before installation is not necessarily a good one because shrinkage may result, with possible development of voids when excess water leaves the backfill. On the other hand, well-tamped dry backfill tends to expand upon taking up moisture from the surrounding soil, thus ensuring intimate contact throughout the backfill column.

Chapter **10**

Cathodic Protection with Other Power Sources

John A. Beavers

Although most impressed current cathodic protection (CP) systems use AC power supplied by utilities in conjunction with rectifiers as a source of DC current, there are several other power sources that may be used if AC power lines are not available. Some of these have been in use for some time; others are relatively new; and still others are in the development stage. Many of these alternative power sources are expensive; therefore, the corrosion engineer must make certain that the same degree of protection cannot be obtained at less cost by other means such as by galvanic anodes.

ENGINE-GENERATORS

Engine-generator sets may be used to provide the electrical energy for CP rectifiers if a large power source is needed and AC power lines are not available. Gas from the pipeline may be used to power the engine for a CP system on a natural gas pipeline. If the line carries a petroleum product suitable for engine fuel, this may be taken directly from the line as well. Otherwise, fuel must be brought to the generator station periodically.

Present practice is to use an engine coupled with an AC generator (alternator). The power from the alternator is fed to a conventional rectifier that supplies the direct current energy required for the CP installation, as shown in Figure 10.1. The DC power output from the rectifier is used in the conventional manner to supply current to ground beds (surface or deep well) as discussed in Chapter 7.

The reasons for using an alternator and conventional rectifier rather than generating direct current are the following:

1. The alternator requires less maintenance on its slip rings than a DC generator requires with its commutator, and

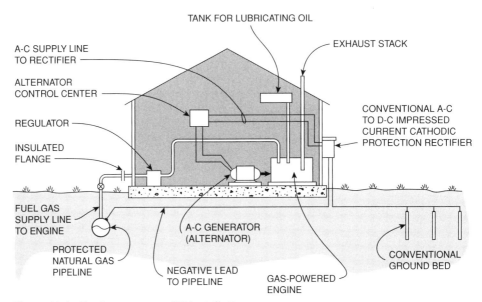

TANK FOR LUBRICATING OIL

A-C SUPPLY LINE
TO RECTIFIER

EXHAUST STACK

ALTERNATOR
CONTROL CENTER

REGULATOR

INSULATED
FLANGE

CONVENTIONAL A-C
TO D-C IMPRESSED
CURRENT CATHODIC
PROTECTION RECTIFIER

FUEL GAS
SUPPLY LINE
TO ENGINE

A-C GENERATOR
(ALTERNATOR)

PROTECTED
NATURAL GAS
PIPELINE

NEGATIVE LEAD
TO PIPELINE

GAS-POWERED
ENGINE

CONVENTIONAL
GROUND BED

Figure 10.1   Engine-generator CP installation.

2. Control of DC output voltage over a wide range is accomplished more readily with rectifiers than by controlling the output of a DC generator.

Engine-generator installations must be designed with reliable equipment that will operate unattended for several weeks. The cost of operating such an installation will be relatively high, particularly if engine fuel must be brought in. The installations should be inspected frequently, preferably at least every two weeks. Periodic overhauling of the rotating equipment (particularly the engine) should be planned to assure continued effective operation. Intervals between overhauls will depend on the engine manufacturer's recommendations and operating experience with the equipment.

TURBOGENERATORS

Closed cycle vapor turbogenerators (CCVTs) are commercially available as power sources for remote CP systems. The available CCVT systems can supply up to 5000 W and 100 V. The system consists of a Rankine cycle turbine and an alternator. A schematic is shown in Figure 10.2 and an actual installation is shown in Figure 10.3. A burner heats an organic liquid that vaporizes and expands. The vapor is directed through the rotating turbine wheel, providing power to the alternator. The vapor is passed into a condenser where it is cooled and returns to the liquid state. The liquid is then pumped back into the vapor generator. The common shaft connecting the turbine wheel, generator, and

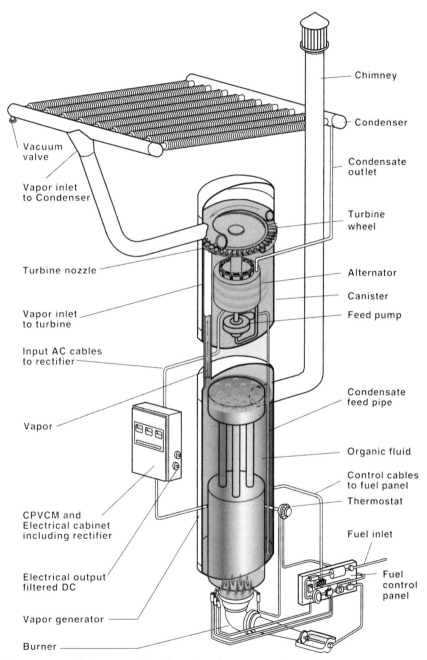

Chimney

Condenser

Condensate outlet

Turbine wheel

Alternator

Canister

Feed pump

Condensate feed pipe

Organic fluid

Control cables to fuel panel

Thermostat

Fuel inlet

Fuel control panel

Vacuum valve

Vapor inlet to Condenser

Turbine nozzle

Vapor inlet to turbine

Input AC cables to rectifier

Vapor

CPVCM and Electrical cabinet including rectifier

Electrical output filtered DC

Vapor generator

Burner

Figure 10.2 Schematic of a closed cycle vapor turbogenerator. (Courtesy of Ormat.)

Figure 10.3   Installation of a closed cycle vapor turbogenerator on a gas pipeline in the western United States. (Courtesy of Ormat.)

pump is the only moving part in the system. This shaft is supported by working fluid film bearings, minimizing wear and associated maintenance.

CCVT systems can operate on a variety of fuels, including natural gas, liquified petroleum gas, kerosene, jet fuel, and diesel fuel. With natural gas, the burner should be inspected and cleaned, if necessary, annually. More frequent cleaning may be required if less clean fuels are used.

THERMOELECTRIC GENERATORS

It has long been known that heating a junction of certain dissimilar metals could generate electricity. These junctions (thermocouples) are used widely as a means of measuring temperature—the voltage output of the heated junction being fed to a voltmeter calibrated in degrees. In the earliest attempts to use this principle as a CP power source, large numbers of low-capacity metallic junctions were connected in series-parallel combinations and heated with a gas flame to attain the necessary DC output capacity. These designs were not particularly successful because of failure of the junctions used.

In recent years, there has been rapid development of higher capacity semiconducting thermoelectric materials designed specifically for power-generation use. Figure 10.4 is a

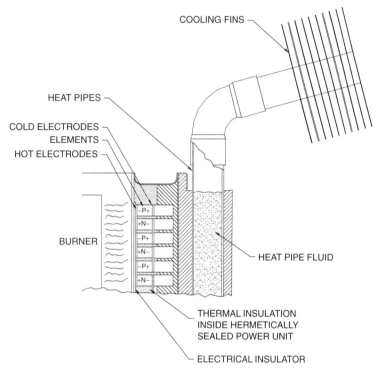

COOLING FINS

HEAT PIPES

COLD ELECTRODES
ELEMENTS
HOT ELECTRODES

BURNER

HEAT PIPE FLUID

THERMAL INSULATION
INSIDE HERMETICALLY
SEALED POWER UNIT

ELECTRICAL INSULATOR

Figure 10.4 Schematic of a thermoelectric generator. (Courtesy of Global Thermoelectric, Inc.)

schematic showing the operation of a thermoelectric generator and Figure 10.5 shows an actual installation. A thermocouple is formed by a P type and an N type thermoelectric leg joined together electrically by a hot junction electrode. Adjacent thermocouples are joined together by cold junction electrodes with each pair producing about 90 mV. Several hundred thermocouple pairs are connected in series to provide the desired output voltage. The hot junction is maintained at a high temperature (about 1000°F) using natural gas or propane while the cold junction is cooled with heat pipes to maintain a lower temperature (about 325°F). The heat pipe is hermetically sealed and contains a special fluid in equilibrium with its vapor. As heat is applied to the fluid, it boils, carrying heat with it. The vapor rises to the finned portion of the pipe and condenses because of the cooling effect of the fins.

Standard thermoelectric generator units are available at power outputs up to 600 W and voltages up to 48 V. Higher power outputs can be achieved by adding parallel units. If higher voltages are required for a CP installation, it is also possible to convert the low DC voltage from the generator to a higher DC voltage. The converters, although of high efficiency, do cause some power loss. For this reason, maximum efficiency will

Figure 10.5 Installation of a thermoelectric generator. (Courtesy of Global Thermo-electric, Inc.)

result if ground beds can be built to directly use the output of the thermoelectric generator. Designing ground beds without carbonaceous backfill will reduce the applied voltage requirement by reducing the groundbed back voltage substantially. When planning an installation where a thermoelectric generator may be applicable, check with the equipment manufacturers for the latest equipment specifications. Since thermoelectric generators contain no moving parts, maintenance is minimal. Annually, it is necessary to replace the fuel filter and clean the fuel orifice.

SOLAR ELECTRIC POWER SYSTEMS

In areas where sunlight can be expected for relatively large percentages of the time, a combination of solar cells and storage batteries can be used to provide a continuous flow of current to a CP installation. A typical installation is shown in Figure 10.6. Solar cells rely on the photoelectric effect: a process in which a material liberates an electric charge when electromagnetic radiation (sunlight) is incident on the material surface. Solar cells are typically P-N junction semiconductors fabricated of crystalline silicon and doped to provide the desired photovoltaic properties.

Figure 10.6 Typical solar electric CP installation. (Courtesy of Kyocera Solar, Inc.)

The initial cost of the solar electric powered CP systems has dropped dramatically over the past 20 years as the technology has advanced. This advancement has occurred, in part, as a result of rapid development in the semiconductor industry in general. Solar electric power systems also are used for other applications such as satellite communications and cellular telephony. Systems are now available that operate at power outputs up to 1000 W, voltages up to 20 V, and currents up to 50 A. Battery storage capacities up to 3200 A-h (at 12 V) are available. Such a battery backup could supply a 10 A rectifier for almost two weeks with no recharging.

BATTERIES

The cost of electrical energy from batteries is high. Occasionally, however, they have been used to supply CP current to isolated sections of well-coated pipe where power lines are not available and where galvanic anodes will not supply the necessary protective current at less cost. Figure 10.7 illustrates the use of batteries on a well-coated river crossing.

Note that the ground bed shown in the figure is scrap steel. High silicon cast iron anodes without carbonaceous backfill may be used also. Graphite anodes or other anodes backfilled with carbonaceous material are not favored because of the characteristic back voltage (usually around 2 V) which would have to be overcome with extra battery capacity.

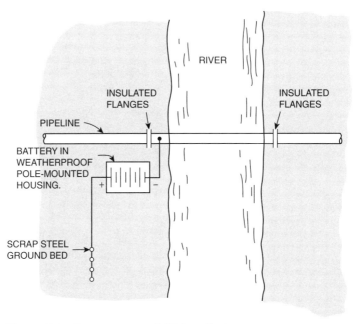

Figure 10.7   Battery-powered CP installation.

WIND-POWERED GENERATORS

Wind-powered generators may be used as a source of power in areas where prevailing winds are of sufficient intensity and duration. Such units were used fairly extensively in the early days of pipeline CP. However, they are expensive and require quite a lot of maintenance. Their use for this application has declined with the development of more cost-effective, reliable power sources, such as solar cells, CCVTs, and thermoelectric generators. Nevertheless, wind-powered generators may be considered as one method of providing power for CP systems in remote areas. Because the power output from a wind-powered generator will be neither steady nor continuous, some means must be used to assure a steady supply of current to the CP ground bed. This can be done by using storage batteries.

When designing a wind-powered installation, wind conditions must be evaluated thoroughly so that both the generator and storage battery can be sized properly. The storage batteries used must have sufficient capacity to supply the required CP current throughout the duration of the longest probable windless period. Likewise, the generator must have sufficient capacity to both supply the CP current and recharge the batteries during periods of sufficient wind.

Wind-powered generator installations require significant maintenance. Lubrication of the generator bearings and mounting swivel (unless they are the lubricated-for-life type) must be scheduled on a regular basis. Generator commutator and brushes as well as slip rings and brushes at the mounting swivel must be checked periodically, cleaned, and dressed when worn. Storage batteries require close attention to maintain the electrolyte at the proper level.

GAS TURBINES

Gas turbines can be used to drive DC generators on natural gas pipelines if there is an adequate pressure drop available. The installation of such a device across a delivery station is illustrated in Figure 10.8. The gas is diverted to the turbine through a bypass line and returned to the system without loss. Similar systems can be established at other locations on gas systems where reasonably constant pressure drops are available, such as in producing gas fields, at well heads, and on gas transmission pipelines. The principal disadvantage of gas turbine power sources is the restricted number of locations where they can be used. For this reason, they are not widely installed.

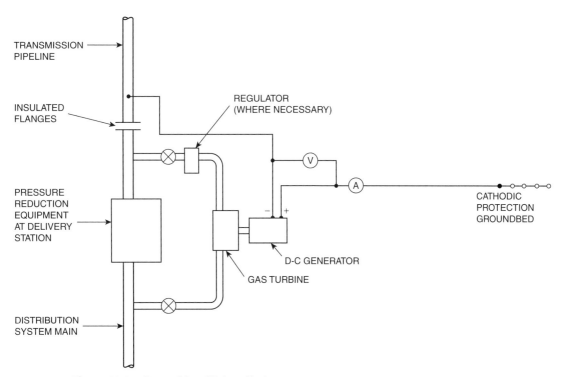

Figure 10.8   Gas turbine CP installation.

FUEL CELLS

The fuel cell is still another source of DC energy that is subject to intensive development as a result of space exploration and military applications and, most recently, automotive applications. In its simplest form, the basic fuel cell can be visualized as a sandwich of two porous electrically conducting plates (or electrodes) with an electrolyte filling the space between the plates. A gaseous fuel such as hydrogen is forced through one plate into the cell, and an oxidizing agent such as oxygen gas is forced through the other plate.

Within the porous electrodes, the fuel and oxidant react electrochemically with the electrolyte to produce electricity and water. Leads from the two porous electrodes serve to remove the electricity generated. Cell developments are in the areas of porous electrode formulation, electrolytes, and catalysts that will permit long-term cell performance at optimum output. Development is active also in the technology of fuel cells that use fuels other than hydrogen and oxygen. The pipeline corrosion engineer will have another useful DC power source for impressed current CP installations when fuel cells are developed commercially at practical cost that can use natural gas or propane as fuels.

Chapter 11

Stray Current Corrosion

Michael J. Szeliga

The major emphasis of the preceding chapters has been on corrosion and the use of corrosion control methods to combat it successfully. The stray currents associated with pipeline corrosion problems are, as the designation implies, direct currents flowing in the earth from a source other than that associated with the affected pipeline. To cause corrosion on a pipeline, stray direct current (DC) must flow from an outside source onto the pipeline in one area and then flow along the line to some other area or areas where they leave the pipe to reenter the earth (with resulting corrosion) and complete the circuit by returning to the original DC power source. Stray currents are either static (nonvarying) or dynamic (varying). Stray current sources include the following: impressed current cathodic protection (CP) systems on other pipelines, DC transit systems, DC mining operations, DC welding operations, high voltage DC transmission systems and disturbances of the earth's magnetic field. On occasion, AC current flow to ground on electrical distribution systems may be rectified if environmental conditions are such that rectifying junctions can be formed such as certain copper oxide films on copper or copper jacketed ground rods. The resulting direct current could create a stray current problem (usually minor) that can be mitigated by the procedures described below for the more usual sources of stray DC currents.

The purpose of this chapter is to outline the fundamentals involved in recognizing, testing for and correcting stray current corrosion conditions. The ability to deal with such situations is important to the pipeline corrosion engineer. This is because the magnitude of stray current discharge from a pipeline at a given point may be far greater than that of galvanic corrosion currents experienced elsewhere on the line. Failure to correct stray current discharge, can lead to early pipeline leaks.

STRAY CURRENT FROM CATHODIC PROTECTION INSTALLATIONS

Impressed current CP systems can cause stray current interference on adjacent pipelines depending on the location of the ground beds, the exact location of the pipeline and the

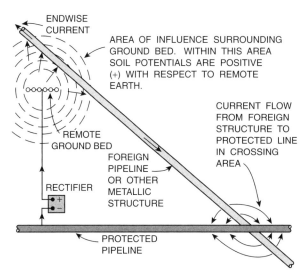

Figure 11.1 Foreign pipeline damage by cathodic protection installation—case 1.

operating characteristics of the CP system. Figures 11.1 to 11.4 illustrate the conditions that can result in this type of stray current interference.

Testing for Interference

Testing for static stray DC current interference caused by CP systems is reasonably straightforward in areas where there are no complications caused by the presence of

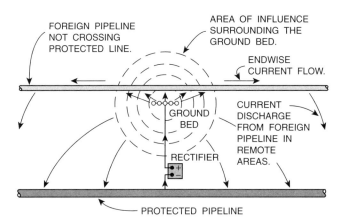

Figure 11.2 Foreign pipeline damage by cathodic protection installation—case 2.

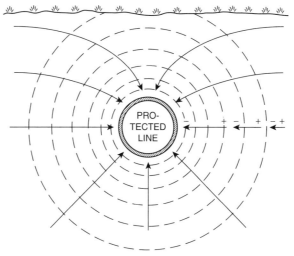

Figure 11.3 Potential gradients in earth around cathodically protected pipeline.

superimposed dynamic (variable) stray currents from sources such as DC powered transit systems. Figure 11.5 illustrates an example where an impressed current CP system (incorporating a rectifier as a DC power source) has been applied to a section of coated pipeline that has several foreign pipelines crossing it. Assume that at each foreign line crossing, a test station has been installed, as shown in the detail on the figure, with two

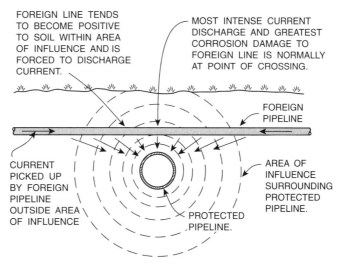

Figure 11.4 Effect on foreign pipeline passing through earth potential gradients around cathodically protected bare line.

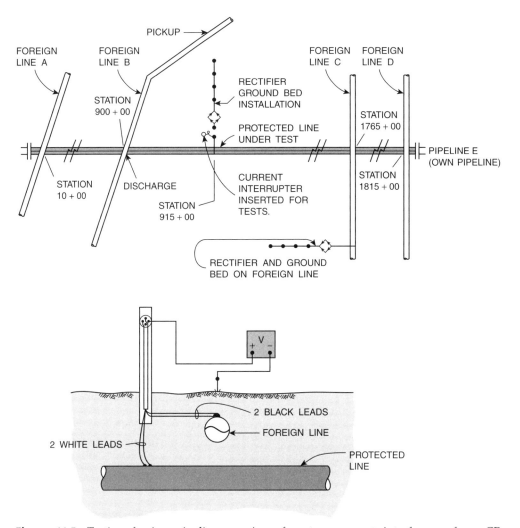

Figure 11.5 Testing foreign pipeline crossings for stray current interference from CP installations.

color-coded leads brought to the test station terminal board from each pipe. An automatic current interrupter (a device for automatically opening and closing an electrical circuit at preset time periods) may then be installed in the output of the rectifier as shown. The interrupter may be set to operate at a cycle such as 20 seconds, current ON, and 10 seconds current OFF, so that the effect of the CP current on the foreign pipelines can be clearly distinguished. With the current interrupter operating, each foreign line crossing is visited and the potential of each line is measured under both current ON and current OFF conditions. For these tests, the copper sulfate electrode (CSE) is placed directly over the point of crossing. If there is any question as to the crossing location, a pipe locator

Table 11.1 Survey Notes on Stray Current Investigation

Foreign Line Designation & Location		Potential Vs Close (CSE)					
		(E) Own Pipeline, V			Foreign Pipeline, V		
		With Current			With Current		
Name	Pipeline Station	ON	OFF	ΔV	ON	OFF	ΔV
A	10 + 00	−0.88	−0.85	−0.03	−0.87	−0.89	+0.02
B	900 + 00	−1.98	−1.02	−0.96	−0.32	−0.68	+0.36
C	1765 + 00	−0.68	−0.64	−0.04	−0.78	−0.78	0
D	1815 + 00	−0.95	−0.91	−0.04	−0.68	−0.68	0

should be used to determine exactly where it is. See Chapters 5 and 6 on instrumentation and techniques for information on equipment and test procedures.

Data taken at the several pipeline crossings of Figure 11.5 may be recorded as shown in Table 11.1. The data shown in the table illustrate various types of stray current interference effects that may be encountered. In addition to the data shown for this illustration, field data sheets should include full information on the line protected, date, current output of the interrupted rectifier and other pertinent facts. Following are some conclusions that can be reached from the data as well as notes on supplementary tests that can be made where appropriate.

Crossing A

Pipeline E (own pipeline) is fully protected, but may have a substantial coating holiday in the vicinity of the crossing because the potential of the foreign line decreases when the interrupted rectifier switches from OFF to ON. This indicates that there is appreciable current flowing to the line under test, creating more negative soil locally around the foreign line.

The foreign line in this instance appears to be cathodically protected as indicated because its potential at the crossing, with the line E rectifier turned OFF, is −0.89 V. The potential of pipeline A becomes less negative (−0.87 V) when the line E rectifier is ON. This indicates that the line E rectifier is reducing the protective potential on pipeline A. However, the reduction is probably not sufficient to suggest a loss of protection. To verify full protection on line A, additional testing should be performed with the CP system for the foreign line interrupted while the rectifier for pipeline E is turned ON. The data indicate that no corrective measures would probably be required for pipeline A.

Crossing B

Pipeline E is fully protected. Pipeline B is not cathodically protected (at least not fully) because its potential is well below −0.85 V to CSE with the line E rectifier OFF. With the line E rectifier ON, the potential on line B is shifted severely in the less negative direction, indicating the probability of severe stray current corrosion damage to the foreign line. Corrective measures will be required to protect line B from stray current corrosion damage.

From the location of line B, crossing only 1,500 ft from the line E rectifier and its route carrying into the vicinity of the line E ground bed, the interference can be expected to result from current pickup by line B where it passes through the area of influence surrounding the line E ground bed. Two verification tests can be made. First, if the potential of Line E is the same, or nearly so, with reference to a remote electrode as it is to the electrode directly over the point of crossing, coating damage on line E is not probable as was the case at the crossing with line A. Second, if the potential of line B to an electrode placed directly over it in areas where it approaches the ground bed swings in the negative direction when the rectifier is switched ON, current pickup by line B is indicated.

Finally, where interference is found (as in this case) it is necessary to determine if the actual point of crossing is the point of maximum exposure. This is done by moving the electrode a few feet at a time, five ft to start, first in one direction and then in the other away from the point of crossing and directly over line B to see if there is an area in which the positive delta voltage swing is greater than at the point of crossing. If such an area is found, the electrode may be moved by smaller distance increments within this area until the point of maximum exposure is found. Identify the location and record the ON, OFF and delta voltages at this point. Rarely will it be necessary to go more than 100 ft in either direction from the point of crossing. The maximum exposure point may be other than at the point of crossing if soil resistivity varies appreciably in the crossing area or if the coating (if any) on the foreign line varies in quality.

Crossing C

Line E, at the crossing with line C, is receiving inadequate protection, apparently because of interference from the CP system for Line C. If the potential of line E is measured to a CSE that is remote from both pipelines, and this potential is found to be representative of normal protective potentials (above -0.90 V in this case), the low potential at the crossing is a localized condition that is probably caused by the CP system on line C. Corrective measures will be required. The length of the line under test that is below -0.85 V can be determined by taking readings to an electrode placed directly above line E in each direction from the point of the crossing with line C. If the data, when plotted, give a curve similar to that in Figure 11.6, interference from the protection system on line C is confirmed. Pipeline C, in this case, is not affected adversely by the CP system for line E. There was no change in the line C potential with the line E rectifier ON and OFF.

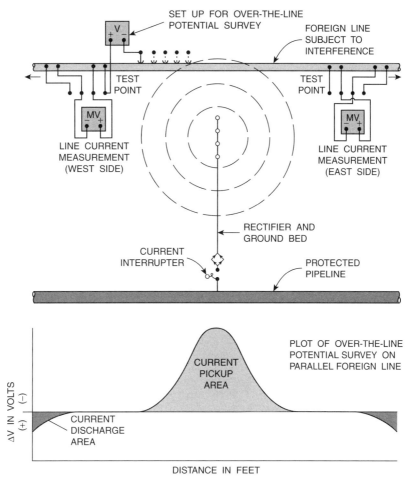

Figure 11.6   Testing noncrossing foreign pipelines for stray current interference from installations.

Crossing D

Pipeline E is protected adequately. Pipeline D does not have full protection but is not affected by the CP system on the line under test. No corrective action is required.

Another possible situation involving interference can exist with a foreign pipeline that passes through the area of influence of a rectifier ground bed, but never actually crosses the protected pipeline. Testing for interference on such a line is illustrated by Figure 11.6. As shown in the figure, the foreign line can be tested by making an over-the-line potential profile in the ground bed area. This can be supplemented, if the profile indicates a current

Table 11.2 Survey Notes on Investigation of Interference from Ground Bed

| Electrode Location with Respect to Starting Point-Ft | Over-the-Line Potentials—Volts on Foreign Pipeline | | | |
	Rectifier ON	Rectifier OFF	ΔCSE[1]	Remarks
0	−0.48	−0.52	+0.04	Exposure
100	−0.58	−0.58	0	
200	−0.64	−0.63	−0.01	
300	−0.69	−0.64	−0.05	
400	−1.01	−0.69	−0.32	
500	−1.20	−0.77	−0.43	
600	−1.37	−0.81	−0.56	Opposite
700	−1.18	−0.78	−0.40	Ground Bed
800	−0.99	−0.71	−0.28	
900	−0.66	−0.65	−0.01	
1000	−0.64	−0.64	0	
1100	−0.57	−0.59	+0.02	Exposure
1200	−0.48	−0.53	+0.05	Exposure

[1] Values to be plotted

| Foreign Pipeline Line Current Measurement | Potential Drop Rectifier ON | | Potential Drop Rectifier OFF | | Change in Potential Drop | | Calculated Interference Current | | |
	mV[1]	Flow	mV[1]	Flow	ΔmV	Flow	Amp/mV	Amps	Flow
West Side	0.62	West	0.08	East	0.70	West	3.8[2]	2.66	West
East Side	0.53	East	0.02	East	0.51	East	4.1	2.09	East

[1] mV readings corrected for lead resistance.
[2] Amp/mV factors for the specific voltage drop span.

pickup area, by pipeline current measurements to determine the magnitude of current pickup. With an interrupter operating at the rectifier on the protected line, the data might appear as shown in Table 11.2.

The first set of data in Table 11.2, with highly negative values of delta voltage opposite the ground bed, indicate definite current pickup. The positive delta voltage values indicate the beginning of a current discharge area. The portion of the foreign pipeline that is picking up current starts at the 100 ft point and continues to the 1,000 ft location for a total distance of 900 ft.

The foreign pipeline current flow measurements (second set of data in Table 11.2) indicate definite stray current flow along the pipeline with the rectifier ON. The magnitude of the current flow indicated is high for this type of interference condition. Serious damage to the foreign line could be expected at an early date if the condition were allowed to exist without correction.

HOW TO REDUCE STRAY CURRENT INTERFERENCE

Some of the methods used to reduce or eliminate stray current interference from CP installations include bonds between the offending and affected pipelines, use of galvanic anodes at the point of crossing, use of coatings, and use of electrical shields. In some instances, the corrective measures required may be so complicated or expensive that relocating the offending rectifier installation may be the more economical solution. To illustrate how the various corrective procedures may be used, the examples of interference described above in "Testing for Interference" will be used to demonstrate the specific corrective procedures.

Drainage Bonds

Table 11.1 shows that foreign pipeline B is subject to stray current damage from the impressed current CP system on pipeline E, see Figure 11.5. A commonly used method to correct this condition involves connecting a resistance bond between the two pipelines with the amount of resistance in the bond adjusted to drain just enough current from the affected line to eliminate the damaging condition. Normally, this is done during cooperative tests with the corrosion engineer representing the foreign pipeline owner unless the owner has given specific permission to make the bond installation without representation on his part. Permission should be in writing.

The accurate determination of when the stray current interference effect has been eliminated is critical. To determine this, the bond is adjusted with the current interrupter operating at the rectifier on the pipeline causing the interference (as in Figure 11.5) and with a voltmeter set up to measure the potential of the foreign line to CSE at the point of crossing (or at the point of maximum exposure if other than at the actual point of crossing). The bond resistance is made such that the foreign line potential with the affecting rectifier ON is the same as was observed and recorded for it with the rectifier OFF prior to the installation of the bond. In other words, the foreign pipeline potential is restored to its original value. A typical foreign line test point with a bond in place is illustrated by Figure 11.7, together with the instrument connections for measuring the pipe-to-soil potentials on affected pipeline.

Assuming that the point of crossing is also the point of maximum exposure in this instance (crossing B, Figure 11.5), the original readings for the foreign line are −0.32 V, ON, and −0.68 V, OFF. With the resistance bond adjusted properly, the foreign line potential with the rectifier ON should be −0.68 V.

A method of adjusting bonds frequently used, calls for adjusting the bond resistance until there is no swing (delta voltage) on the foreign pipeline at the point of maximum exposure as the affecting rectifier is switched ON and OFF. This no potential shift procedure has been shown over the years[1] to be ultra conservative in that more current is drained by the bond than is necessary to clear the interference. Although this does no harm to the foreign line, the cathodically protected line may be unnecessarily penalized.

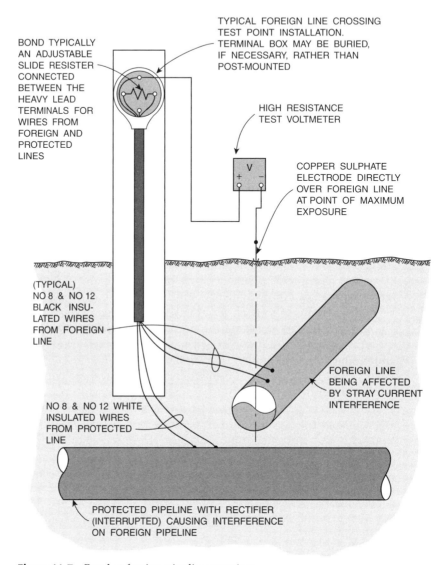

BOND TYPICALLY AN ADJUSTABLE SLIDE RESISTER CONNECTED BETWEEN THE HEAVY LEAD TERMINALS FOR WIRES FROM FOREIGN AND PROTECTED LINES

TYPICAL FOREIGN LINE CROSSING TEST POINT INSTALLATION. TERMINAL BOX MAY BE BURIED, IF NECESSARY, RATHER THAN POST-MOUNTED

HIGH RESISTANCE TEST VOLTMETER

V + −

COPPER SULPHATE ELECTRODE DIRECTLY OVER FOREIGN LINE AT POINT OF MAXIMUM EXPOSURE

(TYPICAL) NO 8 & NO 12 BLACK INSU-LATED WIRES FROM FOREIGN LINE

FOREIGN LINE BEING AFFECTED BY STRAY CURRENT INTERFERENCE

NO 8 & NO 12 WHITE INSULATED WIRES FROM PROTECTED LINE

PROTECTED PIPELINE WITH RECTIFIER (INTERRUPTED) CAUSING INTERFERENCE ON FOREIGN PIPELINE

Figure 11.7   Bond at foreign pipeline crossing.

Had the foreign pipeline in this example been cathodically protected such that full protective potentials were lost with the affecting rectifier ON, full return to the original potential might not be necessary. Assume that, when the crossing was tested, the readings were the following: −0.55 V, ON; −0.91 V, OFF; +0.36 V, delta voltage. By adjusting the bond with the rectifier ON until the foreign line reads −0.85 V at point of maximum exposure, corrosion would be prevented with no need to return the foreign pipeline potential to the full −0.91 V. The stray current drainage bond would require bi-monthly inspections by qualified personnel to verify that it was in place and operating properly.

Situation Involving Poorly-Coated Line

Table 11.1 shows that the crossing of pipeline E with foreign line C on Figure 11.5 involves interference conditions which may not be solved with a bond. Test data taken on this foreign line suggest that the foreign line causing interference is bare or very poorly coated at the crossing. Assume, as suggested in proceeding discussion, that the potential of the line under test is measured to a remote CSE and found to be −0.93 V with its rectifier ON, even though a value far below this is measured to an electrode placed at the crossing as a result of the interference. With the rectifier on the foreign pipeline interrupted, the potential of the line under test to the electrode at the point of crossing could have, typically, values as follows: −0.68 V, ON; −0.91 V, OFF; +0.23 V, delta voltage. The ON reading needs to be corrected to at least −0.85 V to eliminate interference, meaning that if a bond is used, it will have to drain current from the line under test. If, however, the potential of the foreign line is measured to the remote reference electrode and found to be, for example, only −0.83 V with its rectifier ON, it becomes apparent that a bond between the two lines will not drain current from the pipeline, as would be necessary to correct the interference. A bond, under these conditions, would not correct the interference, but would impose needless additional burden on the CP system for the coated pipeline under test.

Knowing that a relatively high current density that is flowing through the soil onto the bare foreign line results in a localized reduction in the protective potential on the line under test, one solution is to reduce the density of current flow to the foreign line in the crossing area. This may be done with coatings as illustrated by Figure 11.8. By applying a quality coating to the foreign pipeline causing the interference in the crossing area, current flow through the soil to the foreign line is reduced greatly. This means that the voltage drops in the earth (cathodic field) around the foreign line become negligible and no longer cause a severe local depression of protective potentials on the line under test. The length of foreign line to be coated can be based on the over-the-line potential profile on the line under test, as shown in Figure 11.9, which identifies the length of line subject to interference. Coated lengths of foreign line are equated with the interference profile length as shown in Figure 11.8.

Use of Galvanic Anodes

Another means of correcting the interference involves the use of galvanic anodes attached to the line under test through the area subject to interference from the foreign line as illustrated by Figure 11.10. Basically, this approach involves using the anodic potential gradient fields surrounding galvanic anodes to offset the cathodic potential gradient field surrounding the pipeline. For most applications of this type, a single line of anodes between the affected pipeline and the one causing the interference will be sufficient to

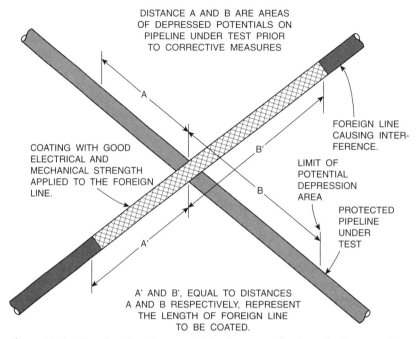

DISTANCE A AND B ARE AREAS
OF DEPRESSED POTENTIALS ON
PIPELINE UNDER TEST PRIOR
TO CORRECTIVE MEASURES

A

B'

B

FOREIGN LINE
CAUSING INTER-
FERENCE.

LIMIT OF
POTENTIAL
DEPRESSION
AREA

PROTECTED
PIPELINE
UNDER
TEST

COATING WITH GOOD
ELECTRICAL AND
MECHANICAL STRENGTH
APPLIED TO THE FOREIGN
LINE.

A'

A' AND B', EQUAL TO DISTANCES
A AND B RESPECTIVELY, REPRESENT
THE LENGTH OF FOREIGN LINE
TO BE COATED.

Figure 11.8   Use of coating to correct interference at foreign pipeline crossing.

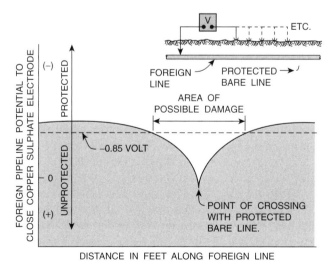

Figure 11.9   Pipe-to-earth potentials on foreign pipeline passing through area of influence around cathodically protected bare line.

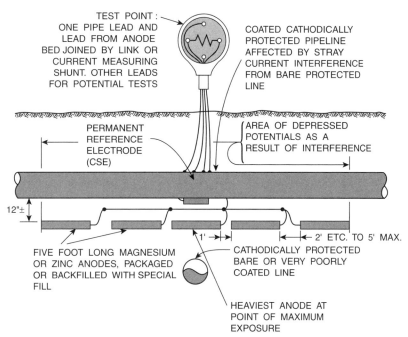

TEST POINT :
ONE PIPE LEAD AND
LEAD FROM ANODE
BED JOINED BY LINK OR
CURRENT MEASURING
SHUNT. OTHER LEADS
FOR POTENTIAL TESTS

COATED CATHODICALLY
PROTECTED PIPELINE
AFFECTED BY STRAY
CURRENT INTERFERENCE
FROM BARE PROTECTED
LINE

PERMANENT
REFERENCE
ELECTRODE
(CSE)

AREA OF DEPRESSED
POTENTIALS AS A
RESULT OF INTERFERENCE

12"±

1'

2' ETC. TO 5' MAX.

FIVE FOOT LONG MAGNESIUM
OR ZINC ANODES, PACKAGED
OR BACKFILLED WITH SPECIAL
FILL

CATHODICALLY PROTECTED
BARE OR VERY POORLY
COATED LINE

HEAVIEST ANODE AT
POINT OF MAXIMUM
EXPOSURE

Figure 11.10   Use of galvanic anodes to correct interference at foreign pipeline crossing.

mitigate the harmful effects of the interference. There still will be current discharge but the discharge will be from the anodes rather than the previously affected pipeline. Where potential differences are very great as occurs occasionally with stray current from DC transit systems or mining substations, several strings of anodes may be required forming a cage around the affected line. In such a case, however, anode life may be short unless soil resistivity is high.

As shown in the figure, the heaviest anodes would be used at the point of crossing where the exposure is most intense while lighter anodes may be used elsewhere. Magnesium anodes are used successfully because they have higher anodic potential gradient fields than do zinc anodes. The length of the anode string is determined by the length of the depressed potential area on the affected pipeline. A test point is desirable to permit measuring anode output periodically and to facilitate potential measurements. In addition to the normal surface potential measurements, a permanent reference electrode placed as shown in the figure will permit checking the underside of the affected line at the point of maximum exposure. A prepackaged, permanent, CSE placed below the pipeline makes an excellent installation.

Information in proceeding chapters is applicable when working out the design for installations of this type. Factors to be considered include soil resistivity, voltage difference between the lines, length of exposure area, and desired life.

Use of Electrical Shield

Where a pipeline passes through the area of influence surrounding a ground bed, it is possible to reduce the amount of stray current the line will pick up by using electrical shields. Situations where this may be a solution include examples such as represented by foreign line B in Figure 11.5 and that illustrated by Figure 11.6. The Figure 11.6 condition is used to illustrate the application of electrical shields as shown by Figure 11.11.

The reason electrical shields of bare pipe may be useful is that they permit utilization of the cathodic potential gradient fields surrounding the bare pipe connected to the rectifier negative terminal. With the foreign line lying between the two shields as shown,

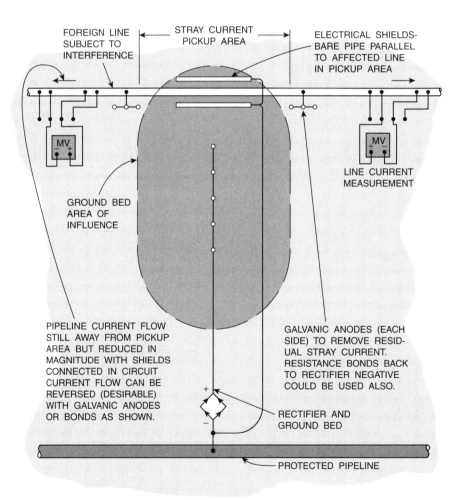

Figure 11.11   Use of electrical shields to reduce stray current interference.

it is completely within the gradient field. This cathodic field is in opposition to the positive ground bed field. The net result is a reduction in the amount of stray current picked up by the foreign line. The effect is quite similar to that which has been described for a coated and cathodically protected pipeline crossing a cathodically protected bare line, with local loss of protection on the coated line because of a reduction in current pickup from the soil caused by the cathodic potential gradient field.

The shields shown in the figure will reduce the stray current pickup on the foreign line, but will seldom eliminate it. Interference current still can be expected to flow away from the pickup area to remote discharge points at which the pipe will be corroded. This current flow needs to be reversed. This may be done with galvanic anodes or bonds, as suggested on the figure, if the shields have reduced stray current pickup to a reasonably small magnitude.

Using shields as described has many disadvantages. The bare pipe shields connected to the rectifier negative may consume a large portion of the rectifier current output and thus possibly reduce protection of the line to which the rectifier is connected. The bare pipe used as shields may be kept small (3/4-in diameter pipe should be satisfactory in most cases) to keep the current demands within reason. A shield installation as described can be expensive to install and expensive to maintain because, probably, a substantial percentage of the rectifier operating costs will be due to the shields. Because of these considerations, the pipeline corrosion engineer should consider other alternatives carefully before using shields to be sure that it would not be less expensive, in the long run, to relocate the rectifier and ground bed.

Notification Procedures

An essential part of the pipeline corrosion engineer's job involves cooperating with owners of other pipelines or buried metallic structures. This is necessary in order that all parties may plan and operate their corrosion control systems with the least practical effect on structures belonging to others. Corrosion engineers should, when cathodically protecting a pipeline, notify all owners of underground structures crossing their pipeline that a CP system is planned. This should be done before the CP system installations are made. These foreign structure owners should be given the location, type, and size of protection installations to be installed in the vicinity of their crossing or crossings. They should be told when the system is to be energized and they should be invited to participate in cooperative tests at points of crossing. They may be promised copies of data taken at their crossings if they do not elect to send a representative for cooperative tests. They should be asked if they have additional crossings not known to the engineer issuing the notifications. For clarification, the written notice may be accompanied by a strip map of the pipeline (or pertinent portions thereof) marked to show the foreign line crossings of the company being notified and the proposed CP installations in the vicinity of those crossings.

Some geographical areas, typically large urban areas, have organized corrosion coordinating committees that have established procedures for disseminating information to companies within their area. The corrosion coordinating committee will typically have specific notification procedures and possibly specific forms to be filled out and submitted to impacted utility companies and the committee recording secretary. In areas which are not served by corrosion coordinating committees, the pipeline corrosion engineer will have to determine the appropriate offices of foreign structure owners to which notifications will be sent.

STRAY CURRENT FROM TRANSIT OR MINING SYSTEMS

Stray current problems on pipelines arising from direct current transit systems and mining operations can be very severe. Solving such problems is more complicated than treating those discussed in the preceding sections. This is because of the continuously varying nature of the exposure as the load on the DC power sources varies. This type of problem is affecting an ever growing portion of the utility operators in North America because of the widespread construction of new DC powered rail transit systems in urban areas throughout the continent and the expansion of existing transit systems. The two types of DC powered rail transit systems that are becoming more common are heavy rail (the typical subway system) and light rail (the typical street railway). The terms heavy rail and light rail do not refer to the weight of the transit vehicles. The terms relate to the general operating characteristics of the rail vehicles. Typically heavy rail transit systems will operate with greater accelerations, higher speeds, longer trains, and higher current demands than will light rail transit systems. No such generalities may be made as to which type of system creates the highest overall levels of stray current activity. The amount of stray current generated by a specific transit system will depend upon the resistance-to-earth of the running rails and the level of voltage on the running rails. A simplified version of the problem is illustrated by Figure 11.12.

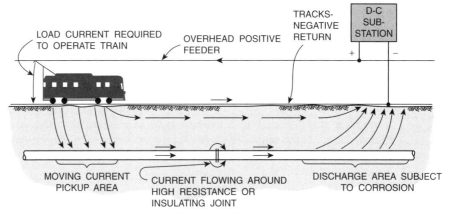

Figure 11.12   Stray current corrosion caused by DC transit systems.

DC light rail transit systems, as shown in Figure 11.12, are operated normally with the overhead insulated feeder connected to the positive bus of the DC traction power substation. The load current which is typically measured in thousands of amperes is supposed to return to the substation via the tracks (the running rails) which are connected to the negative bus at the substation. A common operating potential for transit systems is 750 volts. Because running rails are laid at ground level and are not fully insulated from earth, some part of the load current will enter the ground where the running rails are most positive (at the load) and take an earth path back to the substation. The current which flows through the ground is called stray current. Pipelines in the area constitute a good return path for a portion of the total stray current. Such a pipeline will carry the current to a location in the vicinity of the DC substation where it will flow from the pipeline to earth and return to the negative bus of the substation. Severe pipe corrosion will result if corrective measures are not used. Where the pipeline is picking up current near the train, it is receiving CP. In severe cases, the pipe may be many volts negative to adjacent earth in this area and, at the same time, many volts positive to earth in the exposure area near the DC substation. If there are high resistance joints in the pipeline, as shown in Figure 11.12, there may be enough driving voltage to force current to bypass the joint and corrode the pipe on the side where the current leaves the pipe. It is important to note that the location where the stray current returns to the negative return system is not always going to occur in the vicinity of the traction power substations. The stray current may return at any location on the transit system where the track-to-earth resistance is low. This means that any evaluation of stray current activity on a pipeline must first determine the locations of stray current discharge from the pipeline before any possible stray current control measures may be considered.

As mentioned earlier, the illustration of the Figure 11.12 is a simple condition involving one load (train) and one substation. In actuality, operating systems will have a number of trains in operation at any one time depending on the traffic load. This means that the severity of exposure conditions is subject to constant variations that makes the evaluation of the stray current activity very complex. Ideally, if the transit system running rails were perfectly isolated from earth, they would return all of the DC current to the substations and there would be no stray current to affect pipelines in the area. How closely any given transit system will approach this condition depends on several factors including the type of negative return system, the type of track construction, the level of track maintenance, and the overall dryness of the trackwork.

Most new transit systems are designed with ungrounded negative return systems. The ungrounded negative return system is intended to electrically isolate the return system from earth and provides the highest level of stray current control. The ungrounded transit systems are also typically designed with multiple traction power substations that are intended to maintain running rail voltages at safe levels. This also helps to reduce stray current activity by keeping running rail voltages relatively low.

Diode grounded transit systems may have electrically isolated running rails for stray current control, but the negative return system is deliberately grounded through diodes at the traction power substations. This allows a relatively high level of stray current activity. Some transit systems will use diode grounding for running rail voltage control.

The running rails and substations are normally isolated from earth. Sensing circuits monitor the running rail voltages and when preset limits (unsafe voltages) are reached, switches close that temporarily ground the negative return system though diodes. The period of time when the return system is grounded will produce relatively high overall stray current levels.

Grounded transit systems operate with the negative return system permanently connected to earth at the substations. No special measures are typically implemented to electrically isolate the running rails from earth. High stray current activity is caused by these grounded transit systems. Typically, it is only the very old, existing transit systems that are operated with their negative return system deliberately connected to ground. Old, existing transit systems also have an additional problem that new transit systems do not have. New transit systems are constructed with welded running rails and insulating rail joints are installed only at specific locations, such as at crossovers, where they are required for automatic train control operations. These insulating rail joints are bonded across with impedance bonds that allow the return of DC current through them while blocking the AC current of the train control system. Old, existing transit systems were not constructed with welded running rails. Therefore, each rail joint has bond cables welded across it to assure proper return of the negative current. If these rail bonds are broken, as may occur during normal rail operations, then the return current cannot flow through the bond cables and all of the return current passes through earth. Extremely high stray current activity will occur under these circumstances. Old, existing transit systems should have a program in place to periodically inspect and repair these critical rail bonds.

Underground mining operations that are DC powered have negative return systems that operate in much the same manner as has been described for transit systems. Because most of these systems are underground, pipelines will seldom be as close to the running rails as is the case with surface transit systems. Stray current effects on pipelines can still be severe in some situations. DC substations may be located underground rather than at the surface. This can result in problems in applying corrective measures as will be seen in later sections of this chapter.

Testing for Exposure Areas

Suitable time based recording instruments are critical when locating exposure areas. The instruments may include paper strip chart recorders or electronic data loggers. Both types of equipment have advantages and disadvantages for field evaluations. The most appropriate type of equipment for your particular application should be determined. Locations where tests may be made are selected from a knowledge of all pipeline routes in the area as well as those of the transit or mining system. The location of all DC substations and their operating schedules must be known. Testing should always be performed in the vicinity of DC traction power substations as these are likely locations for the pipeline to be in exposure, especially if the substation is grounded. Testing should never be limited solely to the vicinity of traction power substations as the pipeline may be in exposure in other locations due to low track-to-earth resistance values on the transit system.

Exposure can be experienced on pipelines which do not come close to a DC substation. If, for example, a pipeline crosses a DC traction system, stray current may be picked up at the point of crossing as trains pass. This stray current may flow in both directions from the crossing and discharge at remote locations. If a pipeline parallels a transit line for a distance, but does not approach a DC substation closely, current will be picked up by the pipeline as trains pass the parallel section. This current will be discharged from the ends of the parallel section. In finding its way back to the DC substation, stray current may jump from pipeline to pipeline at crossings in order to follow the most direct or lowest resistance path. Therefore, a pipeline that is not in close proximity to a transit system may cross a pipeline that is. The pipeline that is close in proximity to the transit system may carry the stray currents to the pipeline that is not in close proximity. Corrosion damage at these pipeline crossings that are remote from a transit system can be severe. Tests for exposure should be made at such possible points of current interchange. This emphasizes the need to know the routes of all foreign lines in an area where conducting tests.

Recording voltmeters are used to measure and record pipe-to-earth potentials at locations selected for test. The potential will be measured to adjacent earth in most instances. Changes in the pipe-to-earth potentials are greater per unit of current discharge on coated lines than on bare lines. Where the pipeline potential becomes more positive during periods of stray current activity, current discharge is indicated. Experience with this type of testing is most helpful in planning the recording instrument test program and when interpreting the data taken.

Figure 11.13 is a representation of the results that may be obtained at a stray current discharge area on a pipeline adjacent to a transit system. The chart shows that the pipeline is affected by stray current activity when the transit system is in operation, but that the pipeline only goes into exposure during the morning and afternoon rush hour periods.

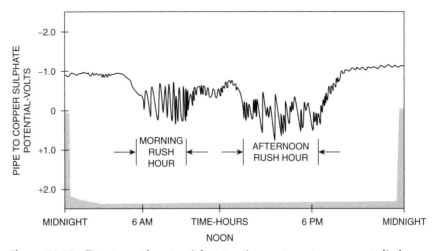

Figure 11.13 Pipe-to-earth potential at traction system stray current discharge area.

It becomes apparent from a study of the chart that observation of an indicating meter for any reasonable period of time is not apt to give a true picture of the full range of potential variations. The evaluation of the stray current activity indicated on the chart in Figure 11.13 must focus on the time periods when the pipeline is in exposure. The duration of the individual exposures must be determined as well as the expected impact on the pipeline itself. If the pipeline goes into exposure for only very limited time periods, then the pipeline may not be experiencing corrosion damage and no stray current mitigation measures may be necessary.

Recording millivolt meters may be used to measure pipeline current on calibrated pipe spans. Where sufficient test spans exist or can be installed, two or more such recording millivolt meters may be used to record the current flow at adjacent test points in areas where exposure is suspected. By comparing the charts taken at any two adjacent test points, current loss in the section may be detected. Current loss between test points may be determined with indicating millivolt meters also. This necessitates having an observer at each test point. A series of simultaneous readings are made and compared to ascertain whether or not current loss is occurring. Although a synchronized timing schedule, typically using computer data loggers, may be used to obtain simultaneous readings, direct communication (as by cellular phone) is more reliable and should be used to verify that the test equipment is actually synchronized.

When working with bare pipe, carefully conducted current loss surveys will indicate the point of maximum voltage exposure (by showing where current loss is greatest) unless there is wide variation in soil resistivity. On coated lines, however, the point of maximum current discharge can be some distance from the point of maximum voltage exposure. This can happen when the coating at the point of maximum exposure, for example, is in substantially better condition than at other locations in the area.

Once the general location of the point of maximum exposure has been determined, it may be pinpointed more precisely by the use of X/Y plotters or two indicating voltmeters (two identical voltmeters are required to assure consistency of data). This is done by correlating the pipe-to-earth potential at the test point with the potential between the pipeline and the transit system negative return. Correlations are made at a series of locations through the exposure area. At each location, a number of simultaneous readings are taken at various degrees of intensity of the stray current effect. Carefully recorded data, when plotted, will fall along a generally straight line. The slope of the line is a measure of exposure: the greater the slope, the greater the exposure. The calculated slope at each test point may be referred to as the Beta for that point. The diagram obtained by plotting the slope, or Beta, against the test point locations may be referred to as a Beta Profile or an Exposure Profile. The general procedure is summarized by Figure 11.14.

Because of the possibly very marked and quick stray current variations, it is essential that indicating instruments of identical characteristics be used in obtaining simultaneous readings. Rapid response is necessary. If characteristics are not identical, particularly with regard to response speed, good correlation of simultaneous readings cannot be obtained. It is obvious that a lot of work is involved in taking and plotting data and obtaining slopes at each test point to produce an exposure profile. X/Y plotters are available which will record both values simultaneously and show the line of slope. Where much of this

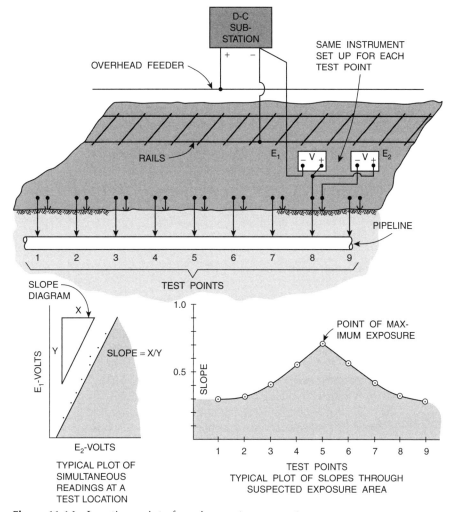

Figure 11.14 Locating point of maximum stray current exposure.

type of work is to be done, such instruments will save a great deal of time. High input impedance and rapid response are essential characteristics to be looked for in selecting such a recorder.

CORRECTIVE MEASURES

Transit System Action

One approach to stray current mitigation involves the elimination of excessive stray current activity at its source. This involves the assistance of the transit system operator and is often only feasible with the newer, nongrounded transit systems. Most transit systems have a corrosion engineer on staff or a corrosion engineering consultant available to deal with these types of stray current interference problems. The utility operator should request a meeting with the transit system corrosion engineer to review the field data and discuss what action is available to the transit system. Typically, the transit system engineer will perform track-to-earth resistance and track-to-earth voltage testing in the vicinity of the pipeline to determine if a problem exists on the transit system. If a problem is found to exist, the transit system will usually make the necessary repairs and the excessive stray current activity may be eliminated. The typical repairs will include cleaning of wet and dirty trackwork, replacement of damaged track fasteners, removal of inadvertent contacts between the negative return system and ground, and/or correction of improper positive system operation. Retesting of the pipeline, after the repair of the transit system, will have to be performed to verify that the excessive stray current activity has been mitigated and that any remaining stray current activity is at tolerable levels.

Pipeline Modifications

Another approach to stray current mitigation involves making modifications to the pipeline to reduce its susceptibility to stray currents and to provide a safe means of stray current discharge. The modification of the pipeline to reduce stray current activity maintains all control for the stray current measures directly in the hands of the pipeline operator.

The first consideration for pipeline modification involves the installation of insulating joints. The proper placement of insulating joints in a pipeline can dramatically reduce the overall stray current activity on the pipeline by making the pipeline less susceptible to stray current pickup and discharge. By installing insulators, the pipeline operator is increasing the overall resistance of the pipe to earth, thereby reducing its tendency to pick up stray currents. This approach may require modifications to the CP system for the pipeline to assure that full protection is maintained on the pipeline after the insulating joints are installed.

Another possible pipeline modification involves the installation of magnesium anodes on the pipeline at the locations where the pipeline is going into stray current discharge. The magnesium anodes can provide a low resistance discharge point for the stray currents so that no stray current actually discharges directly from the pipeline. The stray current activity must be carefully re-evaluated after the magnesium anodes are installed to verify that the stray current is discharging fully from the anodes. If magnesium anodes are installed where the pipeline both picks up and discharges stray current, then the installation of diodes with the magnesium anodes may be necessary to assure that the anodes discharge stray current, but do not collect stray current. The installation of magnesium anodes may be required at insulating joints where stray current may be discharging around the joints.

Another possible pipeline modification involves the installation of a potentially controlled rectifier and impressed current ground bed where the pipeline is going into stray

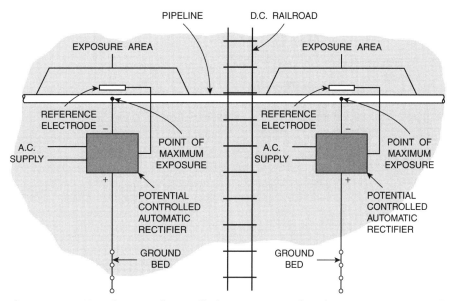

Figure 11.15   Use of potential controlled automatic rectifiers for stray current control.

current discharge. The output of the rectifier would automatically adjust itself to supply additional CP current to the pipeline when stray current was being discharged. This would maintain acceptable CP levels on the pipeline at all times. This approach is only effective and feasible if the pipeline has a very limited number of areas where the stray current is discharging from the pipeline. Figure 11.15 shows a potentially controlled rectifier installation.

The pipeline should be evaluated to determine if its CP system is operating properly. It is possible that the existing CP system would be sufficient to overcome the stray current activity if it were operating properly. The repair of defective rectifiers, damaged external coatings, defective insulating joints and the removal of any inadvertent contacts to grounded structures may sometimes greatly reduce stray current effects and eliminate possible stray current damage. Always make sure that everything on the pipeline is operating as intended and that the CP system is functional before performing any evaluations to determine what additional stray current mitigation measures are required.

Stray Current Drainage Bonds

The measure of last resort that may be implemented for stray current mitigation is the installation of a drainage bond between the pipeline and the transit system negative return system. Figure 11.16 shows a drainage bond installation. The installation of a

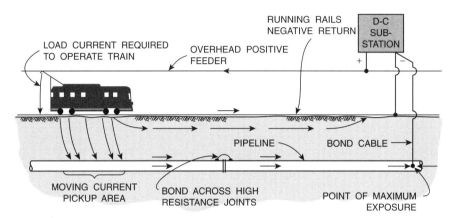

Figure 11.16   Bond between pipeline and DC substation.

drainage bond should only be considered if all other stray current control (on the transit system) and stray current mitigation measures (on the pipeline) prove ineffective. The installation of a stray current drainage bond requires a direct connection between the pipeline and the negative return of the transit system. The connection to the negative return is made at a traction power substation if at all possible to avoid interfering with any automatic train control equipment on the running rails. The installation of a drainage bond should safely drain the stray current from the pipeline. However, it will also result in a decrease in the transit system's overall negative return resistance-to-earth. This will result in a significant increase in total stray current activity associated with the transit system and will probably result in excessive stray current interference on pipelines that were previously being subjected to only minor stray current effects. This is likely to lead to the need for additional stray current drainage bonds and the distribution of the stray current over an ever increasing larger area with an increase in the number of utilities being adversely impacted by the stray current activity.

The bond must have adequate conductivity to remove all stray current and clear the exposure condition. In designing a bond, it should have, ideally, just enough conductivity to clear the exposure. If the conductivity is higher than necessary, more current will be drained. This may not be harmful to the pipeline to which the bond is connected but will cause it to become more highly negative to earth than necessary. This may in turn increase the likelihood of exposure at crossings with other pipelines. If the pipeline being bonded to the substation is coated, potentials should not be allowed to become more negative to earth than necessary so that, insofar as possible, coating damage may be avoided.

Although a bond resistance value may be obtained by installing a temporary cable and determining the degree of clearance per ampere drained, the resistance may be calculated using the following expression:

$$\text{Bond resistance in ohms} = (R_{P-G}/\text{Slope}) - R_{P-N} \tag{1}$$

where:

R_{P-G} is the resistance in ohms between pipeline and ground at point of maximum exposure.

Slope is the slope (expressed as a decimal) previously determined at the point of maximum exposure.

R_{P-N} is the resistance in ohms between pipeline and substation negative bus.

Resistance values are determined by the ammeter-voltmeter method using an interrupted source of DC current connected between the pipeline and substation negative bus. The DC current source used must be of sufficient capacity to override the potential swings caused by the stray current activity. The average of a number of readings will be required to obtain reliable data. Taking such readings at a time when the load on the substation is at a minimum will facilitate good data. Once the bond cable size is determined, a trial installation is recommended to determine the impacts on other adjacent utilities from the installation of a bond. This will allow testing to be performed to determine if other utilities will require a bond to the pipeline or to the transit system. This testing may determine that a different size bond cable than that originally calculated will be required. The bond cable that is installed must have sufficient current carrying capacity to handle the maximum current drained without burning out.

A simple bond to a DC substation as discussed is ample where that substation is the only one supplying current to the traction or mining system. If, however, there are several substations on the system and the one to which the bond is connected is lightly loaded or out of use during part of each 24 hour period, having the bond permanently connected becomes a disadvantage. This is because the direction of current flow in the bond can reverse and feed stray current to the pipeline. This reverse current flow will increase exposure conditions at other points on the pipeline.

To prevent this reverse current flow, various types of reverse current switches may be used in the bond cable installed between pipeline and negative bus. These may take the form of relay-actuated switches which open automatically when the current tends to reverse. Diodes may also be used to block any reverse current flows. A stray current drainage bond should always have some kind of device to block the flow of reverse current. In the event of a change in the transit system operations, the bond should not be allowed to carry current directly to the pipeline. If this happens, stray current will be discharged from the pipeline at a location remote from the drainage bond. This could result in serious corrosion damage on the pipeline. When reverse current blocking devices of either type are used, allowances must be made in the bond resistance design for any voltage drop (effective resistance) interposed by the blocking device.

The installation of bond cables between a pipeline and a DC substation is seldom easy, particularly in urban locations where a practical route for heavy drainage cable must be selected. A special problem is associated with underground substations on mining systems. If a bond is unavoidable, it may be necessary to drill a bore hole from the surface to the mine gallery where the substation is located. This requires careful selection of the hole location in cooperation with the mine surveyor, and the drilling of a straight hole. Before undertaking such action, however, it is wise to find out how long the underground substation will remain in its present location. This is because mining substations are apt to be moved as mining progresses. If it is found that the substation is to be moved in the near future, the bore hole installation would not be economical.

Underground Corrosion Coordinating Committees

As was discussed under Notification Procedures in the section covering stray current from CP installations, the pipeline corrosion engineer should utilize the services of the underground corrosion coordinating committees. By attending committee meetings regularly, the engineer will have advance information pertaining to any changes in stray current sources or corrective action by others which may have an effect on the engineer's own system.

Stray Current from Magnetic Disturbances

Occasionally, varying pipe-to-soil potentials and/or pipeline currents will be encountered in areas where there is no known source of man-made stray direct current. These pipe-to-soil variations usually are associated with disturbances in the earth's magnetic field. Such disturbances have been found most active during periods of severe sun spot activity. Stray current from this source is termed telluric. The reason for the effect on pipelines may be associated with the buildup and collapse of the earth's magnetic field in the area of the pipeline. In an electric generator, voltage is produced by passing an insulated conductor through a magnetic field in such a manner that the conductor cuts the magnetic lines of force. Likewise, a voltage is generated on a pipeline due to the variations in the earth's magnetic field along the pipeline route.

Telluric effects may be identified with recording instruments. A 24-hour record of pipeline current or pipe-to-soil potential, if the effect is telluric, will not show any identifiable pattern as is the case when the stray current is of man-made origin. Fortunately, although occasionally intense, telluric current effects on pipelines are seldom of long duration and may not even be localized at specific pickup or discharge areas for any length of time. For this reason, corrective measures are not often required. Should areas be found, however, where the condition occurs frequently enough and is of serious intensity, corrective measures discussed earlier in the chapter may be adapted to counteract the telluric effect.

REFERENCES

R. L. Seifert, Practical Interference Current Testing on Underground Metallic Structures, *Materials Protection and Performance*, Vol. 11, 41 October 1972.

M. J. Szeliga, ed., Stray Current Corrosion: The Past, Present and Future of Rail Transit Systems, NACE International, Houston, TX, 1994.

Chapter 12

Construction Practices

Ronald L. Bianchetti

Areas covered in this section that apply to the overall corrosion control program include pipeline coatings, test points, cased crossings, insulated joints, galvanic and impressed current cathodic protection (CP) installations, and inspection requirements.

PIPELINE COATINGS

Pipeline coatings were detailed in Chapter 2. Although precautions to be observed were discussed in that chapter, additional points applicable specifically to construction are described below.

Handling Mill Coated Pipe

If mill coated pipe is used, start at the mill to verify that all coating steps are strictly in accordance with the specifications established. This includes surface preparation, priming, application of specified coating materials, holiday tests and holiday repairs, and yard racking of the coated pipe. Check also to see that the pipe is handled carefully during loading out for truck or rail delivery so that coating damage will be at a minimum. Also see that coated pipe lengths are padded adequately and secured solidly on rail cars or trucks so that damage cannot develop under normal shipping conditions. Shipping requirements should be covered by careful specifications designed to accomplish the desired result.

If shipping is by rail, the coated pipe either will be transferred from the rail cars directly to trucks or will be placed first in field storage and then loaded onto the trucks. Again make sure that the coated pipe is handled and protected with care and arrange for specifications that will cover every phase of this work.

When trucks arrive at the job site, facilities must be available for placing the coated pipe on the ground—not dumping it directly from the truck. Coated pipe should not be placed directly on the ground unless the ground is free of material that could damage the coating. Preferably it should be placed with skids or supports under the bare pipe ends where the coating has been cut back; this is seldom possible, however, because of pipe length variation. The best alternative is the use of supports padded properly to prevent damage to the coating. Check with the coating manufacturer for padding recommendations as well as the number of layers permissible in the pipe pile.

Lengths of mill coated pipe should be handled with belt slings or end hooks. Chains or cables around the coated pipe must not be permitted. Belt slings must be wide enough so that they will bear the full pipe weight without distorting the coating. End hooks (one to engage each end of the pipe using a cable sling and spreader) must be designed so that the pipe ends will not be distorted by their use. If a length of coated pipe is handled with a single belt sling, its swing should be restricted with ropes or other suitable means to prevent accidental swinging into equipment with attendant coating damage.

When coated pipe is taken from the ground after stringing for lining up and welding into the pipeline, it usually will be laid up on skids under coated portions to free the ends for welding. Suitable padding must be used between the coating and timber skids to avoid damage.

Pipe Coating over the Ditch

In addition to making sure that the coated pipe is handled as carefully as described for mill coated pipe, the corrosion engineer must verify that the coating application is in strict accordance with tight specifications as was discussed in Chapter 2.

This applies to every phase of pipe cleaning, priming and application of coating materials such as cold applied tapes, wax coatings, heat-shrink sleeves, and wraps. Be sure materials are handled carefully in the field. They must be kept free of dirt and other foreign matter. Wrapping material must be kept dry.

The manufacturer of coating materials should have a technical advisor on a pipeline project. If problems develop under unusual application conditions, the advisor should be consulted at once. Advisors are interested in how their material performs and will be able to recommend application or material modifications to meet the special situation encountered.

Holiday Detection and Repair

Refer to Chapter 2 for further information on the use of holiday detectors. This is an important part of the over-all coating procedure. The corrosion engineer should be assured that detector operators are trained properly in the use of the equipment and that they are using appropriate procedures to verify adequate detector performance at all times.

Because the holiday detector test usually is the last opportunity to verify coating integrity before it is backfilled, this test must be thorough with all holidays well marked for repair. If the coated pipe is laid up on skids prior to lowering into the ditch, be sure that the pipe is checked after lifting from each skid.

The holiday repair crew is as important as the holiday detection crew. Those making such repairs must be trained to repair coating defects properly and apply the repair materials in such fashion that the repaired holiday will be as strong, electrically and mechanically, as the original coating. Preparation includes removing broken and disbonded material and, for best performance when working with enamel or other thick coatings, feathering the edges of the break with a draw knife or equivalent tool. This assures a better bond between the repair materials and the original coating. If there is an outer wrap, it must be removed from around the break to obtain good bonding of repair materials at the overlap. The repair materials themselves must be handled carefully and in accordance with good coating practice.

Good Practices Save Money

Good coating construction practices produce results. Insistence on good coating procedures from the beginning of construction should be the function of the responsible corrosion engineer.

TEST POINT INSTALLATIONS

Test points are the best means of electrically examining a buried pipeline to determine whether or not it is cathodically protected as well as making other tests associated with corrosion control work. Types of test points needed have been mentioned in preceding chapters. To serve their purpose over the years, these test points must be convenient to use and must be so constructed to minimize future damage to the test station.

Types of Test Points

Test point types by function are illustrated in Figure 12.1. The types shown are not necessarily representative of any particular standard but are intended to represent the variety that may be encountered. A color code is shown to illustrate a system whereby leads may be identified. Whatever color code is adopted should be made standard throughout your pipeline system.

The two-wire potential test point is the one used most frequently. Two wires make it possible to check pipe-to-earth potential with one while test current is being applied to the line (if desired) using the other.

The four-wire insulated joint test point permits measuring pipe-to-earth potentials on each side of an insulated joint. The second pair of heavier gauge wires are available for inserting a resistance or solid bond across the insulated joint if necessary.

The four-wire calibrated line current test point permits accurate measurement of pipeline current flow as discussed in Chapter 5.

The six-wire combination insulated joint and line current test point is useful, particularly at terminal insulated flanges, because it permits positive measurement of current

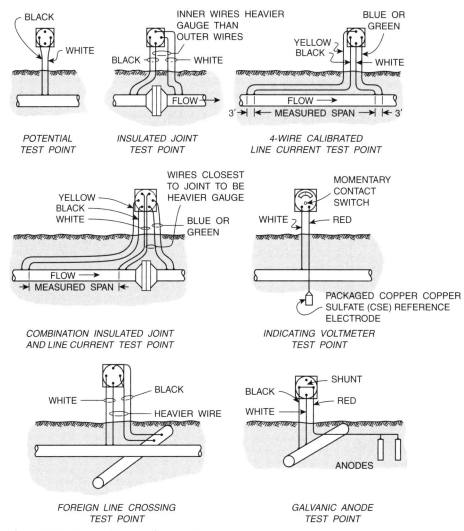

Figure 12.1 Typical types of test station.

flow through an insulated flange should the flange become totally or partially shorted for any reason. Likewise, it will measure the current flowing through a solid or resistance bond should such measurement be necessary. One heavier gauge wire is provided on each side of the insulated joint for bonding purposes (if required).

An indicating voltmeter test point is installed at key points on some systems. These meters may be read by operating personnel on a routine basis and the indicated values recorded and reported to the corrosion engineer. As shown in Figure 12.1, a voltmeter may be connected between the pipe and a reference electrode suitable for underground service.

The foreign line crossing test point provides two wires to each line. One wire is used for potential measurements or other tests as required while the other (the heavier gauge wire) is available for installing a bond when needed. It should be noted that test wires should never be attached to another company's pipeline unless the pipeline owner authorizes it. Further, many companies will allow such attachments only if made by their own personnel or if their own representatives are present while the attachments are being made.

The galvanic anode test point is typically used primarily in connection with anodes at one location. Such a test point is shown in greater detail in Chapter 9 (Figure 9.9).

Test Point Construction

Test points should be located where they will be as convenient as practical for the corrosion engineer. While some type of post mounting is preferable, in some areas test points may have to be in grade level boxes or even buried.

Typical methods of mounting above-ground test points are illustrated by Figure 12.2. Terminal boxes used should be of heavy cast metal construction to resist gunfire—test points in rural areas become convenient targets. Many terminal boxes and matching terminal blocks are available commercially. Terminal blocks obtained to fit the box selected should have heavy studs (at least 0.25 in) of solid brass (may be nickel or

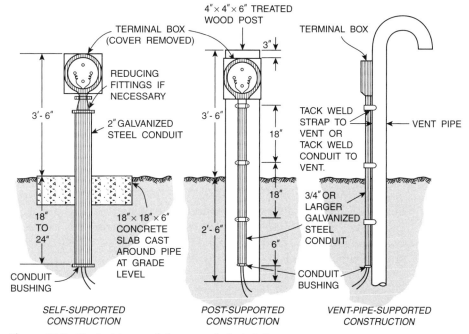

Figure 12.2 Typical types of above grade test stations.

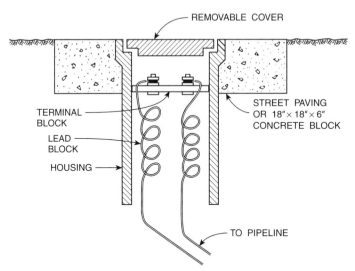

Figure 12.3 Typical at-grade types of test stations.

cadmium plated), with hex nuts and washers. If a rigid steel conduit is used it should be reamed carefully after cutting to length to remove all sharp edges and a conduit bushing should be installed at the lower end as shown. Each wire terminated in the box should have at least 12 in of slack coiled as shown. The last two requirements are necessary to prevent the insulation from being cut through or having them pulled off the terminals in case the wires are subjected to tension by backfill settlement. Where a test point conduit is tack welded to vent pipes or other steel structure, all welding should be done before wires are pulled in so that there will be no heat damage to insulation.

Test points installed at grade level may use an arrangement such as that illustrated by Figure 12.3. In its simplest form, the grade-level test point uses a common street valve box with a cover that has test wires coiled and left in the box with their ends taped to avoid contacts. Terminal boards may be made to fit such boxes. Test point boxes are available, however, which are manufactured specifically for this purpose and include covers identifying them as such. Some designs are completely watertight.

When installing grade level test points, ample wire slack (typically 18 in) should be left in the housing below the terminal panel to allow for backfill settlement and for withdrawing the terminal panel should it be necessary during test work. Each grade level terminal box should be located precisely with respect to permanent reference points and entered on pipeline maps or other permanent records. This is necessary to avoid time loss in searching for the boxes when they are covered with grass, weeds, dirt or snow, or pavement renewals.

Buried test points may be installed as shown in Figure 12.4. A water tight box as illustrated is preferred. A protective plank should be placed directly above the box and wires as seen in the figure to prevent damage to the wires when excavating the box for test.

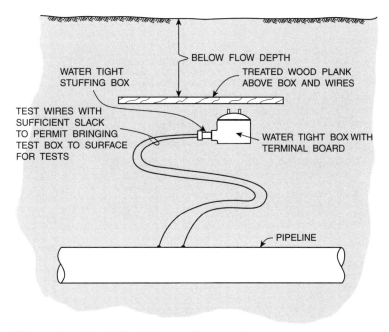

Figure 12.4 Typical buried type of test stations.

Because of the time required for excavating buried test points, they should be used only when there is no alternative. Where possible, it may be preferable to extend leads several hundred feet to a point where an above-ground test point can be installed. This test site must be located precisely with respect to permanent landmarks and the location information recorded where it will be available when tests are made.

Test Wires and Pipeline Connections

Test wires for potential measurements are sized for mechanical strength rather than electrical requirements. As a guide, No. 12 American Wire Gauge (AWG) single conductor stranded wire with 600 V insulation suitable for this service under normal conditions should be used. Such wire may be procured in the various colors needed for test point color coding. For heavier gauge wire shown in some of the sketches in Figure 12.1, No. 6 or No. 4 AWG wire is satisfactory unless the test points are in severe transit or areas of stray current where the wires may carry very large currents. Wire sizing in these cases will depend on experience in similar situations.

If it should be necessary to splice test wires during installation, twisted or bolted splices should not be permitted because they may develop high resistance in time. A soldered splice is preferable, using a good grade of 60–40 lead-tin solder with a

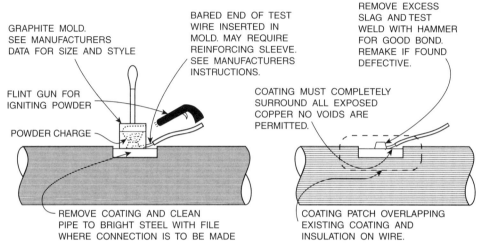

Figure 12.5   Wire connections to pipe.

noncorrosive flux. The splice should be insulated by rubber and plastic tape with the wrapping overlapping the wire insulation sufficiently to render it water-tight.

Test point wires should be so placed that they will not be subjected to excessive strain and damage during backfill operations. Care taken in installation will avoid wire breakage requiring expensive re-excavation for repair. Damage of this nature is most likely to occur where wires are extended along the pipe (as are remote wires for a 4-wire calibrated test point) to reach the test point terminal box. In such instances, the wires may be placed under the pipe as far as they will go before backfilling or they may be run along the top of the pipe and adhered to the pipe with a continuous strip of self-adhesive tape that will also serve to give the wires added mechanical protection.

Permanent low resistance connections are required between test wires and pipeline. Usually these are made using an exothermic welding processes. Currently, practice favors limiting the size of the powder charges to 15-gram when working on high pressure steel lines to minimize localized stresses in the pipe steel caused by the welding heat. The 15-gram charge is adequate for smaller wire sizes. For sizes larger than No. 4, it may be necessary to separate the wire stranding into two or more bundles and powder weld each bundle to the pipe separately. Coating repair is important after wire connections are made. Manufacture literature should be referenced to determine proper powder charge for type and size of pipeline. The essential features of exothermic weld connections and coating repair are shown in Figure 12.5.

Planning a Test Point Location

Prior to construction, the corrosion engineer should study the proposed route and determine the number and types of test points needed. The location and type designation of each test point should be included on pipeline construction drawings so that they will be installed as part of the pipeline construction.

On well coated-pipelines, it is good practice to have four-wire calibrated test points at 3 to 5-mile intervals for measurement of line current and pipe-to-soil potential. Intermediate two-wire test stations should be placed at a minimum of 1/2-mile intervals to a maximum of 1-mile intervals along the pipeline route. Additionally, test points are needed at foreign line crossings, buried insulated joints, and at cased crossings. Test stations should be placed where they will be readily accessible during routine tests.

INSTALLING AND TESTING CASED CROSSINGS

As discussed in Chapter 5 it may be necessary that casing pipe used at road and railroad crossings be electrically insulated from the carrier pipe for adequate CP. Materials are available from a number of manufacturers that make it possible to accomplish this effectively.

Materials

The basic insulating material requirements are shown in Figure 12.6. Insulating spacers, as illustrated in the figure, consist of some type of insulating skid which are strapped

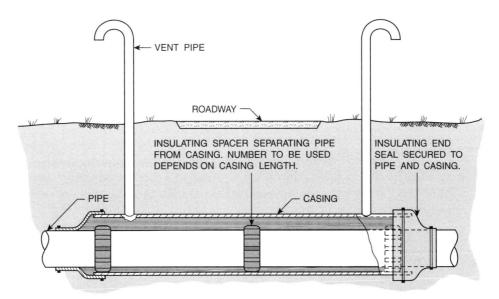

Figure 12.6 Casing installation requirements.

around the pipe through the casing at specific intervals. The various commercially available types of casing insulators range from all-plastic types to models having insulated blocks secured to steel bands (which may be rubber or plastic lined). Skids should be evenly spaced (typically 10 ft max), so that when the carrier pipeline is pulled into the casing, the end insulating spacers will be close to the casing end as shown in the Figure 12.6. Follow manufacturer's recommendations for the number and size of insulating spacers. Top quality materials and careful attention to installation are essential, since stresses on the insulator during installation can be very large. This is particularly true when working with the larger pipe sizes at long-cased crossings. If, during the pulling-in operation, a casing insulator is by accident snagged badly on the casing end, it should be replaced before continuing the installation. After pulling the pipe into final position, if the end insulators are not close to the casing end (such as within 3 ft) additional spacers should be slid into position at the casing ends to maintain positive electrical separation.

End seals shown in the Figure 12.6 are commercially available in various designs. Most designs are arranged to provide a tight, yet flexible, seal between pipe and casing, and most seals are watertight. The style illustrated is typical of synthetic rubber sleeves sized to fit the pipe and casing and strapped to them.

The casing must be prepared properly before the carrier pipe is pulled into it. Welds should be smooth on the inside to prevent damage to insulating spacers. The casing needs to be straight and in round so the carrier pipe, with spacers affixed, can be pulled in without binding. All debris must be removed. If vent pipes are set after the carrier pipe is pulled, burning a hole in the casing may damage the carrier pipe coating, and if the coupon resulting from cutting the hole is allowed to fall into the casing, a short circuit from pipe to casing could result. All welding and hole burning should be done before pulling the carrier pipe.

Test Method for Cased Crossings

After a cased crossing has been completed, it should be checked for adequate insulation before backfilling. Defects can be repaired at that time at a lesser cost than following the completed pipeline installation.

A method of testing cased crossings on completed pipelines is to compare the pipeline potential to soil with the casing potential to soil (electrode at the same location for both tests). A difference in the readings is a qualitative indication of satisfactory insulation between the two pipes. Details of this testing procedure are found in Chapter 5.

Do not use a welding generator to test casing insulation during construction by connecting it between the pipe and casing. If the casing is insulated properly, the generator will not pass current and no harm will be done. If, however, there should be a short, sufficient current may flow to cause a burning effect on the pipe, which could be dangerous in the case of high pressure lines.

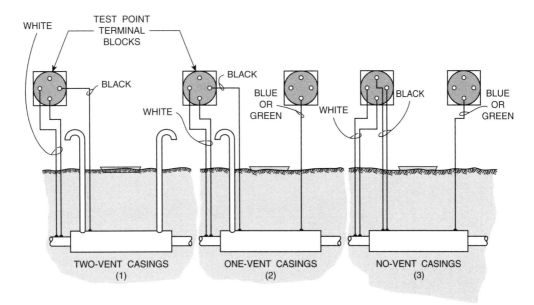

Figure 12.7   Casing test point installations.

Cased Crossing Test Points

The ease with which cased crossings may be tested depends on the type of test point installed. Some suggestions on casing test points are included in Figure 12.7. Although vent pipes may be used in Cases (1) and (2) to indicate whether or not the casing is shorted by using the potential method described above, resistance measurements cannot be made for quantitative results and, if a contact exists, little can be done to locate the fault. To test the nonvented casing (Case 3), test wires are required for routine tests to avoid having to use probe rods to contact the casing.

The four-wire test points (vent pipe serves as one wire in Cases 1 and 2) permit accurate resistance measurements. The additional wire, vent pipe, or probe rod contact at the opposite end of the casing makes it possible to locate the position of a short circuit, should one develop, as discussed in the next section.

Locating Short Circuits in Casings

If a cased crossing becomes shorted in service, being able to identify by testing where the short circuit is located, will save much time and money. This testing can be done as illustrated in Figure 12.8. As shown in the figure, battery current measured with an ammeter is passed between the pipe and casing. This current will flow along the

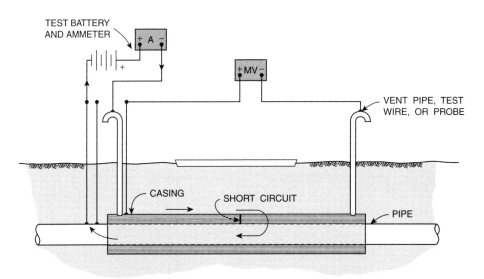

Figure 12.8   Casing short location.

casing to the point of short circuit where it will transfer to the pipe and return to the battery. A millivoltmeter connected between the two ends of the casing will indicate a value dictated by the measured current flowing through the casing resistance within the casing length, which the current actually flows through. The casing size and thickness, or weight per foot, must be known so that its resistance can be estimated using Table 5.3 in Chapter 5.

As an example, assume that the casing in Figure 12.8 is 26-inch pipe, 0.375-in wall thickness and that the span bridged by the millivoltmeter connection is 80 ft. The resistance per foot is 2.82×10^{-6} ohms per foot. The resistance of the 80 ft span would be 225.6×10^{-6} ohms. If the battery current flowing is 10 A and the millivoltmeter reading (corrected for lead resistance) is 1.6 mV, the distance traversed by the current would be the following:

$$\text{Length} = \frac{1.6 \times 10^{-3} \text{ V}}{10 \text{ A} \times (2.82 \times 10^{-6}) \text{ ohms/ft}} = 57 \text{ ft}$$

The short circuit is 57 ft to the right of the voltmeter connection from the left hand end of the casing.

If a short circuit is found more than a few feet in from the ends of the casing (as in the example), it may be very difficult or impractical to clear. Fortunately, many shorts are found at the casing ends where they may be cleared without too much trouble.

In some instances if care is not exercised in placing test leads, an apparent defective casing is actually a short circuit between one of the pipeline test leads and either the casing or vent pipe. Test lead shorts can result if the test wires are wrapped around the vent pipe and subsequently subjected to enough strains to cut through the insulation on the wire.

INSULATED JOINTS

Insulated joints are almost always required in cathodically protected piping systems. On transmission lines, for example, they are used to separate the pipeline electrically from terminal facilities and pumping systems. They may be used also to divide the line into sections so that failure of CP systems or development of contacts with other structures or sections of the pipeline will reduce the loss of protection to an adjacent section. These sections may be reasonably long under normal conditions with distances of 25 to 50 mi being satisfactory. If, however, there are areas where stray currents from mining, traction, or other systems are a problem, closely spaced insulating joints may be helpful in controlling stray current pickup and discharge.

The corrosion engineer should examine proposed construction plans to be sure that adequate provision has been made for placement of insulating joints. The location of insulated joints in such areas will depend on the engineer's knowledge or investigation of areas where stray current influence may be expected.

In planning points of insulation, care must be taken that all possible current paths are insulated. For example, 30 in main line with an insulated flange at a line terminus, can be rendered ineffective by an noninsulated quarter inch instrument line bypassing the flange. Either insulated flanges, or reassembled insulating assemblies, can be used for high pressure line work.

In distribution system piping work, insulated joints maybe used to separate the system into smaller areas for CP purposes. The size of the areas planned will depend on the amount of underground congestion with other pipeline facilities. In downtown sections where underground facilities are dense, individual insulated areas may be limited to a few square blocks. In outlying areas where underground congestion is not great, the insulated areas may be much larger. Separation of areas facilitates maintenance trouble shooting in the event of contact development.

Field assembled or preassembled insulated flanges, or insulated mechanical joints may be used on distribution mains and large service lines. Residential size service lines may be insulated at the meter with various commercially available devices such as insulating bushings, unions, meter bars, meters with insulating swivels, and so forth. Service insulation at the main (if necessary) may be by insulating main tapping fittings, bushings, mechanical couplings, and other kinds of insulation.

Insulated Flanges

The general features of the usual insulated flange assembly are illustrated by Figure 12.9. Flange insulating kits are available from corrosion control supply companies to fit all standard sized flanges. Standard flange bolt holes are 0.125 in larger than standard bolts. Full length insulating sleeves, as shown in the figure, will fit satisfactorily if flanges are aligned properly.

If it is necessary to insulate an existing flange without taking the line out of service, this may be done if the existing gasket is a reasonably good insulating material. Metallized or

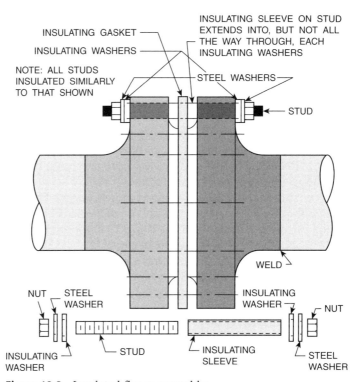

Figure 12.9   Insulated flange assembly.

graphite-impregnated gasket materials normally will make it impossible to insulate the flange without taking it out of service. Assuming that the existing gasket is satisfactory, one bolt may be removed at a time, insulated, and replaced until all bolts have been so treated. Existing flanges, however, are not likely to be sufficiently aligned to permit installing full length insulating sleeves on standard bolts. In this event, insulating and steel washers, and a half-length insulating sleeve may be used on one flange only. The half length sleeve will extend from partway through the insulating washer through the flange being insulated but short of the companion flange. An alternate procedure is to use smaller bolts of higher strength steel such that these smaller bolts with full length insulating sleeves will pass through the misaligned flanges permitting full bolt insulation as illustrated in Figure 12.9.

For new construction, the best practice is to assemble and test the insulated flange before welding it into the line. Shop fabrication and testing allows for perfect flange alignment to be maintained so that undue stresses on insulating materials (particularly the insulating sleeve) will be minimized. Shop fabricated insulated flanges can be tested using a simple ohmmeter. Resistance values in the megohm range should be measured between flanges to indicate proper insulation. The full bolt insulation procedure shown in Figure 12.10 can also be used.

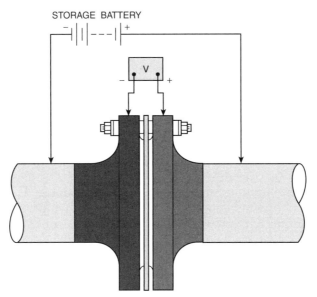

Figure 12.10 Shop testing of Insulating Flanges.

Testing Insulated Joints

When an insulated joint is placed in a pipeline with a substantial amount of pipe on either side of the joint, a simple resistance measurement across the joint may read just a few ohms (or even a fraction of 1 ohm), even though the joint resistance was several million ohms just prior to installation. This method should not be used. The resistance measured with the joint in place consists of two parallel resistances: (1) the joint resistance and (2) the resistance to earth of the pipeline on one side of the joint plus the resistance to earth of the pipeline on the other side of the joint. The resistance measured across a joint, then, (even with perfect joint insulation) will be governed predominantly by the amount of pipe on either side of the joint, the quality of coating (if any), and the average soil resistivity along the pipelines.

More indicative testing of insulated joint effectiveness involves interrupting the CP current source (or test current applied from a temporary d.c. source) on one side of the insulated joint and measuring the potential to a remote copper sulfate electrode. If the joint is effective, the potential on the side with the CP source will change with a positive shift as the current source is interrupted. The unprotected side will remain constant or move in the negative direction. If the measurements are made to a close electrode over or alongside the insulated joint additional information may be gained. For example, if the pipe on the unprotected side swings in the positive direction when the interrupter turns the current source ON (even though there may have been little or no change with respect to the remote electrode), it is an indication that current is flowing through the earth around the insulated flange. This may be a result of defective coating or excessive voltage drop across the flange. Another test is to utilize an insulator tester, which is commonly available. These instruments allow direct measurement of the insulating flange integrity.

If an insulated flange is found defective, it may be possible to repair it without taking the line out of service. This depends on whether the insulating gasket is shorted across or whether it is an insulated bolt sleeve that is broken down. If it is the latter, the shorted bolt may be removed and the insulation replaced. Determining where the trouble is can be accomplished by checking each bolt electrically. If flange bolts are fully insulated per Figure 12.9, an insulator tester should be used to check resistance between pipeline and each bolt. Bolts that are shorted will have zero or low resistance to the pipe. If all bolts have a high resistance to the pipe, a shorted gasket is probably the problem. This assumes that any possible bypassing piping on each side of the flange has been identified and insulated.

In the case of a shorted insulated flange having bolts insulated on one side only, the ohmmeter test will not be acceptable because all bolts will have low resistance to the pipe. Use an insulator checker to identify whether the bolts are shorted or the flanges are shorted.

Grounding Cells for Insulated Joints

Protective devices may be required where insulated joints are subject to damage from lightning-initiated high potential surges. This may be more probable where pipelines closely parallel high voltage electric transmission lines as when a pipeline is installed in the same right-of-way. In such instances, a lightning-initiated fault may cause very high voltages to be induced in the pipeline. If these high voltages are developed across an insulated joint they may cause the joint to arc the current from the lightning flow for a short time. Typically insufficient energy (except in rare cases) is expended to cause the joint to weld across the flange.

Standard lightning arresters may be used effectively. A voltage rating should be selected that will provide adequate protection for the insulation level in the insulating joint being used. Arresters having too high a voltage rating might not divert the high potential appearing across the joint before the insulation fails.

Another protective measure is the grounding cell which combines voltage surge protection with a degree of CP on the unprotected side of the insulating joint. A grounding cell may be constructed as shown, in principle, in Figure 12.11.

Constructed with zinc anodes as illustrated in Figure 12.11, a grounding cell will have a value of resistance between the two closely-spaced anodes depending on the resistivity of the chemical backfill being used. For a properly installed grounding cell, this resistance should be in the range of 0.2 to 0.5 ohms (depending on the backfill used). In the event of a high potential surge, the cell will conduct and the voltage drop across the insulated joint will be limited to 200 to 500 V per thousand amperes of fault current flow. Where very heavy fault currents are anticipated, four anode cells (cross-connected as shown in the detail of Figure 12.11) may be used. These have a lower cell resistance, which limits further the voltage build-up across the insulated flange.

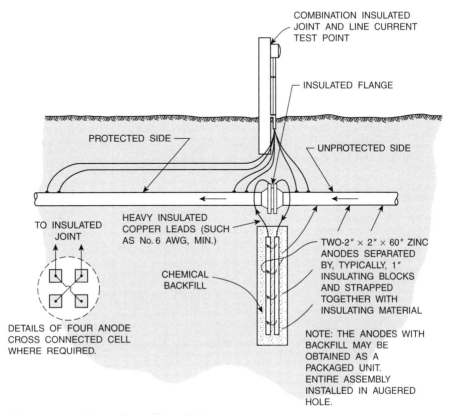

COMBINATION INSULATED JOINT AND LINE CURRENT TEST POINT

INSULATED FLANGE

PROTECTED SIDE

UNPROTECTED SIDE

TO INSULATED JOINT

HEAVY INSULATED COPPER LEADS (SUCH AS No. 6 AWG, MIN.)

CHEMICAL BACKFILL

TWO-2" × 2" × 60" ZINC ANODES SEPARATED BY, TYPICALLY, 1" INSULATING BLOCKS AND STRAPPED TOGETHER WITH INSULATING MATERIAL

DETAILS OF FOUR ANODE CROSS CONNECTED CELL WHERE REQUIRED.

NOTE: THE ANODES WITH BACKFILL MAY BE OBTAINED AS A PACKAGED UNIT. ENTIRE ASSEMBLY INSTALLED IN AUGERED HOLE.

Figure 12.11   Grounding cell installation.

With the grounding cell connected across an insulated joint separating cathodically protected pipe from unprotected pipe, loss of protection current through the cell is limited by cell polarization in addition to the cell resistance. It works in this fashion. The zinc anode connected to the unprotected pipe tends to discharge current to the zinc anode connected to the protected pipe. The anode receiving current, however, will polarize in the negative direction up to approximately −1.5 V with respect to the copper sulfate electrode. The anode discharging current remains at approximately −1.1 V. The cell, then, develops a back voltage up to the difference between the above two figures or 0.4 V. Up to a voltage difference between the two pipelines of this amount, the current flow through the cell will be only that required to maintain polarization. Current flow due to any excess above 0.4 V will be limited by the cell resistance.

In addition to the performance characteristic described above, the zinc anode connected to the unprotected pipeline provides a degree of CP to the unprotected pipe in the flange area. This reduces the possibility of current leaving the pipe in this area to bypass the insulated joint with resulting corrosion of the unprotected pipe.

Where higher cell back voltage is desired, other materials may be used. High silicon cast iron, for example, polarizes in both the negative and positive direction and can develop cell potentials in the order of 2 V or more. If used at an insulated joint separating protected and unprotected pipe, however, the high silicon cast iron anode connected to the unprotected pipe is polarized in the positive direction and will tend to draw current from the unprotected pipe (and corrode) rather than provide a measure of CP as is the case when zinc is used. This can be overcome by using a high resistance container for the cell package (with, however, provision for entry of soil moisture to keep the chemical backfill wet) plus the installation of a local galvanic anode on the unprotected pipe at the insulated joint.

ISP/Polarization Cells

Isolation surge protectors (ISP) and polarization cells are devices that provide excellent grounding and protection for insulating joints. ISP are electronic mechanisms that when placed across an insulating flange block DC current flow and allow AC current to flow. Due to the devices' ability to pass AC current during normal operational, ground fault conditions or lightning strikes, the insulating joint is protected and more importantly the safety of personnel is assured. Since ISP are electronic devices they can automatically reset following a fault condition. Although these devices are more expensive than grounding cells, they provide superior protection. A variety of companies manufacture them and can provide technical support for your particular needs.

GALVANIC ANODE INSTALLATIONS

Although typical galvanic anode installations have been described in Chapter 9, the following pertains to construction practices.

Wire and Connections

All buried wire interconnecting galvanic anodes with the pipeline are cathodically protected. For this reason, insulation level on wire is not critical, but the insulation should be a material which can be expected to resist deterioration under service conditions. Connections between individual anode leads and header wire should be insulated by taping with at least one half-lapped layer of rubber tape and one half-lapped layer of self-adhesive plastic tape (or equivalent insulation) with the joint insulation overlapping the wire insulation. The copper wire connection to the steel main is the most critical insofar as insulation is concerned. At this point, all copper at the connection must be coated completely to avoid the possibility of a shielded copper-steel corrosion cell. All connections must be permanently low resistance. Any gradual development of joint resistance will reduce anode output. Permanent connection such as soldered joints (lead-tin solder or silver solder) or exothermic-welded connections are reliable.

Anode Backfill

The chemical backfill in packaged galvanic anodes will take up moisture slowly even if saturated with water after placing in the auger hole and before completing the earth fill. For this reason, the anode will not attain full output immediately. Depending on the amount of moisture in the earth, it may be a matter of days or even weeks before full output is attained.

CATHODIC PROTECTION SYSTEM INSTALLATIONS

The basic information on ground bed design is contained in Chapter 7 and information on impressed current CP systems is contained in Chapter 8. The following construction notes supplement the information included in those two chapters.

Anodes

Anodes used for ground bed construction, should be transported and handled with care to avoid damage. The insulated leads furnished with the anodes by the manufacturer should be protected from damage to both the wire insulation and the connection between wire and anode. Although these connections are well made, the full anode weight should not be supported by the lead wire alone; although the connection may not fail mechanically, the strain may be sufficient to damage insulating material at the connection. The use of the lead wire to lower anodes into an installation should be prohibited. This may permit current leakage that would cause corrosion failure of the connection. Insulating compounds, taping or specially molded insulating caps of various types are available for reinforcing the insulation provided by anode manufacturers.

Cable and Connections

All underground cable connected to the positive terminal of the rectifier is subject to corrosion at any insulation breaks in the main cable insulation or in field-applied insulation on connections. If a ground bed is to meet its design life expectation without major repairs, all underground cable insulation must be perfect, because the slightest current leakage will result in cable severing.

In selecting insulated cable for ground bed use, follow the cable manufacturer's recommendations for the expected service conditions. Such conditions might include unusually acid or alkaline soils, presence of sea water or brine rather than the usual soil moisture, pressure or abrasive action (cable on ocean or river bottom), solvent action (such as from petroleum product spillage), and other hazards. In recent years, high molecular weight polyethylene insulation has been popular.

Field applied insulation over connections between anode leads and header cable is particularly critical. These connections must be made absolutely waterproof. This can be accomplished by taping after applying insulating putty to break sharp corners at the connection. Four half-lapped layers of top grade rubber splicing compound (overlapping the cable insulation) followed by four half-lapped layers of self-adhesive plastic tape are effective when applied with care. Chemically setting plastic resins poured into molds surrounding connections are also excellent. When the resin and its hardening agent are mixed properly and poured into a correctly applied mold, excellent void-free insulation results.

The more popular methods of making connections between anode leads and header cables are by powder welding or compression connectors using hand or hydraulic compression tools.

Backfill in Cable Trench

Because of the danger of cable insulation breaks, care must be taken to be sure that there are no sharp rocks or other objects in the cable trench bottom that could damage insulation. Should such material be present, the ditch may be deepened and padded with clean earth. The first layer of backfill directly above the cable should likewise be free of cable damaging material. This layer must be of sufficient thickness to prevent penetration by cable-damaging objects in the subsequent fill. Horizontal cable runs are buried, usually, at a minimum depth of 24 in.

Installing Ground Bed Anodes

When installing ground bed anodes according to designs shown in Chapter 8, one of the more critical operations is the installation of coke breeze (or other carbonaceous backfill) around the anode. The fill must be tamped solidly for maximum coupling between anode and earth.

When placing backfill around anodes in vertical holes, continuous tamping is advisable as the backfill is placed layer by layer. This minimizes the possibility of bridging across the hole with void spaces below the bridge. Such voids may increase resistance values and may operate to reduce anode life. When tamping with power tampers (preferred) or by hand, particular care must be exercised to prevent damage to the anode or anode lead wire.

In horizontal installations, ditch width at anode depth should be that of the design width of the carbonaceous backfill layer. Where this is not possible because of trenching conditions, form boards may be used to restrict the backfill. After the carbonaceous backfill and anodes have been placed inside the form boards and the tamped earth outside, the form boards must be withdrawn. The coke breeze should be retamped to fill the space occupied by the form boards.

Rectifier Placement

If possible, rectifiers should be placed where they may be reached for periodic inspection and maintenance with reasonable ease. This may at times necessitate additional cable from the rectifier to the ground bed or pipeline or both. If the amount of additional cable is appreciable, however, the value of having the more convenient rectifier location must be weighed against the increased installed cost of cable and increased power losses in the cable resistance (where significant).

If the proposed rectifier site is in an area where flooding may be a problem, the maximum high water level should be ascertained and the rectifier mounted so that it will be above this level. In the usual instance, however, the rectifier case (if pole mounted) should be placed at a convenient working height.

Before installing a rectifier, the details of the National Electrical Code (NEC) and local electrical codes should be checked. In many areas, rectifier installations must be inspected and passed by an electrical inspector before power service can be obtained. By making the installation conform to the code requirements initially, time will be saved in getting the inspector's certification.

Where power is to be supplied from a local power company by a separate metered service, usually a kilowatt-hour meter base may be obtained from the company. When the installation is completed and inspected (if necessary), the power company can make the necessary connections to the pole top (or other delivery point) and install the kwh meter in the base supplied.

Rectifier cabinets should be grounded separately for safety. Likewise, the power company usually will have pole grounds and a ground rod at the transformer pole serving the rectifier installation. If any of these ground rods are close enough to the ground bed within its area of influence, they will tend to collect current and create a stray current situation on the power system if power distribution is by a grounded neutral system. Locating ground bed anodes too close to ground rods has caused severe instances of stray current damage to power system ground rods and anchors. When there is any question of possible interference from this source, tests should be made and corrective bonds established between the rectifier negative and power system neutral if necessary. In severe instances it could be necessary to install galvanic anodes on ground rods and anchors in current discharge areas to correct the condition, as discussed in Chapter 11.

INSPECTION

Adequate inspection during the construction of corrosion control facilities on pipelines can make the difference between first class performance and a system that may perform poorly and require relatively high maintenance expenditures if ineffective or not inspected.

Test Points, Cased Crossings, and Insulating Joints

Test points must be inspected to assure that installation complies with construction plans. The inspection should make sure that connections to the pipeline are sound and well insulated, that color coding is observed, that wires are so placed in the ditch that backfill will not break them, and that the specified terminal panel and housing is installed properly.

Cased crossings should be inspected as soon as they are installed. This is necessary to ascertain that the casing is electrically insulated from the carrier pipe and to permit correction of defects before backfilling.

Insulating joints installed as complete preassembled, pretested units should be inspected for proper installation at the location indicated on the plans, so that the joint is not subject to undue mechanical strains that could cause early failure of insulating material and that the joint is in fact performing satisfactorily once welded into the line.

The inspectors charged with inspecting the above features must be thoroughly familiar with the use of test points, cased crossings, and insulating joints. They must have the necessary instrumentation to verify the satisfactory performance of the various items prior to acceptance. They should also have the authority to see that corrections are made should defects be found.

Cathodic Protection Installations

Inspectors responsible for CP installations must be fully familiar with all details of good CP construction practice as well as with the specific provisions of the installations being made.

In some instances field modifications may be necessary. This may occur, for example, if vertical anode installations were specified but rock is closer to the surface than expected. A field decision is then necessary to determine whether the type of anode installation may be changed from vertical to horizontal or if best results will be obtained by boring the rock. Occasionally what appears to be solid rock is actually a relatively thin layer with good soil underneath. The inspector must be qualified to evaluate all such situations when encountered. If major modifications are advisable, the inspector should check with the designer of the installation to be sure that the system performance will not be affected adversely.

At galvanic anode installations, one of the more particular points to be watched is the anode backfilling operation to be sure that there are no voids in the fill around the anodes. This can be a problem with packaged galvanic anodes placed vertically in augured holes. If the hole is small, it may be difficult to work earth backfill all around the anode package so that no voids will exist. If voids are present, the chemical backfill material can settle away from the anode, once the container has deteriorated, with probable reduction in anode effectiveness. If anodes and chemical backfill are installed separately, the inspector must verify that the anode is centered in the hole or trench as specified and that the fill is so placed and compacted that no voids can exist. All other details of galvanic anode installations must be verified by the inspector as being in accordance with good practice for such construction.

When inspecting impressed current ground beds, anode placement and backfilling operations must be given careful attention to ensure installation at the design location and to avoid voids in special carbonaceous backfill which would tend to increase anode resistance and shorten life. Adequate compacting of carbonaceous backfill materials is important and the inspector must verify that this is done effectively but in a way that will not damage the anode proper or its connecting cable.

Probably the most important single feature of impressed current ground beds to be verified by the inspector is the insulation on all positive header cable, anode connecting cable, and connections between the two. The inspector must be sure that no damaged cable insulation is buried without being repaired and that the insulation of all splices and tap connections are such that they will be permanently watertight so no current leakage can occur. Likewise, the inspector must be sure that the cable trench bottom that can damage the cable insulation and that the backfill in contact with the cable is free of insulation-damaging material.

When rectifier installations are involved, the inspector verifies that the rectifier unit has been placed at the specified location and in the specified manner, that all wiring is correct and that requirements of the power company and of NEC and local jurisdictional codes have been satisfied. If power supplies other than rectifiers are used, the inspector must be familiar with the details of the power source specified so that he may verify that the installation is being made properly.

Chapter 13

Maintenance Procedures

Ronald L. Bianchetti

Pipeline corrosion control measures as described in the preceding chapters can be highly effective if properly designed and installed, but only if they are maintained adequately. Without a suitable maintenance program, money spent for designing and installing corrosion control can be wasted. There have been many instances, for example, of the system owner paying for the installation of cathodic protection (CP) on sections of their system without establishing any means for ongoing maintenance. Although they may feel that their troubles are over, this false sense of security can be short-lived if corrosion failures continue to occur. The tendency is to blame the design, but from experience the fault in most cases is simply failure to keep the system operating continuously and effectively. The purpose of this chapter is to present suggestions for maintenance programs that will help to keep corrosion control measures operating at maximum effectiveness.

REQUIREMENTS FOR A MAINTENANCE PROGRAM

The following items should be included, as applicable, in a maintenance program for a pipeline corrosion control system:

- Periodic surveys to determine the status of CP and related items
- Coating maintenance procedures
- Maintenance procedures for current sources and ground beds in impressed current CP installations
- Maintenance procedures for galvanic anode CP installations
- Maintenance procedures for test points
- Maintenance procedures for cased crossings
- Maintenance procedures at foreign line crossings.

Each of the above will be discussed in detail in the following sections.

PERIODIC SURVEYS

On cathodically protected pipelines, the following data should be taken as outlined in NACE INTERNATIONAL RP0169 (latest revision) and code of Federal Regulations-Transportation Section 49, Part 192:

- A potential survey along the protected pipeline. This should include, on a coated pipeline, potentials to close copper sulfate electrode (CSE) at all test points along the line
- On coated pipelines, data for calculation of effective coating resistance
- At each rectifier installation, DC current and voltage, the efficiency of the rectifier and the kilowatt hour meter reading
- At other DC power sources, the DC current and voltage as well as pertinent supplementary information which may apply to the particular power source
- The resistance of each impressed current ground bed
- The current output and resistance of each galvanic anode installation
- Potentials of the line surveyed and of the foreign line at foreign line crossings. Where intersystem bonds exist, measure the bond current and direction of flow
- At cased crossings, the resistance between carrier pipe and casing plus the potential to reference electrode of both pipeline and casing
- In variable stray current areas, verification that bonds, electrolysis switches or other corrective measures are operating properly and are providing the required degree of protection
- Verification that insulated joints are effective and that any protective lightning arresters, spark gaps, grounding cells, and polarization cells are performing their function effectively
- Notes on maintenance requirements on any of the physical features associated with the corrosion control system.

In addition to the required surveys, a more frequent check of protective potentials should be made in areas where there is pipeline congestion with many foreign line crossings, where variable stray current interference is a problem, or where particularly critical or hazardous environmental conditions exist. In this category may be included interference correction bonds between pipelines where the bond carries more than some established value (5 A for example) as well as bonds, electrolysis switches, or other facilities for stray current electrolysis correction in DC transit system, mining, or other similar problem areas.

Standard printed forms should be used to record the field data. These may be planned by the pipeline corrosion engineer to suit particular requirements. Such forms serve two important functions. First, they save field time by minimizing the amount of writing necessary on the part of field test personnel. Second, they establish a uniform manner for recording data which is important if a number of different people are participating in the surveys throughout the pipeline system. A form that may be used for recording the protective potential data is shown by Figure 13.1.

XYZ PIPE LINE COMPANY
CORROSION CONTROL DEPARTMENT
POTENTIAL SURVEY TEST DATA

Date ___7-8-68___ Test Engineer(s) ___John Doe___ Sheet No. _2_ of _3_

Pipeline ___Omega 30" Main Line No. 1___ Mileposts ___9___ to ___23___

Between Compressor Stations ___C___ and ___D___

Test Meter: ___MCM B-3___ Meter No. ___123___ Scale ___1-Volt and 2-Volt___

MILE POST NUMBER	TEST POINT DESIGNATION	PIPE-TO-SOIL POTENTIAL-V (CSE)				REMARKS
		OVER THE LINE	REMOTE			
			DISTANCE	DIRECTION	VALUE	
15.33	CD-TP7-I	−0.605	100'	West	−1.05	−0.601 P/Sc Opp. Side Flange
16.34	CD-TP-8	−0.638				
17.36	CD-MG-3	−0.765				

NOTES: _____

Figure 13.1 Form for potential test data.

Other forms may be used for line current data and calculations, for coating resistance test data and calculations, for galvanic anode or impressed current source tests, for cased crossing rests, for stray current tests, and for other special tests that may be made as a matter of routine during periodic survey work.

Although areas requiring additional protection may be determined by inspection of the data sheets, the best understanding of the results may be achieved by plotting the protective potentials versus line length. Master sheets may be prepared for each line with all test points, impressed current or galvanic anode installations, insulating joints, taps, and other pertinent information shown in their correct position above the area in which the data are plotted. Results of each survey may be plotted on a print of the master sheet together with a plot of the last survey made. This permits readily determining areas where there may have been reduction or loss of protection since the last survey was made. This will show graphically where improvements in the protection system may be required. A portion of such a data plot is illustrated by Figure 13.2.

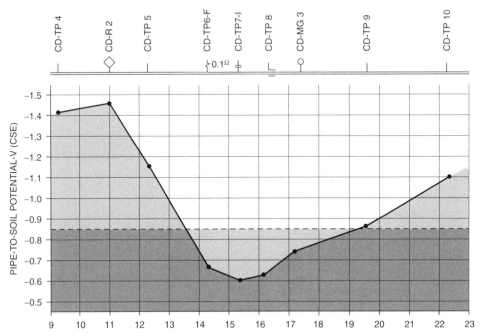

Figure 13.2 Protective potential profile.

As shown in the figure, there is an area near the center where there has been a loss of protective potential throughout a substantial area. From the line plot above the graph, it can be seen that there is an insulated main line tap, a cased crossing, a bond to a foreign structure, and a magnesium anode installation within this area. Difficulty with any one or several of these items could have contributed to the loss of protection. Comparison of the most recent survey data at each of these sites with similar data taken during the last preceding survey should give a quick indication of the probable source of the trouble—shorted insulation in the lateral tap, shorted cased crossing, changed conditions at the foreign line crossing, or magnesium anode installation starting to fail.

Note also from Figure 13.2 that items such as test points and CP current sources are given identifying numbers (arbitrary in this case). For a pipeline network covering an extensive area, it is helpful to establish some system of designations that will identify the location within the network. In the illustration, for example, CD-TP6-F could indicate the section between compressor stations C and D with TP6 indicating test point No. 6 and F indicating a foreign line test point. Similarly, CD-Mg3 could indicate magnesium anode installation No. 3 in the same section. In setting up a system, the overall requirements of the pipeline network should be analyzed and a uniform designation code established that will satisfy fully the requirements of that particular network.

Original survey data and completed survey plots should be bound in suitable ledgers or otherwise stored in such fashion that they may be reviewed conveniently. Such data may become of great importance in the event of litigation involving the need to demonstrate that a section of line has been placed under CP and maintained adequately.

As soon as a periodic survey is completed it should be analyzed promptly. In areas where required, corrective action should be taken immediately. The corrosion engineer should recommend, obtain approval for, and organize standard procedures for having required maintenance work done through established channels consistent with company policy. This will make it a routine matter for requesting maintenance work when and as needed to keep the corrosion control system operating at optimum effectiveness.

COMPUTER PROGRAMS

Computers today provide the capability for the pipeline company to manage and analyze large amounts of data in a relatively short time. Experience shows that the development and use of computer programs to save, sort, and analyze data provides the corrosion engineer an invaluable tool for operation and maintenance of the corrosion control system. Programs can be written to automatically flag such things as protective potentials below predetermined levels, rectifier efficiencies that have dropped to an uneconomic level requiring stack replacement, anode installations that have dropped below a predetermined output level, and other items of a similar nature as required. The time spent in getting such a program organized and established will be repaid in the speed of analyzing data upon conclusion of periodic surveys.

COATING MAINTENANCE

Although coated pipelines are buried and inaccessible under normal conditions, there are things that can be done to maintain coating systems. During normal operations on most pipeline systems the line will be frequently uncovered for other maintenance work. This work may involve damage to the coating or removal of portions of it. Coating repair or replacement should be of a quality at least as good as the original coating. Maintenance crews should be trained in good coating application procedures, care of materials, and compliance with specifications so that acceptable coating work will result.

Maintaining a performance record of pipeline coatings on the system will help the corrosion engineer to prepare and present recommendations for material to be used on new construction. The general electrical condition in terms of effective resistance can be obtained from the periodic corrosion surveys. In some cases, specific information can be obtained by training all line maintenance crews to report on the coating condition whenever pipe is uncovered. Information desirable in such a report includes date, specific location, coating type and description, manufacturer and grade of material (if known) or other identifying information as available or applicable, temperature at the coating surface in place, general condition of the coating, bond quality, evidence of cold flow, evidence of moisture under the coating, evidence of soil stress effects, presence of pitting at holidays (with data on number of pits, depth range, and range of pit diameters), and data on environmental conditions surrounding the pipe that could have an adverse effect on coating. Accumulation of information by this method allows for a continuous reporting procedure to compare historic data, thereby providing the corrosion engineer with knowledge of how the pipeline's coatings are performing.

Where anomalies are found as part of the ongoing surveys, special dig-ups may be required. These may be caused by conditions where potentials are declining along a specific section of pipeline with no apparent cause. Actual points to be excavated are typically selected on the basis of areas of low potentials, sections with higher than normal current demands, and areas having the more severe holiday indications following holiday detection.

Although uncovering a pipeline and replacing a coating is expensive, it may be necessary in some instances. This is typically true where coating deterioration is found to be severe over a short length of pipeline because of unusual environmental conditions. This circumstance may result in loss of protective levels of CP over an area of the pipeline. Recoating the section usually restores CP to proper levels over the entire line with no significant changes in the CP system current outputs. If a section is recoated, the chances are that the original coating was not a suitable selection for conditions in that area. The material used for recoating should be selected specifically for its ability to stand up under the particular environmental conditions encountered. Another means of reestablishing proper levels of CP in the deficient area(s) is to provide supplemental localized CP. Economic justification for recoating versus simply adding local CP in the affected area should be evaluated for each case.

RECTIFIER MAINTENANCE

Rectifiers or other impressed current power sources should be inspected on a routine basis. Preferably this should be combined with other pipeline operations to eliminate the need for a separate maintenance trip. The routine established would depend on the procedures followed in a system. Seldom would inspection more than once per week be required, and every two weeks is satisfactory. The interval normally should not exceed a month.

Where longer periods between inspections are unavoidable, units on lines which are air patrolled can be fitted with devices which will give a visual indication of loss of power. The air patrol report will provide prompt notice of unit failure. Monthly power bills on rectifiers equipped with individual kilowatt hour meters will serve also as an indication of whether or not the power is functioning and power consumption is normal. Newer technology which may include remote monitoring systems may be considered for areas where normal inspection intervals cannot be maintained.

Routine inspection of rectifiers consists normally of reading the DC output voltmeter and ammeter as well as reading the AC kilowatt hour meter (if one exists). This latter reading makes it possible, if the unit is found to be out of service, to estimate the approximate time the unit has been off. Readings should be recorded on a form and forwarded to a designated office where they may be posted and compared with prior readings to observe unusual variations. At some locations where seasonal variations cause substantial changes in rectifier current output, rectifier taps may require adjustment during routine inspection to maintain adequate protection.

If a rectifier is found to be off, the inspector should check to see if the trouble is caused by a blown fuse or tripped circuit breaker. If this is found to be the case because of a temporary electric system disturbance (such as may occur during an electrical storm), restoring the circuit may be all that is necessary. If, however, the rectifier cannot be returned to service easily, the responsible corrosion engineer should be notified as soon as is practical so he may investigate the trouble and implement corrective action.

Older rectifiers may be expected to become less efficient as the rectifier stacks age. For small units operating on a minimum power bill basis, this is not significant unless the inefficiency becomes so great that the minimum bill is exceeded. Efficiency is most important, however, on large units. Rectifier stacks on large units should be replaced when they become so inefficient that the increased annual cost of power exceeds the annual cost of the investment required to make the replacement.

In making stack replacements in rectifier units, the use of an element identical to the one being replaced may not be always the right thing to do. The technology of manufacturing rectifying elements has advanced markedly over the years and a stack that may have been the best available when a rectifier was built originally may be outmoded by the time a replacement is needed. For this reason, particularly when replacing stacks in older rectifiers, the new rectifying elements should be specified to match the DC output nameplate rating on the rectifier (plus whether single or three phase, full wave bridge or center tap, and type (silicon, or other) rather than specifying an exact replacement of original equipment. By so doing, gains in efficiency, improvements in aging characteristics, and increases in voltage blocking capacity can be beneficial. Such upgrades provide improved efficiency, reduce operating expense while higher inverse voltages give greater protection and operating flexibility to the rectifier.

At least once per year (usually at the time of the complete annual survey), rectifier components should be systematically inspected and checked as follows:

- Clean and tighten all bolted current-carrying connections.
- Clean all ventilating screens in air cooled units so that air flow will be completely unobstructed.
- Check indicating meters for accuracy.
- Replace insulated wires on which insulation has cracked or been damaged.
- Oil immersed units, check for proper oil level and cleanliness. The oil should be clear and nearly colorless. A failing oil is usually characterized by a murky or cloudy appearance with loss of transparency and should be replaced with a good grade of standard electrical transformer oil unless facilities are available for testing the oil and salvaging by filtration where practicable.
- Check all protective devices (fuses, circuit breakers, or lightning arresters) to be sure that they are undamaged and in satisfactory operating condition.

Other types of direct current sources for impressed current systems, will require routine maintenance to at least an extent equal to rectifiers. Although not detailed here, maintenance programs should be prepared for such power supplies. Programs should have as their prime objective the prevention of unit failures before they occur plus prompt repair should outages develop.

GROUND BED MAINTENANCE

Surface Anodes

Ground bed maintenance will consist of periodic checks to ensure that there has been no disturbance of the earth above the header cable and line of anodes in a conventional (surface) type bed. If any part of the ground bed is subject to washing (by storm water) with exposure of cable, the cable should be covered again for protection. This should be done only after determining that there has been no insulation damage. Washes should be diverted to prevent reexposure of the cable.

If construction activity is noted in the vicinity of the ground bed, the location of the ground bed route should be staked or marked with paint so that inadvertent damage may be avoided. If new construction involves installation of underground structures, tests may be necessary to determine whether or not they will be within the potential gradient field surrounding the ground bed and subject to possible stray current damage.

During routine testing, any significant increases in ground bed resistance (or an open circuit), will prompt additional testing. Measurement techniques will be required to locate cable breaks or anodes that have failed. When an increase in resistance is found, a pipe-cable locator can be used to find the problem. If the locator indicates a continuous cable throughout the ground bed length, one or more anodes may have failed. If there is a header cable break along the line of anodes, the signal will drop to essentially zero in the vicinity of the break.

Where failed anodes are indicated, they may be located by an over-the-line potential profile (made along the line of anodes with the rectifier energized) with the measured potentials being taken between a remote reference electrode and the over-the-line CSE which is moved by two or three foot increments along the line. The potential profile will show positive potential peaks at each working anode. Any areas where peaks in potential are not found represent anodes that are no longer working and require repair or replacement. The number and spacing of anodes installed originally should be known.

Deep Well Anodes

Deep well ground beds require preventive maintenance that includes ensuring that cables are well protected between the rectifier cabinet and the well head. Additionally the well head cover or cap should be adequately secured to prevent unauthorized entry and be vented sufficiently to permit escape of any anode-generated gases. If deep well ground anode(s) fail, little can be done if the anode string cannot be withdrawn from the well. If the failure is a result of cable damage at the well top, typically repairs can be made and the functionality of the anode well reestablished.

Increased resistance of a deep well caused by gas blocking can be remedied in some cases by air or water injection through the vent pipe if one exists. If injection of a low resistivity chemical solution is considered, the possible effect on anode material and cable insulation must be studied as well as the possibility of contaminating potable water supplies via underground water seams.

GALVANIC ANODE MAINTENANCE

Maintenance of galvanic anode installations is typically performed to determine that anode leads or header cables have not been exposed or damaged by accident, right-of-way washing or construction work. Where such exposure or damage is found, repairs should be scheduled promptly. At installations having test points, maintaining the connection between the lead from the anodes and that from pipeline is critical. Due to the low driving potential available from galvanic anodes, resistance in the connection can cause a marked decrease in current output. Annually, such connections should be cleaned.

As galvanic anodes approach the end of their useful life, current output will diminish. Replacement of individual anodes or the entire anode ground bed will be required when insufficient current output(s) to maintain protective potentials on the pipeline are identified. Current output can be measured during annual surveys at those installations having test points installed for the purpose. Approximate determination of the useful life of such installations may be predicted from a comparison of the average current output (since installation) with the amount of anode material. See the calculation of anode life in Chapter 9.

If there is a marked decrease in the output of a galvanic anode installation and there is no reason to believe that it is reaching the end of its life, a broken header wire or anode lead may be the cause. If an over-the-line potential profile is made to locate disconnected anodes, the peaks at working anodes will be usually of much less magnitude than those found for impressed current anodes.

TEST POINT MAINTENANCE

Test points are the principal means in evaluating the level of CP on most pipeline systems. Post mounted test stations, from time to time, require replacement of box covers or cover retention screws, cover gaskets or terminal nuts or screws within the test box. Occasionally a test station may be broken or missing as the result of accident or vandalism. Pipeline corrosion personnel, when making routine surveys, should carry a complete stock of spare parts and test boxes so that minor maintenance can be implemented at that time.

Broken wires at test points can be hard to repair if the break is not near the surface. Where test stations are attached to a cased crossing vent pipe, earth settlement at a deeply buried crossing can create enough tension on the wires to break them. While it is good practice to leave slacked wire in the test box to relieve tension, this is not always sufficient.

Occasionally it is found that test wires were tied around the vent pipe to hold it in place while the crossing excavation was being filled and that this tie-off was not loosened when the test point was set. Soil settlement can pull the wires taut at and below the point where they are tied and either snap them or cut through the wire insulation to short circuit the wires to each other or to the vent pipe. In the case of long buried underground conductors along the current measurement spans, backfill settlement around the pipe may be sufficient to snap the wires if they were not placed properly at the time of installation.

Occasionally, a defective exothermic weld connection between test lead and pipe may separate from the pipe and give an open circuit indication. At locations where the test point is located close to the pipe connections, the excavation required to locate and repair the trouble (unless the line is very deep) is rather simple. If the break is in a long wire span, where to excavate becomes important and requires the use of pipe-cable locator tests to determine the break location.

CASED CROSSING MAINTENANCE

Maintaining insulation between carrier pipe and casing is the most important objective at cased crossings. If it is not possible to isolate the casing and the carrier pipe, steps should be taken to eliminate (by methods other than CP) conditions conducive to corrosion on the carrier pipe within the casing. See Chapter 5 on the effect of shorted casings on CP.

The status of isolation at cased crossings should be measured at each annual survey. If a shorted condition is found, immediate repair should be scheduled. Before sending a crew to the site, as much information as possible on the probable location of the short circuit should be determined by electrical measurements.

The first thing to check is the test point at the cased crossing. It is not unusual to find that the short circuit is not in the casing itself, but may result from contacts between the test point wires and the casing vent (or the end of the casing) or between the test wires and test point conduit mounted on the casing vent. Locating and clearing such short circuits is discussed in the preceding section. If the short circuit is between the pipe and casing, it should be determined (if casing and test point construction so permit) whether the short is at one of the two ends or is well inside the casing. This is discussed in Chapter 5. With a contact at one of the two ends, that end may be uncovered, the end seal removed and the short circuit cleared. This may require jacking the pipe and casing apart and inserting additional insulating spacers. Usually, when the contact is at one end, its location and cause are obvious once uncovered and the end seal is removed. The casing end seal should be replaced after the short circuit is cleared and before backfilling.

If tests indicate that the point of contact is well back from the end of the casing, the chances are that it cannot be cleared with any reasonable effort and expense by working from the casing ends. To safeguard the carrier pipe inside such nonclearable casings, the favored procedure is to fill the entire annular space between pipe and casing with a material that will stifle any corrosion tendency. Proprietary casing compounds (greases containing chemical inhibitors) may be used. Companies routinely provide both casing filler compounds and installation of these products.

FOREIGN LINE CROSSINGS

Resistance bonds installed between pipelines for intersystem interference correction require periodic checking (the ones carrying larger amounts of current should be checked frequently). Resistance bonds may be subject to occasional burn-out in the event of high current surges. Prompt replacement is required.

Probably the most important item of preventive maintenance is the timely exchange of operational information resulting from changes in corrosion control systems on existing foreign lines and for new foreign pipeline construction where foreign lines may cross or closely approach the corrosion engineer's system. This information may be obtained by direct contact with the foreign line companies involved and/or through electrolysis committees active in the area. Early information exchange allows planning for cooperative interference tests, design of corrective bonds, or other necessary measures to mitigate interference damage caused to either party.

The matter of information exchange is equally important in stray current electrolysis areas. Advance information on changes in operating schedules, discontinuation, or moving of DC substations are most important. This information will make it possible to coordinate testing and install any required modifications in the corrosion control system to mitigate stray current problems.

Chapter 14

Microbiologically Influenced Corrosion

Brenda J. Little and Patricia Wagner

INTRODUCTION

Microbiologically influenced corrosion (MIC) is corrosion resulting from the presence and activities of microorganisms, including bacteria and fungi. Jack et al. (1996) reported that MIC was responsible for 27% of the corrosion deposits on the exterior of line pipe in one survey of Nova Gas Transmission Ltd. (Calgary, Alberta) lines. Pope and Morris (1995) reported that almost all cases of MIC on external surfaces of pipes were associated with disbonded coatings (Figure 14.1). The following general statements about microorganisms are taken directly from Pope (1986):

1. Individual microorganisms are small (from less than 0.2 to several hundred micrometers (μm) in length by up to 2 or 3 μm in width) a quality which allows them to penetrate crevices and other areas easily. Bacterial and fungal colonies can grow to macroscopic proportions.
2. Bacteria may be motile, capable of migrating to more favorable conditions or away from less favorable conditions, that is, toward food sources or away from toxic materials.
3. Bacteria have specific receptors for certain chemicals which allow them to seek out higher concentrations of those substances that may represent food sources. Nutrients, especially organic nutrients, are generally in short supply in most aquatic environments; but surfaces, including metals, adsorb these materials, creating areas of relative plenty. Organisms able to find and establish themselves at these sites will have a distinct advantage in such environments.
4. Microorganisms can withstand a wide range of temperatures (at least -10 to $99\,^{\circ}$C), pH (about 0–10.5) and oxygen concentrations (0 to almost 100% atmospheres).

Figure 14.1 Disbonded pipeline coating associated with external localized MIC. (Courtesy Dan Pope, Bioindustrial Technologies, Inc.).

5. They grow in colonies which help to cross-feed individuals and make survival more likely under adverse conditions.
6. They reproduce very quickly (generation times of 18 min have been reported).
7. Individual cells can be widely and quickly dispersed by wind and water, animals, aircraft, and other means, and thus the potential for some of the cells in the population to reach more favorable environments is good.
8. Many can quickly adapt to use a wide variety of different nutrient sources. For example, *Pseudomonas fluorescens* can use more than 100 different compounds as sole sources of carbon and energy including sugars, lipids, alcohols, phenols, organic acids, and other compounds.
9. Many form extracellular polysaccharide materials (capsules or slime layers). The resulting slimes are sticky and trap organisms and debris (food), resist the penetration of some toxicants (e.g., biocides) or other materials (corrosion inhibitors) and hold the cells between the source of the nutrients (the bulk fluid) and the surface toward which these materials are diffusing.
10. Many bacteria and fungi produce spores which are very resistant to temperature (some even resist boiling for more than 1 h), acids, alcohols, disinfectants, drying, freezing, and many other adverse conditions. Spores may remain viable for hundreds

of years and germinate on finding favorable conditions. In the natural environment, there is a difference between survival and growth. Microorganisms can withstand long periods of starvation and desiccation. If conditions are alternating between wet and dry, microbes may survive dry periods but will grow only during the wet periods.

11. Microorganisms are resistant to many chemicals (antibiotics, disinfectants, etc.) by virtue of their ability to degrade these chemicals or by being impenetrable to them because of slime, cell wall, or cell membrane characteristics. Resistance may be easily acquired by mutation or acquisition of a plasmid (essentially by naturally occurring genetic exchange between cells, i.e., genetic engineering in the wild).

MECHANISMS FOR MIC

It is established that the most aggressive MIC takes place in the presence of microbial consortia in which many physiological types of bacteria, including metal-oxidizing bacteria, sulfate-reducing bacteria (SRB), acid-producing bacteria (APB), and metal-reducing bacteria (MRB) interact in complex ways within the structure of biofilms (Figure 14.2) (Little et al. 1991). MIC does not produce a unique form of localized corrosion. Instead, MIC can result in pitting, crevice corrosion, underdeposit corrosion and selective dealloying, in addition to enhanced galvanic and erosion corrosion. The principal effect of bacteria under aerobic conditions is to increase the probability that localized corrosion will be initiated. Bacteria can set up the proper conditions for pitting or crevice corrosion. Once localized corrosion has been initiated, microbial reactions can maintain proper conditions (e.g., low oxygen) for continued pit/crevice growth. The rate at which pits propagate can be governed by organic acid production by fungi in aerobic environments and by certain bacteria in anaerobic environments. Under anaerobic reducing conditions, aggressive MIC is observed when there is some mechanism for the removal or transformation of corrosion products (i.e., there are switches from stagnation to flow or from anaerobic to aerobic conditions). The following discussion about individual MIC mechanisms will be related directly to carbon steel.

Sulfate Reduction

SRB are a diverse group of anaerobic bacteria that can be isolated from a variety of subsurface environments. If the aerobic respiration rate within a biofilm is greater than the oxygen diffusion rate during biofilm formation, the metal/biofilm interface can become anaerobic and provide a niche for sulfide production by SRB (Figure 14.3). The critical thickness of the biofilm required to produce anaerobic conditions depends on the availability of oxygen and the rate of respiration. SRB concentrations are always correlated with groundwater sulfate concentration. The distribution of favorable pH ranges from 6 to 12, although they can mutate to accommodate pH conditions. SRB grow in soil,

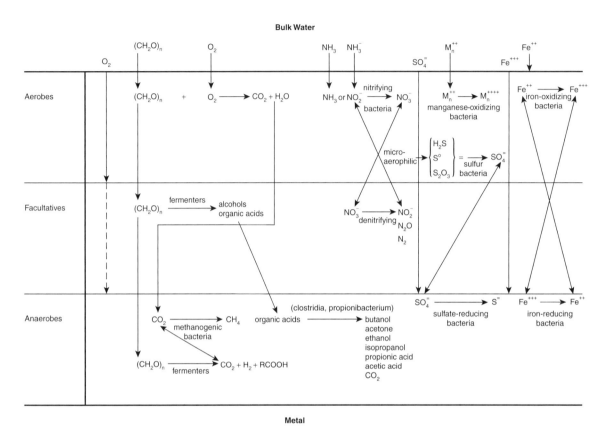

Figure 14.2   Strata within a typical biofilm and possible reactions within the strata.

fresh water, or salt water under anaerobic conditions. Many species of SRB have been identified, differing in morphology and in organic substances that they can metabolize. They have in common the ability to oxidize certain organic substances to organic acids or carbon dioxide by reduction of inorganic sulfate to sulfide. In the absence of oxygen, the metabolic activity of SRB causes accumulation of sulfide near metal surfaces. This is particularly evident when metal surfaces are covered with biofilms. The concentration of sulfide is highest near the metal surface. Iron sulfide forms quickly on carbon steels and covers the surface if both ferrous and sulfide ions are available. Formation of iron sulfide minerals stimulate the cathodic reaction. Once electrical contact is established, a galvanic couple develops with the mild steel surface as an anode, and electron transfer occurs through the iron sulfide. At low ferrous ion concentrations adherent and temporarily protective films of iron sulfides are formed on the steel surface, with a consequent reduction in corrosion rate. Aggressive SRB corrosion requires exposure to oxygen. Hardy and Bown (1984) demonstrated that corrosion rates of mild steel in anaerobic cultures of SRB were low ($1.45\,\mathrm{mg/dm^2/day}$). Subsequent exposure to air caused high corrosion

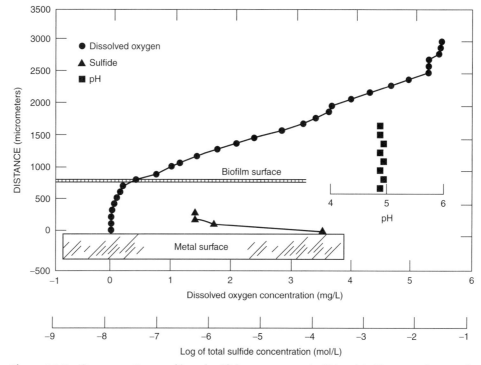

Figure 14.3   Concentration profiles of sulfide, oxygen, and pH in a biofilm on carbon steel. (From *Biofouling*, 1993. Reprinted with permission from Overseas Publishers Association (OPA) and Gordon and Breach Publishers.)

rates (129 mg/dm^2/day). Accordingly, structures that are exposed under fully deaerated conditions generally experience low corrosion rates despite the presence of high concentrations of SRB.

Acid Production

Organic acids can be produced by both bacteria and fungi. Most of the final products of MIC community metabolism are short-chained fatty acids like acetic acid that are very aggressive in the attack of carbon steel, and become especially aggressive when concentrated under a colony or other deposit. This type of attack is accelerated by the addition of chloride. The resulting chloride-rich corrosion products have a greater volume and are less stable, often flaking from the surface. Other bacterial species can produce aggressive inorganic acids, such as H$_2$SO$_4$. Microorganisms in the soil may generate high concentrations of carbon dioxide. The carbon dioxide dissolves in the groundwater, producing carbonic acid. Carbonic acid solution is very corrosive to pipeline steels and can lead to general attack, pitting attack, and stress corrosion cracking.

Metal Deposition

Microorganisms can also affect corrosion by creating differential aeration cells on the surface of the metal and fixing the location of anodic sites beneath colonies of microorganisms. The organisms most often cited as causing differential aeration cells are those organisms capable of depositing iron and manganese oxides.

Manganese oxidation and deposition is coupled to cell growth and metabolism of organic carbon. The reduced form of manganese (Mn^{+2}) is soluble and the oxidized forms (Mn_2O_3, $MnOOH$, Mn_3O_4, MnO_2) are insoluble. As a result of microbial action, manganese oxide deposits are formed on buried or submerged materials including metal, stone, glass, and plastic, and can occur in natural waters that have manganese concentrations as low as 10 to 20 ppb (Figure 14.4). For mild steel corrosion under anodic control, manganese oxides can elevate corrosion current. The current may be significant for biomineralized oxides that provide large mineral surface areas. Given sufficient

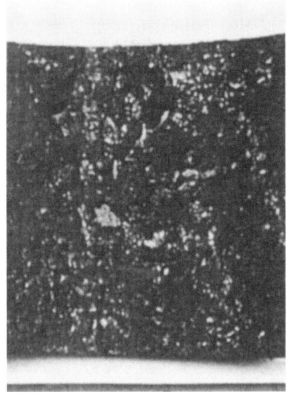

Figure 14.4 Black manganese dioxide deposits on carbon steel caused by metal-depositing bacteria.

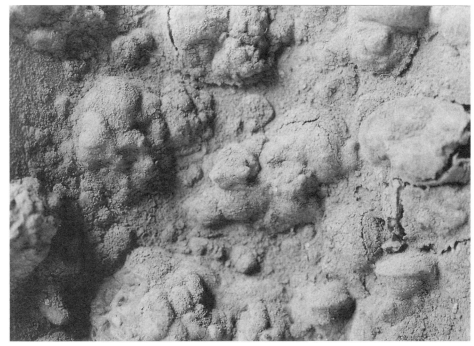

Figure 14.5 Tubercules on carbon steel.

conductivity, manganese oxide may serve as a cathode to support corrosion at an oxygen-depleted anode within the deposit.

Iron-oxidizing bacteria produce orange-red tubercles of iron oxides and hydroxides by oxidizing ferrous ions from the bulk medium or the substratum (Figure 14.5). Iron-depositing bacteria are microaerophilic and may require synergistic associations with other bacteria to maintain low oxygen conditions in their immediate environment. Deposits of cells and metal ions create oxygen concentration cells that effectively exclude oxygen from the area immediately under the deposit and initiate a series of events that individually or collectively are very corrosive. In an oxygenated environment, the area immediately under individual deposits becomes deprived of oxygen (Figure 14.6). That area becomes a relatively small anode compared to the large, surrounding oxygenated cathode. Cathodic reduction of oxygen may result in an increase in pH of the solution in the vicinity of the metal. The metal will form metal cations at anodic sites. If the metal hydroxide is the thermodynamically stable phase in the solution, the metal ions will be hydrolyzed by water, forming H^+ ions. If cathodic and anodic sites are separated from one another, the pH at the anode will decrease and that at the cathode will increase. The pH at the anode depends on specific hydrolysis reactions. In addition, Cl^- ions from the electrolyte will migrate to the anode to neutralize any buildup of charge, forming heavy metal chlorides that are extremely corrosive. Under these circumstances, pitting involves

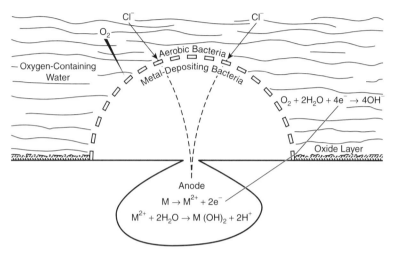

Figure 14.6   Possible reactions under tubercles created by metal-depositing bacteria.

the conventional features of differential aeration, a large cathode-to-anode surface area, and the development of acidity and metallic chlorides. Pit initiation depends on mineral deposition by bacteria. Pit propagation is dependent not on activities of the organisms, but on metallurgy.

Metal Reduction

Dissimilatory iron and/or manganese reduction occurs in several microorganisms, including anaerobic and facultative aerobic bacteria. Inhibitor and competition experiments suggest that Fe^{+3} and Mn^{+4} are efficient electron acceptors that are similar to nitrate in redox ability and are capable of out-competing electron acceptors of lower potential, such as sulfate or carbon dioxide (Meyers 1988). MRB in direct contact with solid iron (Fe^{+3}) and manganese (Mn^{+4}) oxides produce soluble ions (Fe^{+2} and Mn^{+2}). The result is dissolution of surface oxides and localized corrosion that was described by Obuekwe et al. (1981) as anodic depolarization.

MIC ON PIPELINES

Environment

The potential for MIC on buried pipelines is controlled by availability of nutrients, water, and electron acceptors. Peabody (1967) reported data from Harris (1960) indicating that soil moisture content and bacterial cell counts were greater in backfill material than in undisturbed earth adjacent to a pipeline. Trench backfill is not as consolidated and allows greater penetration of moisture and increased oxygen diffusion. Anaerobic bacteria thrive in waterlogged, dense soil. Alternating moisture and oxygen concentrations will influence the growth of bacterial populations. Despite the numerous mechanisms that one would predict for MIC of buried pipelines, most failures have been attributed to the presence and activities of SRB and APB. In general, sandy soils favor APB; high clay soils support populations of both kinds of organisms. To protect against all forms of external corrosion and cracking, several coating materials are used including asphalts, polyolefin tapes, and fusion-bonded epoxies (FBE). Line pipe is further protected by an impressed current or cathodic protection (CP). MIC can occur in the presence of these preventative measures.

Coatings

Because of differing environmental conditions (e.g., soil moisture, microflora, nutrients) in both field surveys and laboratory experiments, it is extremely difficult to interpret comparisons of coating performance. Soil stress or tenting along irregularities on the pipe surface, especially at long seam or girth welds, can create gaps between the tape and the pipe surface that fill with ground water and introduce microorganisms that create corrosion cells under the disbonded coating. Tenting is most prevalent in wet high clay soils, on unstable, geologically active slopes and downstream compressor stations. High service temperatures also promote disbonding. Not all coating materials are affected by soil bacteria under all conditions. Coatings derived from both coal (tars) and petroleum (asphalts) pass some exposure tests and fail others. Materials which by themselves show resistance to attack by microorganisms fail when combined or reinforced with other materials.

Peabody (1967) reported that coal tars, coal tar epoxies, and coal tar enamels were immune to disbonding because of activities of microorganisms. Early coatings based on asphalt were subject to oxidation and loss of low-molecular weight components through biodegradation and biodeterioration, resulting in a permeable, embrittled coatings (Jack et al. 1996). Pendrys (1989) demonstrated that with time asphalt could be degraded by microorganisms selected from soil. Harris (1960) demonstrated that bacteria found commonly in pipeline soils can degrade asphalt, tape adhesives, kraft paper (expendable once line is in place), and binders and fillers used in felt pipeline wrappers. The next generation coatings were based on polyolefin tapes made of polyvinyl chloride (PVC) or polyethylene (PE). The PVC tape was unstable in service. Plasticizers constitute up to 50% of a PVC product and can be effectively lost through biodeterioration and water dissolution. Tape coatings rely on adhesives to attach the polyolefin layer to the primed steel surface.

Jack et al. (1996) demonstrated that certain coatings disbonded more readily after being exposed to soils containing SRB and APB. PE coating damage proceeded linearly with time. PE tape coatings supported higher bacterial counts than extruded PE or fusion-bonded epoxy (FBE), presumably because of the presence of biodegradable adhesive/primer components in the paint system. Susceptibility to disbonding increased in the order: FBE, extruded PE, and PE tape. Two types of coating damage were reported: damage due to water leaching and permeation, which affect intact coatings and coating around holidays. FBE coatings were damaged with increased susceptibility to cathodic disbondment at existing holidays.

The most prevalent mechanism for the observed corrosion in a study reported by Jack et al. (1996) was formation of a galvanic couple between microbiologically produced iron sulfides and steel. The couple is normally short-lived because the iron sulfide matrix becomes saturated with electrons derived from the corrosion process. In the presence of SRB, however, the corrosion process is perpetuated because SRB can remove electrons in the corrosion process from the iron sulfide surface. This process may involve formation of cathodic hydrogen on the iron sulfide or direct transfer of electrons from the iron sulfide matrix to redox proteins in the bacterial cell wall. Corrosion rates associated with this mechanism were proportional to the amount of iron sulfide in the corrosion cell.

Cathodic Protection

Cathodically polarized surfaces attract microorganisms, including SRB, so that, if the CP is interrupted MIC can occur at a higher rate than if CP were not previously present (Sanders and Maxwell 1983). MIC has at least three effects on CP of pipelines. First, where MIC activity is present, the potential level required to mitigate corrosion is moved to more negative values. Pope and Morris (Pope 1995) found that pipeline failures were often in contact with wet clays with little scaling potential, creating the situation in which the demand for CP continued at a high level over long periods of time and in which CP may not be distributed equally over the surface of holidays and surrounding disbondments. Microorganisms colonize and initiate corrosion at such sites. Research by Barlo and Berry (1984) showed that a potential of at least -950 mV (copper/copper sulfate) is required to mitigate MIC, as opposed to the standard NACE International criterion of -850 mV. Second, MIC can increase the kinetics of the corrosion reactions, increasing the CP current necessary to achieve a given level of polarization. Third, microorganisms can attack pipeline coatings, increasing exposed metal surface area and further increasing the CP current required to achieve a given level of polarization. Water intrusion at breaks in the coating may block CP.

Detection

Because microorganisms are ubiquitous, the presence of bacteria or other microorganisms does not necessarily indicate a causal relationship with the corrosion. Microorganisms can always be cultured from natural environments but are not always the cause for corrosion found in their presence. Other factors must be considered in determining a cause and effect relationship. Areas of high SRB activity are generally very negative in potential and can be located by means of a native potential survey if the following conditions are met: (1) area of MIC activity must be large, (2) CP system must be off, and (3) coating cannot shield the metal surface. Once a suspected area of MIC has been located, the presence of bacteria can be confirmed by means of bell hole inspections in conjunction with the application of the analytical techniques described in NACE TPC Publication 3 in (NACE 1990), including culture methods and antibody analyses. A drop of dilute hydrochloric acid placed on corrosion product deposits will produce the odor of rotten eggs when sulfides are present. Detection of SRB or other bacteria in deposits associated with accelerated corrosion does not conclusively establish a casual relationship between the bacteria and the observed corrosion (Little 1996).

SUMMARY

Backfill around pipelines provides an environment that supports microbial growth more than what is expected for undisturbed soil. Nutrients associated with coatings and cathodic polarization encourage microbial settlement on pipeline surfaces. Extensive analyses of field samples indicate that MIC of external surfaces of buried pipeline and other underground structures is most often associated with SRB and APB and disbonded coatings.

ACKNOWLEDGMENTS

Work was performed by the Office of Naval Research, Program Element 0601153N and Defense Research Sciences Program, NRL Contribution Number NRL/BA/7333-97-0056.

REFERENCES

T.J. Barlo, W.E. Berry. *Materials Performance 23*, 9, 1984, p. 9.

J.A. Hardy, J.L. Bown. *Corrosion 40*, 1984, p. 650.

J.O. Harris. *Corrosion 16*, 1960, p. 441.

T.R. Jack, G. Van Boven, M. Wilmott, R. Worthingham. *Materials Performance 35*, 3, 1996, p. 39.

T.R. Jack, M.J. Wilmott, R.L. Sutherby, R.G. Worthingham. *Materials Performance 35*, 3, 1996, p. 18.

W. Lee, Z. Lewandowski, M. Morrison, W.G. Characklis, R. Avci, P. Nielsen. *Biofouling 7*, 1993, p. 217.

B.J. Little, R. Ray, P. Wagner, Z. Lewandowski, W.C. Lee, W.C. Characklis. *Biofouling 3*, 1991, p. 43.

B.J. Little, P.A. Wagner, K.R. Hart, R.I. Ray. Spatial Relationships Between Bacteria and Localized Corrosion. *Corrosion/96*, paper no. 278, Houston, TX: NACE International, 1996.

Microbiologically Influenced Corrosion and Biofouling in Oilfield Equipment. TPC Publication 3, NACE International, Revised September 1990.

C. Myers, K.H. Nealson, *Science 240*, 1988, p. 1319.

C.O. Obuekwe, D.W.S. Westlake, J.A. Plambeck, F.D. Cook. *Corrosion 37*, 8, 1981, p. 461.

A.W. Peabody. *Control of Pipeline Corrosion*, Houston, TX: NACE International, 1967, p. 173.

J.P. Pendrys. *Appl. Environ. Microbiol. 55*, 6, 1989, p. 1357.

D. Pope. A Study of Microbiologically Influenced Corrosion in Nuclear Power Plants and a Practical Guide for Countermeasures. Electric Power Research Institute Report NP-4582, May 1986. Palo Alto, CA.

D.H. Pope, E.A. Morris III. *Materials Performance 34*, 5, 1995, p. 23.

P.F. Sanders, S. Maxwell. Microfouling, Macrofouling, and Corrosion of Metal Test Specimens in Seawater. In: *Microbial Corrosion*, Teddington, UK: Metals Society, 1983, p. 74.

Chapter 15

Economics

Ronald L. Bianchetti

Good economics principles should be used in all pipeline corrosion work. To assure successful implementation of a corrosion control program, the corrosion engineer must be able to express the benefits in terms that management can understand, and that is through economic analysis.

Over the years the cost of implementing a corrosion control system has proven to be extremely beneficial in the reduction of leaks and extension of the useful life of pipelines. Whether by using coating alone or coating with cathodic protection (CP), pipeline owners have obtained very good results when sound corrosion engineering is implemented. The additive cost for corrosion control typically represents a very small percentage of initial pipeline construction costs. With this in mind corrosion control systems should be implemented as a standard operating procedure for all buried pipeline systems to enhance the life of the asset. Some examples of economic considerations are discussed below.

ECONOMIC COMPARISONS

The prime objective in pipeline corrosion control work is to maintain a corrosion-free system at the lowest annual cost. The total annual cost is frequently used as a simple means of comparing the relative cost of alternate means of applying protection to sections of a pipeline system. This cost figure includes the annual cost of the capital invested plus the annual cost of operating and maintaining the system. To make annual cost comparisons that are valid, the pipeline corrosion engineer must know the various component cost items with reasonable accuracy.

Existing Pipelines

When CP is planned for existing pipelines that have an established leak history, it is possible to forecast the number and cost of probable leaks that may occur if CP were not applied to the total cost of CP. These costs are evaluated for a period of time, typically 20 to 50 yr.

New Pipelines

Where CP is installed at the time a pipeline is built, there will be no leak history on which to base the type of comparison previously mentioned. However, established leak histories of other pipelines in the same area can be a valuable guide to indicate the probable savings to be gained by installing CP.

Comparisons can be made for planned pipelines where the choice is between installing CP initially, or installing the pipeline without CP but providing a corrosion allowance such as an extra $\frac{1}{16}$-inch pipe-wall thickness beyond that needed for design operating conditions. The comparison may be based on the annual cost of the CP on the thinner wall pipe versus the annual cost of the investment for the additional steel in the pipe having the corrosion allowance. The probability should be recognized that the pipe having the extra wall thickness ultimately would reach the point where it, too, will require CP.

Cost of Money

The cost of money invested for CP installations or other corrosion control measures is usually developed by the company financial specialists. The money used for such investments can cost more than the simple interest rate. Included also in the cost are such items as taxes and depreciation that increase the real cost to the company of the money invested.

There can be a difference between the cost of money used for installations made under capital expenditure funding versus those made using maintenance funds. The corrosion engineer should determine the difference, because corrosion control installations may be capitalized in some instances (for new pipeline construction) and considered as maintenance costs in others.

Establishing Initial Cathodic Protection System Cost Estimates

When evaluating economic comparisons, estimates of the total installed cost of alternate systems (galvanic anodes versus impressed current) should be considered. Validity of the economic comparisons will depend largely on the accuracy of the cost figures used in compiling the estimates.

An estimate for the installed cost of a CP system includes such items as the following:

- *Engineering time* and associated expenses for field-testing, design, and preparation of plans and specifications.

- *Cost of materials* plus the overhead expense to cover purchasing and storage costs. The overhead factor or other means of determining these costs should be decided for the particular company.
- *Cost of right-of-way* acquisition, if involved. This includes cost of right-of-way easements, time and expenses for right-of-way procurement personnel, and crop damage where applicable.
- *Unit construction costs* for the various components of the systems to be installed. The corrosion engineer will need to establish a working file on costs. If installations are to be made by company crews, review the proposed work with appropriate company personnel for their estimates of all charges that would be made against a work order for the installation. If possible, the estimate should be broken down into unit costs (such as trenching cost per foot, cost per anode for installation, etc.).

If installations are to be made by a CP construction contractor, that person may be willing to provide scoping estimates. The new corrosion engineer may be able to obtain estimating figures from experienced corrosion engineers with neighboring pipeline systems who have direct knowledge of applicable contract construction costs in the same general area. Where corrosion-engineering consultants are used, they can assist the new corrosion engineer by providing established reliable figures for cost estimating purposes.

- *Inspection time* and associated expenses on the part of the corrosion engineer during the actual construction phase.
- *Completed system check out* and associated expenses of the corrosion engineer to verify adequate protection is being achieved. Performing CP current output adjustments as necessary and conducting cooperative interference tests as may be necessary.

Establishing On-Going Operating Cost Estimates

Estimates for the annual operating costs for a pipeline CP installation should include such items as the following:

- *Power costs* where rectifiers are to be used as a current source. Applicable power company rates for the appropriate class of service should be known. If minimum monthly rates apply, they should be taken into account. This usually applies to small rectifier installations. In some instances, however, if the electric company has to build a long power line extension to serve the rectifier, it may establish a fairly substantial minimum monthly billing over a period of years to recover the cost of the line extension. Where other current sources using an outside source of energy are used (thermoelectric generators for example), the cost of fuel required to operate the device must be determined.
- *Maintenance and system checkout costs* include time and associated expenses for routine operational checks (particularly applicable for systems using rectifiers or other DC power sources subject to relatively frequent inspection); time and expense for

periodic corrosion surveys along that section of the system protected by the proposed installation; and an estimate for time, expenses, and materials for corrective repair work.

COST COMPARISON EXAMPLES

To illustrate cost comparisons of different CP systems the following examples are presented to assist the corrosion engineer.

Comparing Alternative Cathodic Protection Systems

Assume a new 50-mile well-coated pipeline to be cathodically protected. Initial corrosion survey tests show that protection can be obtained with 2 A from a single rectifier installation near the center of the line or with 1.5 A from three magnesium anode installations distributed along the line. Less current is required for the magnesium anode system because of reduced attenuation resulting from distributed installations.

Impressed Current System

On the basis of the corrosion survey, it has been determined that the rectifier can be installed at a location where soil conditions are such that a ground bed with three vertical anodes at 20-ft spacing can be placed 300 ft from the pipeline. This system will provide the required 2 A at 5 V. Electric service is available at the installation site and the applicable power rate is 3.5 cents per kwh for the first 250 kwh per month with a minimum monthly bill of $2.50. (Power costs vary from area to area. Actual local rates should be determined.) Right-of-way acquisition will be necessary.

Galvanic Anode System

At the three magnesium anode installations, assume that the initial corrosion survey data have shown that installation sites are available. Soil conditions at the three installations will produce 0.5 A of protection current (with the pipe at protected potentials) using five 20-lb packaged magnesium anodes at 15-ft spacing along the edge of the right-of-way 15 ft from the pipe. No right-of-way costs will be incurred.

To determine which type of installation will be the more economical, the pertinent costs can be compared as shown in Table 15.1. It is assumed that the necessary steps have been taken to obtain reliable estimating figures and that this final comparison summarizes and compares the cost data obtained.

Table 15.1   Economic Comparision Between Alternative CP Systems

Description	Rectifier Installation	Total for 3 Magnesium Anode Installations
A-INSTALLATION COSTS		
1. Time[1] and expense for field tests, design, plans and specifications	$1065	$968
2. Cost of materials including 10 percent for overhead	$2400	$1950
3. Right-of-way acquisition costs	$1000	–
4. Contract installation cost	$4700	$4500
5. Time and expense for construction inspection	$1500	$1500
6. Time and expense for system check-out[2]	$2500	$1500
TOTAL INSTALLATION COST	$13,165	$10,418
ANNUAL COST OF MONEY (Based on an assumed 4 percent for 15 year system life)	$1184	$937
B-OPERATING COSTS		
1. Power cost[3]	$100	–
2. Routine operational checks[4]	$100	–
3. Periodic corrosion survey	$700	$500
4. Time, expenses and materials for corrective repairs[5]	$50	$50
TOTAL ANNUAL OPERATING COST	$950	$550
C-ECONOMIC COMPARISON		
ANNUAL COST OF MONEY (A)	$1184	$937
TOTAL ANNUAL OPERATING COST (B)	$950	$550
TOTAL ANNUAL COST	$2134	$1487

[1]Engineering time charges for operating company personnel include, normally, an overhead charge. This can be determined for the particular company involved.
[2]Additional check-out time for rectifier installations to allow for additional interference checks.
[3]Power consumption is less than minimum billing which applies in this instance.
[4]Based on rect. readings every month.
[5]Estimated annual repair cost.

This comparison indicates that the three magnesium anode installations will have a lower annual cost than the single rectifier and would, therefore, be more economical. Although this is usually the case for lower current outputs (typically less than 2A) used in this example, a similar comparison should be made using the specific factors that apply to the pipeline corrosion engineer's own system.

On the other hand if the amount of current required was higher, an impressed current system tends to become more economical than galvanic anode installations. This is because the additional investment for added rectifier output (in terms of dollars per ampere of capacity) does not increase as rapidly as that for galvanic anode installations.

Comparing Leak Cost and Cathodic Protection Cost

When a section of pipeline system starts to develop leaks, experience has shown that further leaks will develop at a continuously increasing rate. If the accumulated number of leaks repaired is plotted on semilog paper against pipeline age in years, a straight line is the usual result where accurate leak records are available (Figure 15.1). In this

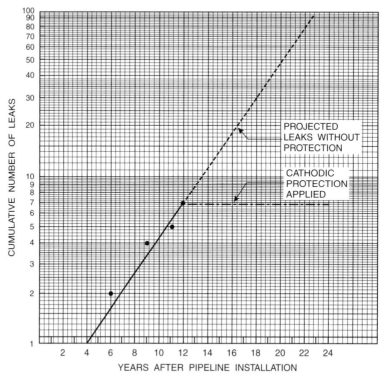

Figure 15.1 Cumulative number of leaks without CP.

instance, the first leak did not develop until the line was 4-yr old and a total of only seven leaks had developed by the time the pipeline was 12-yr old. A definite trend has been established, which shows that in the next 10-yr there will be approximately 70 new leaks, if corrosion is not controlled. The figure also shows that the number of leaks developing each year is increasing at such a rate that the pipeline may become inoperable if the trend is not stopped.

The application of CP as shown in Figure 15.1 can mitigate development of new leaks. The cost of operating a CP system(s) versus the cost of leaks over a period of time can then be economically evaluated. In the case illustrated (Figure 15.1), application of CP at the end of the 12th year would eliminate approximately 70 new leaks over the next 10-yr period. Thus a dollar figure can be developed to represent the cost savings for the anticipated leaks.

To determine the cost of leaks several items should be considered.

- The average cost of a leak repair on the pipeline under study. This should include labor, overhead, materials, transportation costs, and other attendant expenses.
- An average cost for property damages associated with a simple corrosion leak repair. This can vary with the fluid in the pipeline. Such damages tend to be substantially higher, if a pipeline is carrying petroleum or petroleum products versus natural gas.
- The value of product lost from an average corrosion leak. This will depend on the product, the pipeline pressure, the average size of the leak, and the average length of time that/product escapes before the leak repair is accomplished.
- Miscellaneous factors, such as insurance, good will, and other costs.

The total average cost of each leak, will be the sum of the above items plus any associated costs that may be involved for the particular pipeline system under consideration.

Now assume that a coated pipeline having the leak record represented by Figure 15.1 is surveyed during its 12th yr and that design calculations indicate that CP can be applied using a rectifier system. Further assume that the annual cost of the investment for CP plus annual operating costs will be $6,000 per year and it has been established that the average total cost of each leak repaired is $1500. Using these figures, if CP is applied at the end of the 12th yr, comparative costs for the following 10-yr period are as follows:

- Cathodic protection costs: $10 \times \$6000 = \$60,000$
- Savings in leak repair costs: $70 \times \$1500 = \$105,000$

This example indicates that, over the 10-yr period, there will be a net savings of $45,000 with CP installed, if all leaks are avoided.

Greater savings can be shown by projecting the comparison over a longer period because although CP annual costs remain reasonably uniform, the number of projected leaks over that longer period increases very rapidly. (Note, from Figure 15.1, that there would be approximately 20 new leaks in the 23rd yr alone.)

Now look at the comparison that would apply for the same pipeline if CP had been installed when the line was initially constructed. First, the annual cost of CP would be less because the new coating would be better initially. Second, the coating should be substantially better after 12-yr. Third, the full 22-yr of pipeline life is considered in the annual cost analysis, so the annual cost allocation for CP would be $4,000. The total number of leak repairs saved, per Figure 15.1, would be 80 over the 22-yr period. The comparison now is as follows:

- Cathodic protection costs: $22 \times \$4,000 = \$88,000$
- Savings in leak repair costs: $80 \times \$1500 = \$120,000$

Assuming that annual costs for CP have been estimated accurately, there is still a significant saving of $32,000 with CP.

The previous comparison may be used as an argument in favor of deferring the application of CP until leaks have started to develop. This would only be valid if there was a guarantee that all leaks would be simple leaks, as assumed in the cost comparisons, with no risk of exceptional hazard. For pipelines carrying a hazardous product (such as natural gas or petroleum products), there is always the possibility of fire, explosion or loss of life if the leak should develop in the wrong place. Since these are possibilities only (although very real possibilities), a dollar figure cannot be attached readily to the direct cost that might be involved nor to intangible factors such as impaired public good will. Just one serious incident, if it should occur, can more than offset any apparent saving which could be gained by deferring application of CP until leaks start to develop.

Comparing Cathodic Protection with Pipe Corrosion Allowance

A corrosion allowance for example, an additional $\frac{1}{16}$ of an inch of pipe wall thickness (above that needed for pipeline operating considerations) may be considered in lieu of applying CP. This practice is not recommended for underground pipelines, because it does not provide a permanent means of corrosion control but only defers the time when a leak will occur.

Ground Bed Cable Sizing and Anode Spacing

Economic considerations apply to various phases of CP system design. Sizing ground bed cables and determining the economic spacing for impressed current or galvanic anodes are particularly important instances.

Ground Bed Cable Size

Basically, ground bed cable can be increased in size as long as each incremental increase will show a dollar savings in terms of reduced annual power losses in the cable resistance compared with the annual cost of the additional investment for the larger cable size. For rectifier installations, AC power losses (which determine the cost) are the DC power losses in the cable divided by the rectifier efficiency expressed as a decimal.

As was discussed in Chapter 7, the effective resistance of the ground bed cable may be taken as that of the full length of cable between pipeline and first anode plus that of one-half the length of cable along the line of anodes. Power costs at rectifier installations are determined from the power company rate schedule. For small rectifier installations, which do not use enough power to exceed the minimum monthly billing, nothing is gained by using a larger cable size than is necessary for adequate mechanical strength. No. 8 AWG header cable (the same size as the usual anode pigtail cable) may be considered the smallest practical size, although some operators may elect to use no smaller than No. 4 AWG cable for header cable construction.

Power costs at galvanic anode installations vary with the size and type of installation but can be reduced to a cost per kilowatt-hour (kWh). This is performed by first determining the kWh lifetime output of the installation by the expression.

kWh = driving voltage × amps output × 8.76 × installation life in years.

The cost per kWh is then the installation cost in dollars divided by the expected total lifetime power output in kWh.

Although the cost per kWh for a galvanic anode installation usually will be several dollars compared with only a few cents at a rectifier installation (where the monthly minimum bill is exceeded), there may be no economic advantage in using cable larger than needed for strength. This is because the square of the current output of a small galvanic anode installation may be very small compared with that of a rectifier installation (and in addition there is much less cable in the usual galvanic anode installation than in the typical rectifier ground bed).

Anode Spacing

Based on the information on ground bed design discussed in Chapter 7, it is recognized that for soil of uniform resistivity, two boundary conditions for anode spacing exist. These are the following:

- The parallel resistance of two vertical ground bed anodes placed side by side will be only slightly less than the resistance of one anode alone.
- The parallel resistance of two vertical ground bed anodes placed electrically far apart will be approximately one-half the resistance of one anode alone.

Both of these boundary conditions are not economical. The most economical anode spacing is somewhere between these two conditions.

Using proper materials, right-of-way procurement, installation, and power costs, the pipeline corrosion engineer can make an economic analysis to determine the most

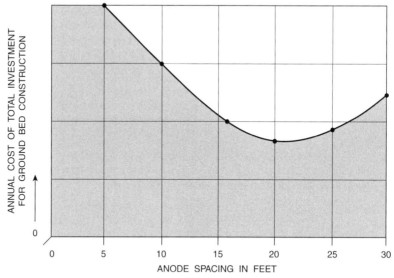

Figure 15.2 Typical plot for economical anode spacing.

favorable spacing for installations. This may be done by calculating, for a typical ground bed resistance in typical soil resistivity, the annual cost of the total investment required for constructing a ground bed at several different anode spacing points. The annual cost of power losses in the cable should be added to the annual cost of the investment. By plotting a total annual cost versus the cost of anode spacing, a curve will be obtained which may appear somewhat as indicated in Figure 15.2. Although the results may vary with costs applicable to a particular system, economical anode spacing of 20 to 25 ft is typical for rectifier ground bed construction.

ECONOMICS OF GOOD MAINTENANCE

The most obvious economic contributor is good maintenance. This means maintaining all CP installations and other corrosion control facilities in optimum operating condition and making sure that full protection is being given the system for the maximum practicable percentage of the time. This is a necessity for proper system performance. Without proper maintenance and system performance the initial investment is not optimized, and the cost of the corrosion control investment represents a wasted expenditure. This is not an acceptable practice and is highly discouraged.

Maintenance economics applies to equipment use in CP installations. At rectifier installations particularly, as discussed in Chapter 8, economies can be gained by replacing rectifying elements (stacks) in older units with new more efficient elements when the annual saving in power cost is greater than the annual cost of the investment for the new stacks. In extreme cases involving large single-phase rectifiers, changing the single-phase unit for a more efficient three-phase rectifier may prove economical on the annual cost basis if three-phase power is available.

COATING ECONOMICS

Chapter 2 emphasized that the most favorable coating system for any given pipeline is the most stable of those available—that is, the coating system with electrical and mechanical characteristics that will deteriorate at the slowest rate with time under the specific installation conditions. Such a coating used with a CP system will be the most economical combination.

Even the most stable pipeline coating system selected will suffer some deterioration with time. Designing and constructing the initial CP system with sufficient reserve capacity to allow for the expected increased current requirements from anticipated coating degradation will result in overall cost savings. This saving tends to be greater in the case of rectifier installations where the cost of providing additional current output capacity can be substantially less than in the case of galvanic anode installations.

The direct cost of the installations will be a function of the electrical resistivity of the coating used. An excellent stable coating properly applied should have a high electrical resistance. Current requirements should be so low that the cost of providing additional capacity will be minimal. On the other hand, a coating initially having a substantially lower electrical resistivity will require correspondingly greater investments for CP and the additional cost for reserve capacity becomes much more significant.

Chapter 16

Fundamentals of Corrosion

John A. Beavers

INTRODUCTION

The fundamentals of corrosion can be divided into the disciplines of thermodynamics and kinetics. Thermodynamics is used to indicate whether a specific corrosion process is possible and kinetics is used to understand and predict actual rates of corrosion. Both topics are discussed in greater detail in this chapter.

THERMODYNAMICS

Gibbs Free Energy

As described in Chapter 1, a significant amount of energy is put into a metal when it is extracted from its ores, placing it in a high-energy state. These ores are typically oxides of the metal such as hematite (Fe_2O_3), for steel or bauxite ($Al_2O_3 \cdot H_2O$), for aluminum. One principle of thermodynamics is that a material always seeks the lowest energy state. In other words, most metals are thermodynamically unstable and will tend to react with something in their environment (e.g., oxygen or water) in order to reach a lower, more stable energy state such as an oxide. As an analogy, consider a baseball. As you raise the baseball in your hand, you are increasing the energy level of the ball. In the case of gravitational energy, the energy $U = mgh$ in which m is the mass of the ball, g is the gravitational constant, and h is the height of the ball. If you let the ball go at a height h_1, it will fall to the floor, which is the lowest possible energy state. The change in energy

$$\Delta U = U_{final} - U_{initial} = mg(0) - mgh_1 = -mgh_1 \tag{1}$$

In other words, the change in energy is negative. A more general term for the energy of a system is the Gibbs Free Energy which uses the symbol G. For a process such as corrosion to be spontaneous, ΔG must be negative. Unfortunately, for most common metals in natural environments, $\Delta G < 0$ and the corrosion process is thermodynamically favored.

Electrode Potentials

The corrosion of most common engineering materials at temperatures near ambient usually involves water and is electrochemical in nature, as described in Chapter 1. The corrosion process occurs with the removal of electrons (oxidation) of the metal and the consumption of those electrons by some other reduction reaction, such as oxygen reduction

$$Fe \rightarrow Fe^{2+} + 2e^- \tag{2}$$

$$O_2 + 2H_2O + 4e^- \rightarrow 4OH^- \tag{3}$$

Note that arrows have been used in the oxidation and reduction reactions listed above indicating that we know the direction of the reactions. Since the oxidation and reduction reactions are different, the corrosion process is not reversible and is not at equilibrium. A system has attained a state of equilibrium when it shows no further tendency to change its properties with time. A corroding metal changes its state with time and is, by definition, not at equilibrium.

The individual oxidation and reduction reactions are referred to as half-cell reactions and can occur locally at the same site on the metal or can be spatially separated. The free energy of each pair of half-cell reactions is related to a reversible electromotive force (E) through the equation

$$\Delta G = -|z| F E \tag{4}$$

in which z is the valence change associated with the reaction and F is Faraday's constant. In other words, E is directly related to the driving force (the change in the Gibbs Free Energy) for the reaction. A positive value of E indicates that the change in Gibbs Free Energy is less than zero, and that the reaction is thermodynamically favored.

> CAUTION: This statement refers to an electromotive force between equilibrium reactions and cannot be directly related to a pipe-to-soil (P/S) potential measurement. P/S potentials are generally negative under corrosive conditions when measured with a copper sulfate reference electrode.

The electromotive force (EMF) is a potential and can be calculated for any set of two half-cell reactions using Equation (4) and standard thermodynamic data for the reactions involved. The hydrogen reduction reaction

$$2H^+ + 2e^- = H_2 \tag{5}$$

has been arbitrarily set at 0.00 V for the series, allowing for the calculation of the EMF of individual half-cell reactions.

A compilation of these EMFs and half-cell reactions, calculated for the reactants at unit activity, is referred to as the electrochemical or EMF series. The activity of a species is a measure of its effective concentration in solution and the activity is equal to the concentration for an ideal solution. When the reactions are written as reduction reactions, the most positive members of the series are the noble metals such as gold and platinum, and the most negative members of the series are the active metals such as sodium and magnesium (see Table 16.1). Note that, in addition to metal reactions, the series also contains reactions for common oxidants found in corrosion such as oxygen.

The potential of any two half-cell reactions can be calculated as shown in the following equation, where the EMF series is written as reduction reactions

$$E = E^\circ_{(\text{reduction})} - E^\circ_{(\text{oxidation})} \tag{6}$$

Table 16.1   Standard Electrochemical Series for Some Common Metals and Reactions

	Reaction	Standard Reduction Potential V (SHE)
↑ Noble	$Au^{3+} + 3e^- = Au$	+1.498
	$Pt^{2+} + 2e^- = Pt$	+1.200
	$Pd^{2+} + 2e^- = Pd$	+0.987
	$Ag^+ + e^- = Ag$	+0.799
	$Hg_2^{2+} + 2e^- = 2Hg$	+0.788
	$O_2 + 2H_2O + 4e^- = 4OH^-$	+0.401
	$Cu^{2+} + 2e^- = Cu$	+0.337
	$2H^+ + 2e^- = H_2$	0.000
	$Pb^{2+} + 2e^- = Pb$	−0.126
	$Sn^{2+} + 2e^- = Sn$	−0.136
	$Ni^{2+} + 2e^- = Ni$	−0.250
	$Co^{2+} + 2e^- = Co$	−0.277
	$Cd^{2+} + 2e^- = Cd$	−0.403
	$Fe^{2+} + 2e^- = Fe$	−0.440
	$Cr^{3+} + 3e^- = Cr$	−0.744
	$Zn^{2+} + 2e^- = Zn$	−0.763
	$Al^{3+} + 3e^- = Al$	−1.662
	$Mg^{2+} + 2e^- = Mg$	−2.363
Active	$Na^+ + e^- = Na$	−2.714
↓	$K^+ + e^- = K$	−2.925

For example, for the reactions; $Au^{3+} + 3e^- = Au$ and $Al = Al^{3+} + 3e^-$, the potential is

$$E^\circ = 1.498 - (-1.662) = 3.160 \text{ V} \tag{7}$$

Since the EMF is positive, $\Delta G < 0$, and the reactions will proceed as written. Had the direction of the reactions been reversed, the calculated EMF would have been negative, indicating that the reactions would not proceed as written. Therefore, with this information, one can use the series to determine whether a set of reactions is possible. Corrosion of a metal in the presence of a possible oxidant will occur if the reduction potential of the metal is less positive than the reduction potential of the oxidant. For example, oxygen reduction cannot support corrosion of gold but can promote corrosion of the common materials of construction such as iron.

The EMF series is calculated for the reactants at unit activity. These potentials shift as a function of concentration according to the Nernst equation. For any electrochemical reaction

$$a A + b B = c C + d D \tag{8}$$

$$E = E^\circ - \frac{RT}{|z|F} \ln \frac{(a_C)^c (a_D)^d}{(a_A)^a (a_B)^b} \tag{9}$$

in which E is the cell potential, E° is the standard cell potential, R is the gas constant, T is the absolute temperature, $|z|$ is the number of electrons transferred, F is Faraday's constant, and $(a_C)^c$ is the activity of species C raised to the c power.

As described in the preceding section, the EMF series can be generated from standard thermodynamic data. In theory, the EMF series also could be generated experimentally by measuring the potential difference between each of the metals at equilibrium in solutions of unit activity and the hydrogen electrode, as shown in Figure 16.1. When a potential is measured in this fashion, it is referred to as an electrostatic potential or a standard electrode potential, rather than an EMF. The hydrogen electrode consists of an inert platinum wire immersed in an acidic solution of H^+ ions at unit activity with H_2 gas bubbled through it at 1 atm. A shorthand description of the cell is often written

$$Pt|H_2/H^+(a = 1)||M^{n+}(a = 1)|M \tag{10}$$

and the potential of the cell is $E^\circ = E_{M/M^{n+}} - E_{H_2/H^+} = E_{M/M^{n+}}$. The solid vertical line represents a phase change (for example, between the metal M and the solution). The || indicates the presence of a porous barrier that allows electrical communication between the two half cells but minimizes mixing of the electrolytes. The superscript "$\circ$" on the E indicates that the potential is a standard electrode potential at unit activity ($a = 1$).

For the measurement to be accurate, the reactions must be at equilibrium, which implies that no net current can flow in the measurement circuit. This can be accomplished by using a high input impedance voltmeter for the measurement. The hydrogen

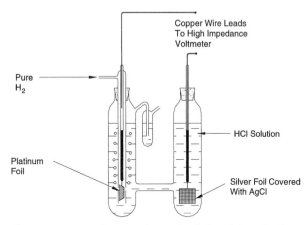

Figure 16.1   Hydrogen electrode (left side) and silver metal electrode in cell for standard EMF determination.

electrode used as shown in Figure 16.1 is referred to as a reference electrode. In practice, a hydrogen reference electrode is rarely used because of the difficulty in constructing and maintaining the electrode. Other types of reference electrodes are described in the following section.

In practice, standard electrode potentials cannot be measured for many metals because they react with water; water is reduced and the metal is oxidized. Therefore, the metal cannot be present at equilibrium in aqueous solutions. These metals include iron and common anode metals such as aluminum, zinc, and magnesium. For these metals, the standard half-cell potentials are generated from thermodynamic data.

Reference Electrodes

One definition of a reference electrode is "a reversible electrode used for measuring the potentials of other electrodes". As described in the previous section, a reversible electrode must be at equilibrium, which means that there is no net change in the electrode over time. Desirable properties of a good reference electrode include the following:

- Easy to use and maintain
- Stable potential over time
- Potential varies little with current flow (does not polarize readily)
- Not easily contaminated
- Does not contaminate what is being measured.

The hydrogen electrode can be used as a reference electrode but it is cumbersome, even in the laboratory. Other common reference electrodes include silver-silver

Table 16.2   Potentials of Common Reference
Electrodes

Electrode	Potential (V) @ 25°C
$Cu^{2+}/CuSO_4$ (Saturated) [CSE]	+0.300
Calomel (Saturated KCl) [SCE]	+0.241
$Ag^+/AgCl$ (Saturated KCl)	+0.196
$Ag^+/AgCl$ (0.6 M Cl^-) [seawater]	+0.250
Standard Hydrogen Electrode [SHE]	0.000
Zinc (Seawater)	−0.800

chloride, calomel, and copper-copper sulfate. Their potentials are given in Table 16.2. Each reference electrode potential is based on the equilibrium reaction for the respective metal

$$Ag^+ + e^- = Ag \text{ (silver-silver chloride)} \tag{11}$$

$$Hg_2^{2+} + 2e^- = 2Hg \text{ (calomel)} \tag{12}$$

$$Cu^{2+} + 2e^- = Cu \text{ (copper-copper sulfate)} \tag{13}$$

The potential of the reference electrode is dependent on the aqueous environment used. For example, silver-silver chloride reference electrodes are normally filled with potassium chloride (KCl) solution and can be purchased with KCl concentrations ranging from 0.1 M up to saturated KCl, with a corresponding range of potentials. Since silver chloride (AgCl) has very limited solubility in KCl, the silver wire in the reference electrode is normally coated with AgCl to establish the equilibrium reaction and associated potential.

The copper-copper sulfate reference electrode (CSE) is the most common reference electrode used for underground corrosion. It is frequently referred to as a half-cell based on the copper half-cell reaction. A schematic of the CSE is given in Figure 16.2. As shown in the figure, a heavy gauge copper wire is used for the electrode and the cell is filled with a saturated solution of copper sulfate. Saturated solutions are commonly used in reference electrodes since salt crystals can be added to the cell to ensure that saturation is maintained. It is very important to maintain the desired concentration of the solution in the reference electrode to ensure that it has a stable potential over time.

The standard procedure for performing potential measurements (such as a pipe-to-soil potential measurement) is to connect the positive terminal of the voltmeter to the reference electrode and the negative terminal to the structure. When recording the reading, the sign of the reading must be reversed. The measurement has historically been performed in this manner to produce a positive deflection on an analog meter (pipe-to-soil potentials are usually negative values).

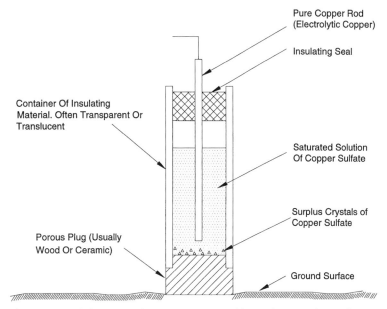

Figure 16.2   Schematic of copper-copper sulfate reference electrode.

Galvanic Series

As described in the section on electrode potentials, the electrochemical series is derived from thermodynamic data and represents equilibrium conditions. One rarely encounters such conditions in the real world except for the case of reference electrodes. A galvanic series is similar in appearance to an electrochemical series but represents actual potential measurements made on common engineering materials in everyday environments. Table 16.3 shows a galvanic series produced on a number of metals in soil. The series was generated by measuring the stable potential between the metal and a CSE in a neutral soil. This potential is referred to as a corrosion potential, an open circuit potential, or a native potential. Note that the potentials measured may vary considerably, depending on the temperature, the type of soil, the moisture content of the soil, and the amount of time the metal is in contact with the soil before the measurement. Nevertheless, the galvanic series provides an indication of the relative reactivity of the different metals.

A corrosion potential is not an equilibrium potential. The metal never reaches a state of equilibrium in corrosive environments. There is net oxidation of the metal to produce metal ions and corrosion products, and net reduction (and consumption) of some other species, such as oxygen, hydrogen, or water. These reactions are not reversible. If it were possible to measure the equilibrium potential for the metal in soil, it would be found to lie at a more negative value than the corrosion potential. Similarly, the equilibrium potential for the reduced species (oxygen, for example) is a more positive potential. Thus, the corrosion potential is somewhere between the equilibrium potentials of the two

Table 16.3   Practical Galvanic Series for Metals in Neutral Soils and Water

Metal	Potential V (CSE)[1]
Carbon, Graphite, Coke	+0.3
Platinum	0 to −0.1
Mill Scale On Steel	−0.2
High Silicon Cast Iron	−0.2
Copper, Brass, Bronze	−0.2
Mild Steel In Concrete	−0.2
Lead	−0.5
Cast Iron (Not Graphitized)	−0.5
Mild Steel (Rusted)	−0.2 to −0.5
Mild Steel (Clean and Shiny)	−0.5 to −0.8
Commercially Pure Aluminum	−0.8
Aluminum Alloy (5% Zinc)	−1.05
Zinc	−1.1
Magnesium Alloy (6% Al, 3% Zn, 0.15% Mn)	−1.6
Commercially Pure Magnesium	−1.75

[1]Typical potentials normally observed in neutral soils and water, measured in relation to copper sulfate reference electrode.

reactions. Both reactions are polarized from their equilibrium values. The metal oxidation reaction is anodically polarized and the reduction reaction is cathodically polarized. These reactions are commonly called the anodic and cathodic reactions, respectively.

Potential measurements are powerful tools for studying electrochemical processes such as corrosion. However, potential measurements do not directly provide information on the corrosion rate of a material. The rate must be inferred through knowledge of the relationship of the potential and the electrode kinetics.

KINETICS

As described in the previous section, the oxidation and reduction reactions on a corroding metal are polarized from their equilibrium values. A definition of polarization is "the deviation (change) in potential of an electrode as a result of the passage of current." The potential deviation (polarization) can be measured from the equilibrium potential or from the corrosion potential. The amount of polarization is referred to as the overvoltage or overpotential and is assigned the term eta (η).

One type of polarization commonly observed in corroding metal systems is activation polarization. In the case of activation polarization, the rate of the corrosion reaction is limited by the electron transfer reaction at the metal surface. This electron transfer process has an associated activation energy and the rate of this process is exponentially related to the free energy change. Since the free energy is directly related to the potential, and the rate is directly related to the electrical current, the relationship becomes the following

$$\Delta I \propto e^{\eta/RT} \tag{14}$$

in which I is the corrosion current, R is the gas constant, and T is the absolute temperature. Upon taking the log of both sides of the equation, the relationship becomes the following

$$\text{Log}(\Delta I) \propto \frac{\eta}{RT} \tag{15}$$

Rather than using equations, a better way of visualizing the relationship between potential and current is by means of Evans diagrams (E-log i plots), where potential is plotted on the vertical (Y) axis and log current or log current density is plotted on the horizontal (X) axis (see Figure 16.3). In this example, the equilibrium potentials for the reduction reaction, hydrogen reduction, and the metal oxidation reactions are indicated as E_{H^+/H_2} and $E_{M^{2+}/M}$, respectively. Note that at the equilibrium potential of each reaction,

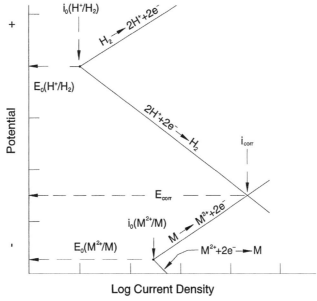

Figure 16.3 Evans diagram (potential versus logarithm of current density) for metal M in deaerated acid solution.

there is an associated current. This current is referred to as an exchange current i_0. At equilibrium, the exchange current for the oxidation and reduction reactions are equal and the net rate is zero. The exchange current of a reaction is different depending on the type and nature of the surface on which it is occurring. For example, the exchange current for the hydrogen reaction is higher on a clean metal surface such as platinum than on a metal surface with an oxide film present.

The corrosion potential for a metal in an environment is established at a potential where the net sum of the reduction reactions is equal to the net sum of the oxidation reactions. This is because there can be no net accumulation of charge; all of the electrons liberated by the oxidation of the metal must be consumed by the reduction reactions. The value of the corrosion potential, E_{corr}, is indicated in Figure 16.3. Note in the example in Figure 16.3 that the oxidation reaction for hydrogen and the reduction reaction for the metal are ignored in the summation process. This is because the current scale is logarithmic and the rates for these reactions are negligible near the free corrosion potential.

The curves in Figure 16.3 show the current-potential relationships of the individual oxidation and reduction reactions. The net current (difference between oxidation and reduction currents), plotted as a function of potential, has the form shown in Figure 16.4. The net current is zero at the free corrosion potential and only approaches the curves shown in Figure 16.3 at overpotentials greater than about 75 mV from E_{corr}. At overpotentials less than this value, the net current is affected by both the anodic and

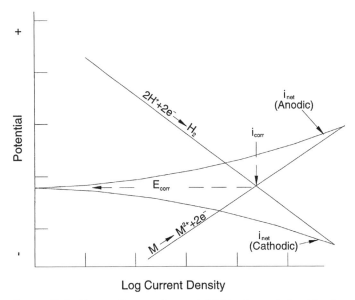

Figure 16.4 Evans diagram for metal M in deaerated acid solution, showing net anodic and cathodic currents.

cathodic reactions. The equation describing the net current has a form similar to the classical Butler-Volmer equation

$$i_{\text{net}} = i_{\text{corr}}\left[e^{2.3\eta/\beta_a} - e^{-2.3\eta/\beta_c}\right] \qquad (16)$$

in which β_a and β_c are the slopes of the anodic and cathodic components of the corrosion reactions, in millivolts per decade of current. These slopes are referred to as Tafel Slopes. In general, the anodic and cathodic Tafel slopes are different.

The anodic (corrosion) current at the corrosion potential is I_{corr} which is the corrosion rate. When written as a large I, the units are generally in amperes (A). This current can be converted into a corrosion rate if one knows the surface area over which the current occurs. When this is known, the current is written as a current density (i) with units of A/cm^2 or A/ft^2. This current can be converted to an actual corrosion rate using Faraday's Law

$$\frac{m}{at} = \frac{iM}{nF} \qquad (17)$$

in which m is the mass loss of the metal in grams, t is the time in seconds, a is the exposed surface area of the metal in cm^2, i is the current density in A/cm^2, M is the atomic weight of the metal in grams, n is the number of electrons transferred, and F is Faradays Constant (96,500 Coulombs/mole of e^-). The left-hand side of the equation can be converted to a corrosion rate by dividing by the density (ρ), in grams/cm^3 and converting the units to the desired values.

$$\text{corrosion rate (cm/s)} = \frac{(1/\rho)m}{at} \qquad (18)$$

For example, as written, the units are in cm/sec, which are not commonly used. This can be converted to thousandths of an inch per year (mils per year or mpy) by multiplying the number by 1.242×10^{10}.

$$\text{corrosion rate (mils per year)} = \text{Corrosion Rate(cm/s)} \times (1.242 \times 10^{10}) \qquad (19)$$

A good number to remember is that 1 mpy for iron is equal to a current density of 2.17×10^{-6} A/cm^2, which is equivalent to 2.02 mA/ft^2.

Another type of polarization commonly observed is concentration polarization. A definition of concentration polarization is "The portion of the polarization of a cell produced by concentration changes resulting from passage of current through the electrolyte." Concentration polarization is most commonly associated with the reduction reaction and is shown graphically in Figure 16.5. In this example, the diffusion of oxygen to the metal surface limits the rate of corrosion. Note that the rate of the reduction reaction is independent of potential when concentration polarization occurs.

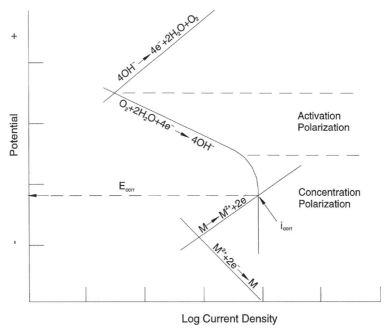

Figure 16.5   Evans diagram for metal M where the concentration of oxygen is limiting rate of corrosion.

Differential Aeration Cells

In the corrosion cells described above, the oxidation and reduction reactions occur physically at or very near the same location on a metal. At any given moment, one atom is being oxidized while the reduction reaction is occurring at an adjacent atomic site. Corrosion of a metal in an acid solution is a common example of this type of behavior. It is also possible for the oxidation and reduction reactions to be separated on a metal surface, where the metal oxidation occurs predominantly at one site while the reduction reaction occurs predominantly at another site. This is referred to as a differential corrosion cell. One common differential corrosion cell is a differential aeration cell, shown in Figure 16.6. In this example, the paved road lowers the oxygen concentration in the soil around the pipeline. This region of the pipeline becomes the anode in the differential corrosion cell. Current leaves the metal surface in this region, increasing the corrosion rate, and flows to the cathodic areas where the oxygen concentration is higher.

The Evans diagram for a differential aeration cell is shown in Figure 16.7. Note that each of the two sites has its own free corrosion potential. At the cathodic site, the primary reduction reaction is oxygen reduction while water reduction is indicated as the primary reduction reaction at the anodic site. The oxidation reactions at the two sites are the

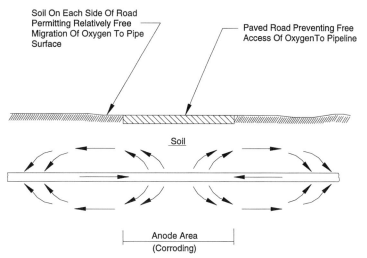

Figure 16.6 Schematic showing differential aeration cell developed on a pipeline beneath a paved road. Arrows indicate direction of current flow.

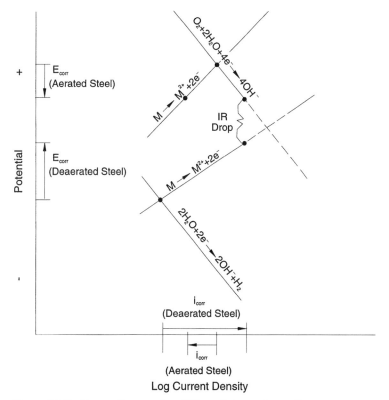

Figure 16.7 Evans diagram for differential aeration cell.

same: oxidation of iron in this case. However, the Tafel slopes for the oxidation reactions are different because oxygen promotes the formation of protective oxide films. Figure 16.7 shows that the cathodic site, where net reduction occurs, is polarized cathodically (in the negative direction) from its free corrosion potential. The anodic site, where net oxidation occurs, is polarized anodically (in the positive direction) from its free corrosion potential. After polarization, the two sites are not usually at the same potential because of an ohmic potential drop in the electrolyte, which is also indicated in the figure.

The differential aeration cell is probably the most common corrosion cell found on pipelines or other underground structures. The upper parts of the structure are exposed to higher concentrations of oxygen and become the cathodes in the cell while the lower parts of the structure are oxygen deficient and become the anodes. Books on CP commonly state that the following four conditions are required for a corrosion cell to function:

1. There must be an anode.
2. There must be a cathode.
3. There must be a metallic path electrically connecting the anode and cathode. (Normally, this will be the pipeline itself.)
4. The anode and cathode must be immersed in an electrically conductive electrolyte (normally, moist soil).

The earlier edition of this book also stated that there must be an electrical potential between the anode and cathode. However, the principles of electrode kinetics show that a potential difference between the anode and cathode is not required for all types of corrosion. For example, an electrical potential between the anode and cathode is not necessary for uniform corrosion to occur. In the case of uniform corrosion, the anode and the cathode can be adjacent atoms on a metal at the same potential. The anodic and cathodic reactions must be polarized from their equilibrium values for corrosion to occur: the cathodic reaction is cathodically polarized and the anodic reaction is anodically polarized. The polarization of these reactions generates net oxidation and reduction currents that produce corrosion. Nevertheless, the vast majority of cases of corrosion on underground structures occur as a result of differential cells where the four conditions are present and a potential difference between the anode and cathode is present.

Other Differential Corrosion Cells

Galvanic Corrosion

The differential aeration cell is one example of a differential corrosion cell. Galvanic corrosion is another example. In the case of galvanic corrosion, the potential difference is created by the presence of different metals. Referring to the galvanic series described in the thermodynamics section, each material has a different corrosion potential in a given environment. When these metals are electrically coupled, the metal with the most positive corrosion potential is cathodically polarized, reducing its corrosion rate, while the more negative member of the couple is anodically polarized, increasing its corrosion rate. Galvanic corrosion can be very detrimental to an underground structure. Examples include the corrosion of iron in contact with copper or stainless steel fittings. However, galvanic corrosion can be used as an effective means of CP, as described in the section on CP.

Mill Scale Corrosion

Although not a metal, mill scale on hot rolled steel acts like a dissimilar metal in contact with the pipe steel. As shown by the practical galvanic series of Table 16.3, pipe steel will be anodic to mill scale. This can result in severe corrosion in low resistivity soils.

New and Old Pipe

A condition closely related to dissimilar metal corrosion occurs when new steel pipe, as shown in Figure 16.8, is intermixed with old steel pipe. This has often been found in older distribution piping systems where a section of pipe has been replaced because of corrosion damage. The new piece of pipe, exposed to the same corrosion conditions, logically would be expected to last as long as the original section. However, the new section will usually fail sooner than expected unless it is electrically insulated from the remainder of the system. This is simply an application of the practical galvanic series of Table 16.3, which shows that the potential of bright new steel is markedly different

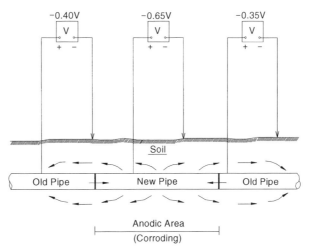

Figure 16.8 Schematic showing a differential corrosion cell created by replacement of a section of pipe.

from that of old rusted steel. The new steel is anodic and corrodes more rapidly than the old rusted steel. A similar corrosive condition can occur if, during work on an existing piping system, tools cut or scrape the pipe and expose areas of bright steel. These bright spots will be anodic and can result in accelerated corrosion in low resistivity soils.

Dissimilar Soils

A steel pipeline passing through dissimilar soils can establish corrosion cells in much the same manner that corrosion cells can be established with dissimilar metals. This is illustrated by Figure 16.9, which shows a pipeline passing through two dissimilar soils. The potential of the pipeline in soil A is slightly different from the potential in soil B. As indicated in the section of the book on the galvanic series, the corrosion, or native potential of a metal can vary with differences in the environment. This causes the potential difference illustrated and satisfies the conditions necessary to establish a differential corrosion cell. In the figure, the pipe in soil A is anodic to that in soil B and is corroding as indicated by the current discharge. This behavior is sometimes made strikingly apparent when excavating an old bare pipeline in which some areas

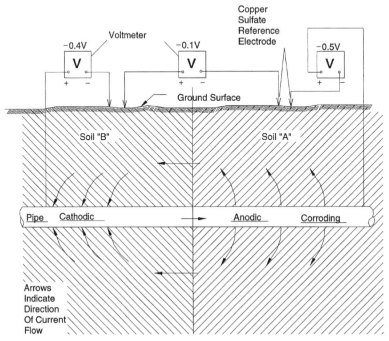

Figure 16.9   Schematic showing differential corrosion cell created by dissimilar soils.

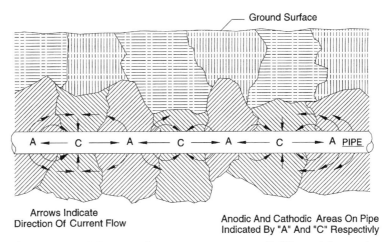

Figure 16.10   Schematic showing numerous small differential corrosion cells created by different soils.

(cathodic) are in excellent condition but other areas (anodic) only a few feet away are severely corroded. The middle voltmeter illustrates that the potential difference between soil types can be measured. This type of measurement is used during pipeline surveys as outlined in Chapter 5.

Figure 16.10 illustrates the effect of adjacent soil types of different character on differential cell corrosion. In some instances, different soil types are layered so that the backfill contacting the pipe will be a mixture of soil types when a pipeline trench is excavated and the pipe is laid and backfilled. This produces many small corrosion cells at the pipe surface that are not necessarily detectable by potential measurements taken at the surface of the ground.

A specialized differential corrosion cell involves steel in concrete versus steel in soil. Figure 16.11 indicates that the portion of a steel pipe which is embedded in concrete will be more noble (positive) than adjacent pipe sections buried in soil. The electrolytic environment of moist concrete, being entirely different from the surrounding soil, results in substantial differences in the steel-to-environment potential as illustrated in Table 16.3. Practically, this will always make the steel in soil more negative (active) than the steel embedded in concrete. This is an important source of corrosion activity in some instances.

Relative Size of Anodic and Cathodic Areas

Up to this point, various conditions have been discussed that can cause corrosion current to flow in a differential corrosion cell. The relative size of anodic and cathodic areas has not been mentioned. An understanding of the effect of differences in area relationships

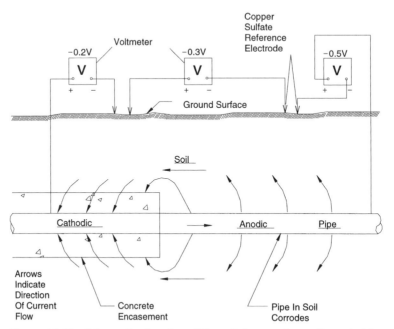

Figure 16.11 Schematic showing differential corrosion cell created by concrete encasement of pipe. Note that the indicated polarities of the potentials are reversed.

is important for an appreciation of why, for example, a dissimilar metal combination can cause very rapid corrosion under certain area relationships and relatively little in others. Figure 16.12 demonstrates the effect of anode to cathode area ratio on galvanic corrosion. The left-hand sketch in Figure 16.12 shows a small anode (a galvanized cap on a service stub on a bare steel pipeline) in contact with a large cathode (the bare steel line). Under such a condition, the small anode will be subject to a high density of current discharge per unit area, with the total amount of current flowing governed by the kinetics of the oxidation and reduction reactions and the soil resistivity. The current collected per unit area on the cathode is relatively low and may not be sufficient to result in any degree of polarization which would tend to limit corrosion current flow as discussed earlier. Under these conditions, in a low resistivity environment, corrosion can be serious and rapid.

By contrast, the right-hand sketch in Figure 16.12 shows a large anode (the steel pipeline) and a small cathode (the brass valve in the steel system). With such a combination, a high current density may be collected per unit area at the cathode, but the total cathodic current will be relatively small because of the small area of the cathode (total current = current density × area). The corrosion current density discharged from the steel will be even smaller because the small current is distributed over a large surface area. From this discussion, we may conclude that no matter what condition has

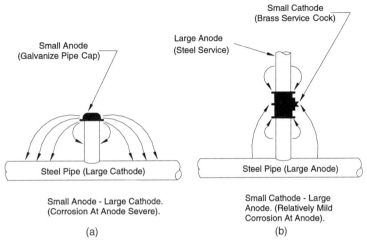

Figure 16.12 Schematic showing the effect of anode to cathode area ratio on galvanic corrosion.

initiated the differential corrosion cell, if the anodic area is relatively small in relation to the cathodic area, corrosion will be severe. If, on the other hand, the anodic area is large as compared to the cathodic area, corrosion will be relatively mild.

CATHODIC PROTECTION

The principal methods for mitigating corrosion on underground pipelines are coatings and CP. A primary function of a coating on a cathodically protected structure is to reduce the surface area of exposed metal on the pipeline, thereby reducing the current necessary to cathodically protect the metal. CP is defined as "a reduction of the corrosion rate by shifting the potential of the structure toward a less oxidizing potential by applying an external current." This can be shown graphically on an Evans diagram as indicated in Figure 16.13. In the illustration, the potential of the metal is shifted from the free corrosion potential, E_{corr} to the value E_{CP} by the application of the CP current, $i_{applied}$. As the potential becomes more negative, the corrosion rate decreases, as defined by the anodic kinetics, while the rate of the cathodic current increases. This difference between the anodic and cathodic kinetics is the amount of current required to maintain the indicated potential and is equivalent to the CP current applied to a structure.

It is important to note that complete protection is not achieved until the potential of the metal is shifted to the equilibrium potential, E_{equil}. At this potential, the net corrosion rate is zero. Usually, it is not practicable to achieve complete protection because of the high current required; the applied current increases exponentially with decreasing potential. Since anodic Tafel slopes are typically around $100\,mV$, a $100\,mV$ negative shift in the

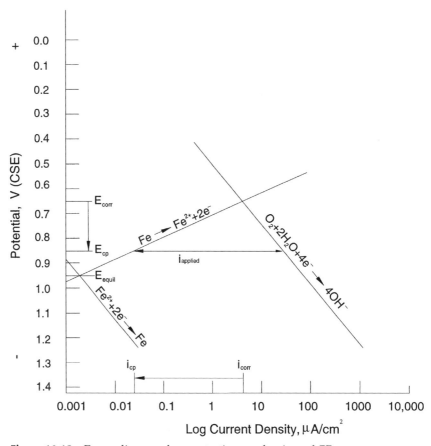

Figure 16.13   Evans diagram demonstrating mechanism of CP.

potential will decrease the corrosion rate by a factor of 10. This magnitude of decrease is typically considered to be adequate to protect most structures.

The required shift in potential can be achieved by means of an external power source (referred to as impressed current CP) or by utilizing a sacrificial anode. The impressed current system uses a power supply, referred to as a rectifier, and an anode buried in the ground to impress a current on the structure. The sacrificial anode system uses the galvanic relationship between a sacrificial anode material, such as zinc or magnesium, and the pipe steel to supply the required CP current.

ENVIRONMENTAL POLARIZATION

The concepts presented for CP are fundamentally correct at the instant that CP is applied but are too simplistic to consider the time-dependant behavior of a cathodically protected underground structure. At the surface of a structure under CP, a number of changes in the environment occur that are beneficial in mitigating corrosion. They have been referred to as environmental polarization. As shown in Figure 16.13, the rate of the reduction reaction is increased when the CP is applied. The reduction reactions generate OH^- or consume H^+

$$O_2 + 2H_2O + 4e^- \rightarrow 4OH^- \tag{3}$$

$$2H^+ + 2e^- \rightarrow H_2 \tag{5}$$

$$2H_2O + 2e^- \rightarrow 2OH^- + H_2 \tag{20}$$

Thus, an increase in the rate of these reactions causes a pH increase to occur at the metal surface, creating a less acidic (more basic) environment. This pH increase is beneficial because the corrosion rate of steel decreases with increasing pH, even under freely corroding conditions. The decrease in corrosion rate is the result of the formation of a protective oxide film on the metal surface in the elevated pH environment, a process referred to as passivation. On an Evans diagram, this process corresponds to an increase in the anodic Tafel slope and a resulting shift in the oxidation kinetics to the left. The flow of electrical current also causes damaging negatively charged ions (anions), such as chloride, to migrate from the metal surface.

NACE Glossary of Corrosion-Related Terms

Courtesy of Technical Coordination Committee and Reference Publications Committee.

A

Abrasive Small particles of material that are propelled at high velocity to impact a surface during abrasive blast cleaning.

Abrasive Blast Cleaning Cleaning and roughening of a surface produced by the high-velocity impact of an abrasive that is propelled by the discharge of pressurized fluid from a blast nozzle or by a mechanical device such as a centrifugal blasting wheel. (Also referred to as *Abrasive Blasting*.)

Accelerator A chemical substance that increases the rate at which a chemical reaction (e.g., curing) would otherwise occur.

Acrylic Type of resin polymerized from acrylic acid, methacrylic acid, esters of these acids, or acrylonitrile.

Activator A chemical substance that initiates and accelerates a chemical reaction (e.g., curing). Heat and radiation may also serve as activators for some chemical reactions.

Active (1) The negative direction of electrode potential. (2) A state of a metal that is corroding without significant influence of reaction product.

Aeration Cell [See *Differential Aeration Cell.*]

Air Drying Process by which an applied wet coat converts to a dry coating film by evaporation of solvent or reaction with oxygen as a result of simple exposure to air without intentional addition of heat or a curing agent.

Airless Spraying Process of spraying coating liquids using hydraulic pressure, not air pressure, to atomize.

Alkyd Type of resin formed by the reaction of polyhydric alcohols and polybasic acids, part of which is derived from saturated or unsaturated oils or fats.

Alligatoring   Pronounced wide cracking over the surface of a coating, which has the appearance of alligator hide.

Amphoteric Metal   A metal that is susceptible to corrosion in both acid and alkaline environments.

Anaerobic   Free of air or uncombined oxygen.

Anion   A negatively charged ion that migrates through the electrolyte toward the anode under the influence of a potential gradient.

Anode   The electrode of an electrochemical cell at which oxidation occurs. Electrons flow away from the anode in the external circuit. Corrosion usually occurs and metal ions enter the solution at the anode.

Anode Cap   An electrical insulating material placed over the end of the anode at the lead wire connection.

Anode Corrosion Efficiency   The ratio of the actual corrosion (mass loss) of an anode to the theoretical corrosion (mass loss) calculated from the quantity of electricity that has passed between the anode and cathode using Faraday's law.

Anodic Inhibitor   A chemical substance that prevents or reduces the rate of the anodic or oxidation reaction.

Anodic Polarization   The change of the electrode potential in the noble (positive) direction caused by current across the electrode/electrolyte interface. [See *Polarization*.]

Anodic Protection   Polarization to a more oxidizing potential to achieve a reduced corrosion rate by the promotion of passivity.

Anodizing   Oxide coating formed on a metal surface (generally aluminum) by an electrolytic process.

Anolyte   The electrolyte adjacent to the anode of an electrochemical cell.

Antifouling   Preventing fouling. [See *Fouling*.]

Attenuation   Electrical losses in a conductor caused by current flow in the conductor.

Auger Electron Spectroscopy   Analytical technique in which the sample surface is irradiated with low-energy electrons and the energy spectrum of electrons emitted from the surface is measured.

Austenitic Steel   A steel whose microstructure at room temperature consists predominantly of austenite.

Auxiliary Electrode   An electrode, usually made from a noncorroding material, which is commonly used in polarization studies to pass current to or from a test electrode.

B

Backfill   Material placed in a hole to fill the space around the anodes, vent pipe, and buried components of a cathodic protection system.

Barrier Coating   (1) A coating that has a high resistance to permeation of liquids and/or gases. (2) A coating that is applied over a previously coated surface to prevent damage to the underlying coating during subsequent handling.

Beach Marks The characteristic markings on the fracture surfaces produced by fatigue crack propagation (also known as *clamshell marks*, *conchoidal marks*, and *arrest marks*).

Binder The nonvolatile portion of the vehicle of a formulated coating material.

Bituminous Coating An asphalt or coal-tar compound used to provide a protective coating for a surface.

Blast Angle (1) The angle of the blast nozzle with reference to the surface during abrasive blast cleaning. (2) The angle of the abrasive particles propelled from a centrifugal blasting wheel with reference to the surface being abrasive blast cleaned.

Blowdown (1) Injection of air or water under high pressure through a tube to the anode area for the purpose of purging the annular space and possibly correcting high resistance caused by gas blockage. (2) In conjunction with boilers or cooling towers, the process of discharging a significant portion of the aqueous solution in order to remove accumulated salts, deposits, and other impurities.

Blushing Whitening and loss of gloss of a coating, usually organic, caused by moisture (also known as *blooming*).

Brittle Fracture Fracture with little or no plastic deformation.

Brush-Off Blast Cleaned Surface A brush-off blast cleaned surface, when viewed without magnification, shall be free of all visible oil, grease, dirt, dust, loose mill scale, loose rust, and loose coating. Tightly adherent mill scale, rust, and coating may remain on the surface. Mill scale, rust, and coating are considered tightly adherent if they cannot be removed by lifting with a dull putty knife. [See NACE No. 4/SSPC-SP 7.]

C

Calcareous Coating A layer consisting of calcium carbonate and other salts deposited on the surface. When the surface is cathodically polarized as in cathodic protection, this layer is the result of the increased pH adjacent to the protected surface.

Calcareous Deposit [See *Calcareous Coating.*]

Case Hardening Hardening a ferrous alloy so that the outer portion, or case, is made substantially harder than the inner portion, or core. Typical processes are carburizing, cyaniding, carbo-nitriding, nitriding, induction hardening, and flame hardening.

Casein Paint Water-thinned paint with vehicle derived from milk.

Catalyst A chemical substance, usually present in small amounts relative to the reactants, that increases the rate at which a chemical reaction (e.g., curing) would otherwise occur, but is not consumed in the reaction.

Cathode The electrode of an electrochemical cell at which reduction is the principal reaction. Electrons flow toward the cathode in the external circuit.

Cathodic Corrosion Corrosion resulting from a cathodic condition of a structure, usually caused by the reaction of an amphoteric metal with the alkaline products of electrolysis.

Cathodic Disbondment The destruction of adhesion between a coating and the coated surface caused by products of a cathodic reaction.

Cathodic Inhibitor A chemical substance that prevents or reduces the rate of the cathodic or reduction reaction.

Cathodic Polarization The change of the electrode potential in the active (negative) direction caused by current across the electrode/electrolyte interface. [See *Polarization.*]

Cathodic Protection A technique to reduce the corrosion of a metal surface by making that surface the cathode of an electrochemical cell.

Catholyte The electrolyte adjacent to the cathode of an electrochemical cell.

Cation A positively charged ion that migrates through the electrolyte toward the cathode under the influence of a potential gradient.

Cavitation The formation and rapid collapse of cavities or bubbles within a liquid which often results in damage to a material at the solid/liquid interface under conditions of severe turbulent flow.

Cell [See *Electrochemical Cell.*]

Cementation The introduction of one or more elements into the surface layer of a metal by diffusion at high temperature. (Examples of cementation include carburizing [introduction of carbon], nitriding [introduction of nitrogen], and chromizing [introduction of chromium].)

Chalking The development of loose, removable powder (pigment) at the surface of an organic coating, usually caused by weathering.

Checking The development of slight breaks in a coating which do not penetrate to the underlying surface.

Chemical Conversion Coating An adherent reaction product layer on a metal surface formed by reaction with a suitable chemical to provide greater corrosion resistance to the metal and increase adhesion of coatings applied to the metal. (Example is an iron phosphate coating on steel, developed by reaction with phosphoric acid.)

Chevron Pattern A V-shaped pattern on a fatigue or brittle-fracture surface. The pattern can also be one of straight radial lines on cylindrical specimens.

Chloride Stress Corrosion Cracking Cracking of a metal under the combined action of tensile stress and corrosion in the presence of chlorides and an electrolyte (usually water).

Coat One layer of a coating applied to a surface in a single continuous application to form a uniform film when dry.

Coating A liquid, liquefiable, or mastic composition that, after application to a surface, is converted into a solid protective, decorative, or functional adherent film.

Coating System The complete number and types of coats applied to a substrate in a predetermined order. (When used in a broader sense, surface preparation, pretreatments, dry film thickness, and manner of application are included.)

Cold Shut Horizontal surface discontinuity caused by solidification of a portion of a meniscus during the progressive filling of a mold, which is later covered with more solidifying metal as the molten metal level rises. Cold shuts generally occur at corners remote from the point of pour.

Commercial Blast Cleaned Surface A commercial blast cleaned surface, when viewed without magnification, shall be free of all visible oil, grease, dust, dirt, mill scale, rust, coating, oxides, corrosion products, and other foreign matter. Random staining shall be limited to no more than 33 percent of each unit area (approximately 58 cm^2 [9.0 in.^{2}]) of surface and may consist of light shadows, slight streaks, or minor discolorations caused by stains of rust, stains of mill scale, or stains of previously applied coating. [See NACE No. 3/SSPC-SP 6.]

Concentration Cell An electrochemical cell, the electromotive force of which is caused by a difference in concentration of some component in the electrolyte. (This difference leads to the formation of discrete cathodic and anodic regions.)

Concentration Polarization That portion of polarization of a cell produced by concentration changes resulting from passage of current though the electrolyte.

Conductive Coating (1) A coating that conducts electricity. (2) An electrically conductive, mastic-like material used as an impressed current anode on reinforced concrete surfaces.

Contact Corrosion [See *Galvanic Corrosion.*]

Continuity Bond A connection, usually metallic, that provides electrical continuity between structures that can conduct electricity.

Continuous Anode A single anode with no electrical discontinuities.

Conversion Coating [See *Chemical Conversion Coating.*]

Corrosion The deterioration of a material, usually a metal, that results from a reaction with its environment.

Corrosion Fatigue Fatigue-type cracking of metal caused by repeated or fluctuating stresses in a corrosive environment characterized by shorter life than would be encountered as a result of either the repeated or fluctuating stress alone or the corrosive environment alone.

Corrosion Inhibitor A chemical substance or combination of substances that, when present in the environment, prevents or reduces corrosion.

Corrosion Potential (E_{corr}) The potential of a corroding surface in an electrolyte relative to a reference electrode under open-circuit conditions (also known as *rest potential*, *open-circuit potential*, or *freely corroding potential*).

Corrosion Rate The rate at which corrosion proceeds.

Corrosion Resistance Ability of a material, usually a metal, to withstand corrosion in a given system.

Corrosiveness The tendency of an environment to cause corrosion.

Counter Electrode [See *Auxiliary Electrode.*]

Counterpoise A conductor or system of conductors arranged beneath a power line, located on, above, or most frequently, below the surface of the earth and connected to the footings of the towers or poles supporting the power line.

Couple   [See *Galvanic Couple.*]

Cracking (of Coating)   Breaks in a coating that extend through to the substrate.

Crazing   A network of checks or cracks appearing on the surface of a coating.

Creep   Time-dependent strain occurring under stress.

Crevice Corrosion   Localized corrosion of a metal surface at, or immediately adjacent to, an area that is shielded from full exposure to the environment because of close proximity of the metal to the surface of another material.

Critical Humidity   The relative humidity above which the atmospheric corrosion rate of some metals increases sharply.

Critical Pitting Potential (E_p, E_{pp})   The lowest value of oxidizing potential (voltage) at which pits nucleate and grow. The value depends on the test method used.

Curing   Chemical process of developing the intended properties of a coating or other material (e.g., resin) over a period of time.

Curing Agent   A chemical substance used for curing a coating or other material (e.g., resin). [Also referred to as *Hardener*.]

Current Density   The current to or from a unit area of an electrode surface.

Current Efficiency   The ratio of the electrochemical equivalent current density for a specific reaction to the total applied current density.

D

DC Decoupling Device   A device used in electrical circuits that allows the flow of alternating current (AC) in both directions and stops or substantially reduces the flow of direct current (DC).

Dealloying   The selective corrosion of one or more components of a solid solution alloy (also known as *parting* or *selective dissolution*).

Decomposition Potential   The potential (voltage) on a metal surface necessary to decompose the electrolyte of an electrochemical cell or a component thereof.

Decomposition Voltage   [See *Decomposition Potential.*]

Deep Groundbed   One or more anodes installed vertically at a nominal depth of 15 m (50 ft) or more below the earth's surface in a drilled hole for the purpose of supplying cathodic protection.

Depolarization   The removal of factors resisting the current in an electrochemical cell.

Deposit Attack   Corrosion occurring under or around a discontinuous deposit on a metallic surface (also known as *poultice corrosion*).

Dezincification   A corrosion phenomenon resulting in the selective removal of zinc from copper-zinc alloys. (This phenomenon is one of the more common forms of dealloying.)

Dielectric Coating   A coating that does not conduct electricity.

Dielectric Shield   An electrically nonconductive material, such as a coating, sheet or pipe, that is placed between an anode and an adjacent cathode, usually on the cathode, to improve current distribution in a cathodic protection system.

Differential Aeration Cell   An electrochemical cell, the electromotive force of which is due to a difference in air (oxygen) concentration at one electrode as compared with that at another electrode of the same material.

Diffusion-Limited Current Density   The current density that corresponds to the maximum transfer rate that a particular species can sustain because of the limitation of diffusion (often referred to as *limiting current density*).

Disbondment   The loss of adhesion between a coating and the substrate.

Double Layer   The interface between an electrode or a suspended particle and an electrolyte created by charge-charge interaction leading to an alignment of oppositely charged ions at the surface of the electrode or particle. The simplest model is represented by a parallel plate condenser.

Drainage   Conduction of electric current from an underground or submerged metallic structure by means of a metallic conductor.

Driving Potential   Difference in potential between the anode and the steel structure.

Drying Oil   An oil capable of conversion from a liquid to a solid by slow reaction with oxygen in the air.

E

Elastic Deformation   Changes of dimensions of a material upon the application of a stress within the elastic range. Following the release of an elastic stress, the material returns to its original dimensions without any permanent deformation.

Elastic Limit   The maximum stress to which a material may be subjected without retention of any permanent deformation after the stress is removed.

Elasticity   The property of a material that allows it to recover its original dimensions following deformation by a stress below its elastic limit.

Electrical Isolation   The condition of being electrically separated from other metallic structures or the environment.

Electrochemical Cell   A system consisting of an anode and a cathode immersed in an electrolyte so as to create an electrical circuit. The anode and cathode may be different metals or dissimilar areas on the same metal surface.

Electrochemical Equivalent   The mass of an element or group of elements oxidized or reduced at 100% efficiency by the passage of a unit quantity of electricity.

Electrochemical Potential   The partial derivative of the total electrochemical free energy of a constituent with respect to the number of moles of this constituent where all other factors are kept constant. It is analogous to the chemical potential of a constituent except that it includes the electrical as well as chemical contributions to the free energy.

Electrode   A conductor used to establish contact with an electrolyte and through which current is transferred to or from an electrolyte.

Electrode Potential   The potential of an electrode in an electrolyte as measured against a reference electrode. (The electrode potential does not include any resistance losses in potential in either the electrolyte or the external circuit. It represents the reversible work to move a unit of charge from the electrode surface through the electrolyte to the reference electrode.)

Electrokinetic Potential A potential difference in a solution caused by residual, unbalanced charge distribution in the adjoining solution, producing a double layer. The electrokinetic potential is different from the electrode potential in that it occurs exclusively in the solution phase. This potential represents the reversible work necessary to bring a unit charge from infinity in the solution up to the interface in question but not through the interface (also known as *zeta potential*).

Electrolyte A chemical substance containing ions that migrate in an electric field.

Electrolytic Cleaning A process for removing soil, scale, or corrosion products from a metal surface by subjecting the metal as an electrode to an electric current in an electrolytic bath.

Electromotive Force Series A list of elements arranged according to their standard electrode potentials, the sign being positive for elements whose potentials are cathodic to hydrogen and negative for those anodic to hydrogen.

Ellipsometry An optical analytical technique employing plane-polarized light to study films.

Embrittlement Loss of ductility of a material resulting from a chemical or physical change.

EMF Series See *Electromotive Force Series*.

Enamel (1) A paint that dries to a hard, glossy surface. (2) A coating that is characterized by an ability to form a smooth, durable film.

End Effect The more rapid loss of anode material at the end of an anode, compared with other surfaces of the anode, resulting from higher current density.

Endurance Limit The maximum stress that a material can withstand for an infinitely large number of fatigue cycles.

Environment The surroundings or conditions (physical, chemical, mechanical) in which a material exists.

Environmental Cracking Brittle fracture of a normally ductile material in which the corrosive effect of the environment is a causative factor.

Environmental cracking is a general term that includes all of the terms listed below. The definitions of these terms are listed elsewhere in the *Glossary*:

Corrosion fatigue
Hydrogen embrittlement
Hydrogen-induced cracking—(stepwise cracking)
Hydrogen stress cracking
Liquid metal cracking
Stress corrosion cracking
Sulfide stress cracking

The following terms have been used in the past in connection with environmental cracking but are now obsolete and should not be used:

Caustic embrittlement
Delayed cracking
Liquid metal embrittlement
Season cracking
Static fatigue
Sulfide corrosion cracking
Sulfide stress corrosion cracking

Epoxy Type of resin formed by the reaction of aliphatic or aromatic polyols (like bisphenol) with epichlorohydrin and characterized by the presence of reactive oxirane end groups.

Equilibrium Potential The potential of an electrode in an electrolyte at which the forward rate of a given reaction is exactly equal to the reverse rate; the electrode potential with reference to a standard equilibrium, as defined by the Nernst equation.

Erosion The progressive loss of material from a solid surface due to mechanical interaction between that surface and a fluid, a multicomponent fluid, or solid particles carried with the fluid.

Erosion-Corrosion A conjoint action involving corrosion and erosion in the presence of a moving corrosive fluid or a material moving through the fluid, leading to accelerated loss of material.

Exchange Current The rate at which either positive or negative charges are entering or leaving the surface when an electrode reaches dynamic equilibrium in an electrolyte.

Exfoliation Corrosion Localized subsurface corrosion in zones parallel to the surface that result in thin layers of uncorroded metal resembling the pages of a book.

External Circuit The wires, connectors, measuring devices, current sources, etc., that are used to bring about or measure the desired electrical conditions within an electrochemical cell. It is this portion of the cell through which electrons travel.

F

Fatigue The phenomenon leading to fracture of a material under repeated or fluctuating stresses having a maximum value less than the tensile strength of the material.

Fatigue Strength The maximum stress that can be sustained for a specified number of cycles without failure.

Fault Current A current that flows from one conductor to ground or to another conductor due to an abnormal connection (including an arc) between the two. A fault current flowing to ground may be called a ground fault current.

Ferrite The body-centered cubic crystalline phase of iron-based alloys.

Ferritic Steel A steel whose microstructure at room temperature consists predominantly of ferrite.

Filiform Corrosion Corrosion that occurs under a coating in the form of randomly distributed thread-like filaments.

Film A thin, not necessarily visible layer of material.

Finish Coat [See *Topcoat.*]

Forced Drainage Drainage applied to underground or submerged metallic structures by means of an applied electromotive force or sacrificial anode.

Foreign Structure Any metallic structure that is not intended as a part of a system under cathodic protection.

Fouling An accumulation of deposits. This includes accumulation and growth of marine organisms on a submerged metal surface and the accumulation of deposits (usually inorganic) on heat exchanger tubing.

Fractography Descriptive treatment of fracture, especially in metals, with specific reference to photographs of the fracture surface.

Fracture Mechanics   A quantitative analysis for evaluating structural reliability in terms of applied stress, crack length, and specimen geometry.

Free Machining   The machining characteristics of an alloy to which an ingredient has been introduced to give small broken chips, lower power consumption, better surface finish, and longer tool life.

Fretting Corrosion   Deterioration at the interface of two contacting surfaces under load which is accelerated by their relative motion.

Furan   Type of resin formed by the polymerization or polycondensation of furfuryl, furfuryl alcohol, or other compounds containing a furan ring.

G

Galvanic Anode   A metal that provides sacrificial protection to another metal that is more noble when electrically coupled in an electrolyte. This type of anode is the electron source in one type of cathodic protection.

Galvanic Corrosion   Accelerated corrosion of a metal because of an electrical contact with a more noble metal or nonmetallic conductor in a corrosive electrolyte.

Galvanic Couple   A pair of dissimilar conductors, commonly metals, in electrical contact in an electrolyte.

Galvanic Current   The electric current between metals or conductive nonmetals in a galvanic couple.

Galvanic Series   A list of metals and alloys arranged according to their corrosion potentials in a given environment.

Galvanostatic   Refers to an experimental technique whereby an electrode is maintained at a constant current in an electrolyte.

General Corrosion   Corrosion that is distributed more or less uniformly over the surface of a material.

Graphitic Corrosion   Deterioration of gray cast iron in which the metallic constituents are selectively leached or converted to corrosion products, leaving the graphite intact.

Graphitization   The formation of graphite in iron or steel, usually from decomposition of iron carbide at elevated temperatures. [Should not be used as a term to describe graphitic corrosion.]

Grit   Small particles of hard material (e.g., iron, steel, or mineral) with irregular shapes that are commonly used as an abrasive in abrasive blast cleaning.

Grit Blasting   Abrasive blast cleaning using grit as the abrasive.

Groundbed   One or more anodes installed below the earth's surface for the purpose of supplying cathodic protection.

H

Half-Cell   A pure metal in contact with a solution of known concentration of its own ion, at a specific temperature, develops a potential that is characteristic and reproducible; when coupled with another half-cell, an overall potential that is the sum of both half-cells develops.

Hand Tool Cleaning   Removal of loose rust, loose mill scale, and loose paint to degree specified, by hand chipping, scraping, sanding, and wire brushing. [See SSPC-SP 2.]

Hardener   [See *Curing Agent.*]

Heat-Affected Zone   That portion of the base metal that is not melted during brazing, cutting, or welding, but whose microstructure and properties are altered by the heat of these processes.

Heat Treatment   Heating and cooling a solid metal or alloy in such a way as to obtain desired properties. Heating for the sole purpose of hot working is not considered heat treatment.

High-Pressure Water Cleaning   Water cleaning performed at pressures from 34 to 70 MPa (5,000 to 10,000 psig).

High-Pressure Water Jetting   Water jetting performed at pressures from 70 to 170 MPa (10,000 to 25,000 psig).

High-Temperature Hydrogen Attack   A loss of strength and ductility of steel by high-temperature reaction of absorbed hydrogen with carbides in the steel, resulting in decarburization and internal fissuring.

Holiday   A discontinuity in a protective coating that exposes unprotected surface to the environment.

Hydrogen Blistering   The formation of subsurface planar cavities, called hydrogen blisters, in a metal resulting from excessive internal hydrogen pressure. Growth of near-surface blisters in low-strength metals usually results in surface bulges.

Hydrogen Embrittlement   A loss of ductility of a metal resulting from absorption of hydrogen.

Hydrogen-Induced Cracking   Stepwise internal cracks that connect adjacent hydrogen blisters on different planes in the metal, or to the metal surface (also known as *stepwise cracking*).

Hydrogen Overvoltage   Overvoltage associated with the liberation of hydrogen gas.

Hydrogen Stress Cracking   Cracking that results from the presence of hydrogen in a metal in combination with tensile stress. It occurs most frequently with high-strength alloys.

I

Impingement Corrosion   A form of erosion-corrosion generally associated with the local impingement of a high-velocity, flowing fluid against a solid surface.

Impressed Current   An electric current supplied by a device employing a power source that is external to the electrode system. (An example is direct current for cathodic protection.)

Inclusion   A nonmetallic phase such as an oxide, sulfide, or silicate particle in a metal.

Inorganic Zinc-Rich Coating   Coating containing a metallic zinc pigment (typically 75 wt% zinc or more in the dry film) in an inorganic vehicle.

Intercrystalline Corrosion   [See *Intergranular Corrosion.*]

Interdendritic Corrosion Corrosive attack of cast metals that progresses preferentially along paths between dendrites.

Intergranular Corrosion Preferential corrosion at or along the grain boundaries of a metal (also known as *intercrystalline corrosion*).

Intergranular Stress Corrosion Cracking Stress corrosion cracking in which the cracking occurs along grain boundaries.

Internal Oxidation The formation of isolated particles of oxidation products beneath the metal surface.

Intumescence The swelling or bubbling of a coating usually caused by heating. [The term is commonly used in aerospace and fire-protection applications.]

Ion An electrically charged atom or group of atoms.

Iron Rot Deterioration of wood in contact with iron-based alloys.

K

Knife-Line Attack Intergranular corrosion of an alloy along a line adjoining or in contact with a weld after heating into the sensitization temperature range.

L

Lamellar Corrosion [See *Exfoliation Corrosion*.]

Langelier Index A calculated saturation index for calcium carbonate that is useful in predicting scaling behavior of natural water.

Line Currrent The direct current flowing on a pipeline.

Lining A coating or layer of sheet material adhered to or in intimate contact with the interior surface of a container used to protect the container against corrosion by its contents and/or to protect the contents of the container from contamination by the container material.

Liquid Metal Cracking Cracking of a metal caused by contact with a liquid metal.

Long-Line Current Current though the earth between an anodic and a cathodic area that returns along an underground metallic structure.

Low-Carbon Steel Steel having less than 0.30% carbon and no intentional alloying additions.

Low-Pressure Water Cleaning Water cleaning performed at pressures less than 34 MPa (5,000 psig).

Luggin Probe A small tube or capillary filled with electrolyte, terminating close to the metal surface of an electrode under study, which is used to provide an ion-conducting path without diffusion between the electrode under study and a reference electrode.

M

Martensite A hard supersaturated solid solution of carbon in iron characterized by an acicular (needle-like) microstructure.

Metal Dusting   The catastrophic deterioration of a metal exposed to a carbonaceous gas at elevated temperature.

Metallizing   The coating of a surface with a thin metal layer by spraying, hot dipping, or vacuum deposition.

Mill Scale   The oxide layer formed during hot fabrication or heat treatment of metals.

Mixed Potential   A potential resulting from two or more electrochemical reactions occurring simultaneously on one metal surface.

Modulus Of Elasticity   A measure of the stiffness or rigidity of a material. It is actually the ratio of stress to strain in the elastic region of a material. If determined by a tension or compression test, it is also called Young's Modulus or the coefficient of elasticity.

N

Natural Drainage   Drainage from an underground or submerged metallic structure to a more negative (more anodic) structure, such as the negative bus of a trolley substation.

Near-White Blast Cleaned Surface   A near-white blast cleaned surface, when viewed without magnification, shall be free of all visible oil, grease, dust, dirt, mill scale, rust, coating, oxides, corrosion products, and other foreign matter. Random staining shall be limited to not more than 5% of each unit area of surface (approximately 58 cm^2 [9.0 in.^{2}]), and may consist of light shadows, slight streaks, or minor discolorations caused by stains of rust, stains of mill scale, or stains of previously applied coating. [See NACE No. 2/SSPC-SP 10.]

Negative Return   A point of connection between the cathodic protection negative cable and the protected structure.

Nernst Equation   An equation that expresses the exact electromotive force of an electrochemical cell in terms of the activities of products and reactants of the cell.

Nernst Layer   The diffusion layer at the surface of an electrode in which the concentration of a chemical species is assumed to vary linearly from the value in the bulk solution to the value at the electrode surface.

Noble   The positive direction of electrode potential, thus resembling noble metals such as gold and platinum.

Noble Metal   (1) A metal that occurs commonly in nature in the free state. (2) A metal or alloy whose corrosion products are formed with a small negative or a positive free-energy change.

Noble Potential   A potential more cathodic (positive) than the standard hydrogen potential.

Normalizing   Heating a ferrous alloy to a suitable temperature above the transformation range (austenitizing), holding at temperature for a suitable time, and then cooling in still air to a temperature substantially below the transformation range.

O

Open-Circuit Potential   The potential of an electrode measured with respect to a reference electrode or another electrode in the absence of current.

Organic Zinc-Rich Coating Coating containing a metallic zinc pigment (typically 75 wt% zinc or more in the dry film) in an organic resin.

Overvoltage The change in potential of an electrode from its equilibrium or steady-state value when current is applied.

Oxidation (1) Loss of electrons by a constituent of a chemical reaction. (2) Corrosion of a metal that is exposed to an oxidizing gas at elevated temperatures.

Oxidation-Reduction Potential The potential of a reversible oxidation-reduction electrode measured with respect to a reference electrode, corrected to the hydrogen electrode, in a given electrolyte.

Oxygen Concentration Cell [See *Differential Aeration Cell.*]

P

Paint A pigmented liquid or resin applied to a substrate as a thin layer that is converted to an opaque solid film after application. It is commonly used as a decorative or protective coating.

Paint System [See *Coating System.*]

Parting [See *Dealloying.*]

Passivation A reduction of the anodic reaction rate of an electrode involved in corrosion.

Passivation Potential [See *Primary Passive Potential.*]

Passive (1) The positive direction of electrode potential. (2) A state of a metal in which a surface reaction product causes a marked decrease in the corrosion rate relative to that in the absence of the product.

Passive-Active Cell An electrochemical cell, the electromotive force of which is caused by the potential difference between a metal in an active state and the same metal in a passive state.

Passivity The state of being passive.

Patina A thin layer of corrosion product, usually green, that forms on the surface of metals such as copper and copper-based alloys exposed to the atmosphere.

pH The negative logarithm of the hydrogen ion activity written as:

$$pH = -\log_{10}(a_H^+)$$

where a_H^+ = hydrogen ion activity = the molar concentration of hydrogen ions multiplied by the mean ion-activity coefficient.

Pickling (1) Treating a metal in a chemical bath to remove scale and oxides (e.g., rust) from the surface. (2) Complete removal of rust and mill scale by acid pickling, duplex pickling, or electrolytic pickling. [See SSPC-SP 8.]

Pickling Solution A chemical bath, usually an acid solution, used for pickling.

Pigment A solid substance, generally in fine powder form, that is insoluble in the vehicle of a formulated coating material. It is used to impart color or other specific physical or chemical properties to the coating.

Pipe-To-Electrolyte Potential The potential difference between the pipe metallic surface and electrolyte that is measured with reference to an electrode in contact with the electrolyte.

Pitting   Localized corrosion of a metal surface that is confined to a small area and takes the form of cavities called pits.

Pitting Factor   The ratio of the depth of the deepest pit resulting from corrosion divided by the average penetration as calculated from mass loss.

Plastic Deformation   Permanent deformation caused by stressing beyond the elastic limit.

Plasticity   The ability of a material to deform permanently (nonelastically) without fracturing.

Polarization   The change from the open-circuit potential as a result of current across the electrode/electrolyte interface.

Polarization Admittance   The reciprocal of polarization resistance.

Polarization Cell   A DC decoupling device consisting of two or more pairs of inert metallic plates immersed in an aqueous electrolyte. The electrical characteristics of the polarization cell are high resistance to DC potentials and low impedance of AC.

Polarization Curve   A plot of current density versus electrode potential for a specific electrode/electrolyte combination.

Polarization Decay   The decrease in electrode potential with time resulting from the interruption of applied current.

Polarization Resistance   The slope (dE/di) at the corrosion potential of a potential (E)-current density (i) curve. (The measured slope is usually in good

agreement with the true value of the polarization resistance when the scan rate is low and any uncompensated resistance is small relative to the polarization resistance.)

Polarized Potential   The potential across the structure/electrolyte interface that is the sum of the corrosion potential and the cathodic polarization.

Polyester   Type of resin formed by the condensation of polybasic and monobasic acids with polyhydric alcohols.

Postweld Heat Treatment   Heating and cooling a weldment in such a way as to obtain desired properties.

Potential-pH Diagram   A graphical method of representing the regions of thermodynamic stability of species for metal/electrolyte systems (also known as *Pourbaix diagram*).

Potentiodynamic   Refers to a technique wherein the potential of an electrode with respect to a reference electrode is varied at a selected rate by application of a current through the electrolyte.

Potentiokinetic   [See *Potentiodynamic.*]

Potentiostat   An instrument for automatically maintaining a constant electrode potential.

Potentiostatic   Refers to a technique for maintaining a constant electrode potential.

Pot Life   The elapsed time within which a coating can be effectively applied after all components of the coating have been thoroughly mixed.

Poultice Corrosion   [See *Deposit Attack.*]

Pourbaix Diagram   [See *Potential-pH Diagram.*]

Power Tool Cleaning   Removal of loose rust, loose mill scale, and loose paint to degree specified by power tool chipping, descaling, sanding, wire brushing, and grinding. [See SSPC-SP 3.]

Precipitation Hardening   Hardening caused by the precipitation of a constituent from a supersaturated solid solution.

Primary Passive Potential   The potential corresponding to the maximum active current density (critical anodic current density) of an electrode that exhibits active-passive corrosion behavior.

Prime Coat   [See *Primer.*]

Primer   A coating material intended to be applied as the first coat on an uncoated surface. The coating is specifically formulated to adhere to and protect the surface as well as to produce a suitable surface for subsequent coats. [Also referred to *as Prime Coat.*]

Profile   Anchor pattern on a surface produced by abrasive blasting or acid treatment.

Protective Coating   A coating applied to a surface to protect the substrate from corrosion.

R

Reduction   Gain of electrons by a constituent of a chemical reaction.

Reference Electrode   An electrode whose open-circuit potential is constant under similar conditions of measurement, which is used for measuring the relative potentials of other electrodes.

Reference Half-Cell   [See *Reference Electrode.*]

Relative Humidity   The ratio, expressed as a percentage, of the amount of water vapor present in a given volume of air at a given temperature to the amount required to saturate the air at that temperature.

Remote Earth   A location on the earth far enough from the affected structure that the soil potential gradients associated with currents entering the earth from the affected structure are insignificant.

Rest Potential   [See *Corrosion Potential.*]

Reversible Potential   [See *Equilibrium Potential.*]

Rimmed Steel   An incompletely deoxidized steel. [Also called *Rimming Steel.*]

Riser   (1) That section of pipeline extending from the ocean floor up to an offshore platform. (2) The vertical tube in a steam generator convection bank that circulates water and steam upward.

Rust   Corrosion product consisting of various iron oxides and hydrated iron oxides. (This term properly applies only to iron and ferrous alloys.)

Rust Bloom   Discoloration indicating the beginning of rusting.

S

Sacking   Scrubbing a mixture of a cement mortar over the concrete surface using a cement sack, gunny sack, or sponge rubber float.

Sacrificial Protection   Reduction of corrosion of a metal in an electrolyte by galvanically coupling it to a more anodic metal (a form of cathodic protection).

Scaling (1) The formation at high temperatures of thick corrosion-product layers on a metal surface. (2) The deposition of water-insoluble constituents on a metal surface.

Scanning Electron Microscope An electron optical device that images topographical details with maximum contrast and depth of field by the detection, amplification, and display of secondary electrons.

Sensitizing Heat Treatment A heat treatment, whether accidental, intentional, or incidental (as during welding), that causes precipitation of constituents (usually carbides) at grain boundaries, often causing the alloy to become susceptible to intergranular corrosion or intergranular stress corrosion cracking.

Shallow Groundbed One or more anodes installed either vertically or horizontally at a nominal depth of less than 15 m (50 ft) for the purpose of supplying cathodic protection.

Shop Coat One or more coats applied in a shop or plant prior to shipment to the site of erection or fabrication.

Shot Blasting Abrasive blast cleaning using metallic (usually steel) shot as the abrasive.

Shot Peening Inducing compressive stresses in the surface layer of a material by bombarding it with a selected medium (usually steel shot) under controlled conditions.

Sigma Phase An extremely brittle Fe-Cr phase that can form at elevated temperatures in Fe-Cr-Ni and Ni-Cr-Fe alloys.

Slip A deformation process involving shear motion of a specific set of crystallographic planes.

Slow Strain Rate Technique An experimental technique for evaluating susceptibility to environmental cracking. It involves pulling the specimen to failure in uniaxial tension at a controlled slow strain rate while the specimen is in the test environment and examining the specimen for evidence of environmental cracking.

Slushing Compound Oil or grease coatings used to provide temporary protection against atmospheric corrosion.

Solution Heat Treatment Heating a metal to a suitable temperature and holding at that temperature long enough for one or more constituents to enter into solid solution, then cooling rapidly enough to retain the constituents in solution.

Solvent Cleaning Removal of oil, grease, dirt, soil, salts, and contaminants by cleaning with solvent, vapor, alkali, emulsion, or steam. [See SSPC-SP 1.]

Spalling The spontaneous chipping, fragmentation, or separation of a surface or surface coating.

Standard Electrode Potential The reversible potential for an electrode process when all products and reactions are at unit activity on a scale in which the potential for the standard hydrogen reference electrode is zero.

Standard Jetting Water Water of sufficient purity and quality that it does not impose additional contaminants on the surface being cleaned and does not contain sediments or other impurities that are destructive to the proper functioning of water jetting equipment.

Steel Shot Small particles of steel with spherical shape that are commonly used as an abrasive in abrasive blast cleaning or as a selected medium for shot peening.

Stepwise Cracking [See *Hydrogen-Induced Cracking.*]

Stray Current   Current through paths other than the intended circuit.

Stray-Current Corrosion   Corrosion resulting from current through paths other than the intended circuit, e.g., by any extraneous current in the earth.

Stress Corrosion Cracking   Cracking of a material produced by the combined action of corrosion and tensile stress (residual or applied).

Stress Relieving (Thermal)   Heating a metal to a suitable temperature, holding at that temperature long enough to reduce residual stresses, and then cooling slowly enough to minimize the development of new residual stresses.

Subsurface Corrosion [See *Internal Oxidation.*]

Sulfidation   The reaction of a metal or alloy with a sulfur-containing species to produce a sulfur compound that forms on or beneath the surface of the metal or alloy.

Sulfide Stress Cracking   Cracking of a metal under the combined action of tensile stress and corrosion in the presence of water and hydrogen sulfide (a form of hydrogen stress cracking).

T

Tack Coat   A thin wet coat applied to the surface that is allowed to dry just until it is tacky before application of a thicker wet coat. (Use of a tack coat allows application of thicker coats without sagging or runs.)

Tafel Plot   A plot of the relationship between the change in potential (E) and the logarithm of the current density (log i) of an electrode when it is polarized in both the anodic and cathodic directions from its open-circuit potential.

Tafel Slope   The slope of the straight-line portion of the E log i curve on a Tafel plot. (The straight-line portion usually occurs at more than 50 mV from the open-circuit potential.)

Tarnish   Surface discoloration of a metal resulting from formation of a film of corrosion product.

Thermal Spraying   A group of processes by which finely divided metallic or nonmetallic materials are deposited in a molten or semimolten condition to form a coating.

Thermogalvanic Corrosion   Corrosion resulting from an electrochemical cell caused by a thermal gradient.

Throwing Power   The relationship between the current density at a point on a surface and its distance from the counterelectrode. The greater the ratio of the surface resistivity shown by the electrode reaction to the volume resistivity of the electrolyte, the better is the throwing power of the process.

Topcoat   The final coat of a coating system. [Also referred to as *Finish Coat.*]

Transpassive   The noble region of potential where an electrode exhibits a higher-than-passive current density.

Tuberculation   The formation of localized corrosion products scattered over the surface in the form of knob-like mounds called tubercles.

U-V-W

Ultimate Strength The maximum stress that a material can sustain.

Ultrahigh-Pressure Water Jetting Water jetting performed at pressures above 170 MPa (25,000 psig.)

Underfilm Corrosion [See *Filiform Corrosion.*]

Vehicle The liquid portion of a formulated coating material.

Void (1) A holiday, hole, or skip in a coating. (2) A hole in a casting or weld deposit usually resulting from shrinkage during cooling.

Wash Primer A thin, inhibiting primer, usually chromate pigmented, with a polyvinyl butyral binder.

Water Cleaning Use of pressurized water discharged from a nozzle to remove unwanted matter (e.g., dirt, scale, rust, coatings) from a surface.

Water Jetting Use of standard jetting water discharged from a nozzle at pressures of 70 MPa (10,000 psig) or greater to prepare a surface for coating or inspection.

Weight Coating An external coating applied to a pipeline to counteract buoyancy.

White Metal Blast Cleaned Surface A white metal blast cleaned surface, when viewed without magnification, shall be free of all visible oil, grease, dust, dirt, mill scale, rust, coating, oxides, corrosion products, and other foreign matter. [See NACE No. 1/SSPC-SP 5.]

Weld Decay Intergranular corrosion, usually of stainless steel or certain nickel-base alloys, that occurs as the result of sensitization in the heat-affected zone during the welding operation. [This is not a preferred term.]

Wet Film Gauge Device for measuring wet film thickness of a coating.

Working Electrode The test or specimen electrode in an electrochemical cell.

Wrought Metal in the solid condition that is formed to a desired shape by working (rolling, extruding, forging, etc.), usually at an elevated temperature.

X-Y-Z

Yield Point The stress on a material at which the first significant permanent or plastic deformation occurs without an increase in stress. In some materials, particularly annealed low-carbon steels, there is a well-defined yield point from the straight line defining the modulus of elasticity.

Yield Strength The stress at which a material exhibits a specified deviation from the proportionality of stress to strain. The deviation is expressed in terms of strain by either the offset method (usually at a strain of 0.2%) or the total-extension-under-load method (usually at a strain of 0.5%.)

Additional Important Information on Underground Corrosion Control

Copies of federal regulations concerning the installation and operation of underground pipelines are available as follows:

Transportation of Natural and Other Gas by Pipeline: Minimum Safety Standards. Federal Register, Vol. 35, Number 161, Part II, August 19, 1970. Title 49. Parts 190, 192.

Transportation of Liquids by Pipeline. Federal Register, Vol. 35, No. 218, November 7, 1970. Title 49. Parts 180, 195.

Available from Department of Transportation, Office of Pipeline Safety, Washington, D.C. 20590.

NACE REFERENCED STANDARDS

Standard	Standard Title
Coatings	
MR0274-95	Material Requirements for Polyolefin Cold-Applied Tapes for Underground Submerged Pipeline Coatings-Item No. 21301
RP0185-96	Extruded Polyolefin Resin Coating Systems with Soft Adhesives for Underground or Submerged Pipe-Item No. 21029
RP0190-95	External Protective Coatings for Joints, Fittings, and Valves on Metallic Underground or Submerged Pipelines and Piping Systems-Item No. 21042
RP0399-99	Plant-Applied, External Coal Tar Enamel Pipe Coating System: Application, Performance, and Quality Control-Item No. 21089
RP0394-94	Application, Performance, and Quality Control of Plant-Applied, Fusion-Bonded Epoxy External Pipe Coating-Item No. 21064
RP0375-99	Wax Coating Systems for Underground Piping Systems-Item No. 21013

Surface
Preparation
NACE No.
1/SSPC-SP 5   White Metal Blast Cleaning (RP0494-2000)-Item No. 21065
NACE No.
2/SSPC-SP 10   Near-White Metal Blast Cleaning (RP0594-2000)-Item No. 21066
NACE No.
3/SSPC-SP 6   Commercial Blast Cleaning (RP0694-2000)-Item No. 21067
NACE No.
4/SSPC-SP 7   Brush-Off Blast Cleaning (RP0794-2000)-Item No. 21068
NACE No.
5/SSPC-SP 12   Surface Preparation and Cleaning of Steel and Other Hard Materials by High-
and Ultrahigh-Pressure Water Jetting Prior to Recoating (RP0595-95)-Item No.
21076
NACE No.
8/SSPC-SP 14   Industrial Blast Cleaning (RP0299-99)-Item No. 21088

Holiday
Testing
RP0274-98   High-Voltage Electrical Inspection of Pipeline Coatings Prior to Installation-Item
No. 21010
RP0188-99   Discontinuity (Holiday) Testing of Protective Coatings-Item No. 21038
RP0490-95   Holiday Detection of Fusion-Bonded Epoxy External Pipeline Coatings of 250 to
760 micrometers (10 to 30 mils)-Item No. 21045

Cathodic
Protection
RP0169-96   Control of External Corrosion on Underground or Submerged Metallic Piping
Systems-Item No. 21001
RP0177-95   Mitigation of Alternating Current and Lightning Effects on Metallic Structures
and Corrosion Control Systems-Item No. 21021
RP0200-2000   Steel-Cased Pipeline Practices-Item No. 21091
RP0286-97   Electrical Isolation of Cathodically Protected Pipelines-Item No. 21032
RP0572-95   Design, Installation, Operation, and Maintenance of Impressed Current Deep
Groundbeds-Item No. 21007

Referenced Standards can be ordered from NACE International. Item no. shown is the NACE catalogue order number.

Purchase Information
The Standards listed above may be purchased from NACE International, 1440 South Creek Drive, Houston, Texas 77084. Write or call for prices. Phone: (281) 228-6223.

Note
The above information is revised periodically. Please check current NACE Products Guide or www.nace.org for updates and revisions.

Index